Freud's Mass Psychology

Renewing Philosophy

General Editor: **Gary Banham**

Titles include

Kyriaki Goudeli
CHALLENGES TO GERMAN IDEALISM
Schelling, Fichte and Kant

Keekok Lee
PHILOSOPHY AND REVOLUTIONS IN GENETICS

Jill Marsden
AFTER NIETZSCHE

Céline Surprenant
FREUD'S MASS PSYCHOLOGY

Jim Urpeth
FROM KANT TO DELEUZE

Martin Weatherston
HEIDEGGER'S INTERPRETATION OF KANT
Categories, Imagination and Temporality

Renewing Philosophy
Series Standing Order ISBN 0-333-91928-9
(*outside North America only*)

You can receive future titles in this series as they are published by placing a standing order. Please contact your bookseller or, in case of difficulty, write to us at the address below with your name and address, the title of the series and the ISBN quoted above.

Customer Services Department, Macmillan Distribution Ltd, Houndmills, Basingstoke, Hampshire RG21 6XS, England

Freud's Mass Psychology

Questions of Scale

Céline Surprenant
Lecturer in French
University of Sussex

palgrave
macmillan

First published 2003 by
PALGRAVE MACMILLAN
Houndmills, Basingstoke, Hampshire RG21 6XS and
175 Fifth Avenue, New York, N.Y. 10010
Companies and representatives throughout the world

PALGRAVE MACMILLAN is the global academic imprint of the Palgrave Macmillan division of St. Martin's Press, LLC and of Palgrave Macmillan Ltd. Macmillan® is a registered trademark in the United States, United Kingdom and other countries. Palgrave is a registered trademark in the European Union and other countries.

ISBN 0-333-99742-5

This book is printed on paper suitable for recycling and made from fully managed and sustained forest sources.

A catalogue record for this book is available from the British Library.

Library of Congress Cataloging-in-Publication Data
Surprenant, Céline, 1961–
Freud's mass psychology: questions of scale / Céline Surprenant.
p. cm. – (Renewing philosophy)
Includes bibliographical references and index.
ISBN 0-333-99742-5 (cloth)
1. Psychoanalysis. 2. Psychoanalysis and philosophy. 3. Freud, Sigmund, 1856–1939. I. Title. II. Series.
BF173 .S86 2002
150.19'5–dc21 2002072325

10 9 8 7 6 5 4 3 2 1
12 11 10 09 08 07 06 05 04 03

Printed and bound in Great Britain by
Antony Rowe Ltd, Chippenham and Eastbourne

For my Father

Contents

Series Editor's Preface viii
Acknowledgements ix
Abbreviations x

Introduction 1
1 Psychoanalytic Concepts 13
2 Quantity, Mass and Metaphor 37
3 Sciences of the Crowd 51
4 On a Large Scale 64
5 Figurative Language According to Freud 98
6 Conclusion: 'On Transience' 135

Notes 141
Index 187

Series Editor's Preface to Freud's Mass Psychology

Céline Surprenant's book is an original inquiry into the resources of Freud's use of the notion of the 'mass' exploring the quantitative and metaphorical nature of this notion in a wide range of registers. The work is innovative in eschewing the assimilation of this notion to accounts of 'mass psychology' derived from the late nineteenth and early twentieth centuries and concentrating instead on an analysis of the language of Freud's works. The usual approaches to the analysis of 'mass' in Freud simply present it in terms that assimilate Freud's inquiry to social psychology or view it as an attempt at a 'political' analysis supposedly absent from the other researches Freud was engaged in.

Ranging across Freud's writings and engaging with the most innovative and important philosophical treatments of Freud presented in contemporary writing this work represents a major contribution to philosophical treatments of Freud. In making the case for thinking the mode of address of Freud's writings as containing in itself a substantive contribution to the nature of thinking about thinking the author necessarily is led to state her investigation in terms that themselves invent new techniques of inquiry. Rather than attempting to settle the question about the relation of Freudian thought to philosophy the work enables a questioning of the attempt of many authors to evaluate what is philosophically relevant in Freud.

Renewing Philosophy is a forum for innovative philosophy, philosophy that engages with the history of modernity and its relation to contemporary problems. In setting out on an exploration that requires subtle perception the author renews the philosophical engagement with the conditions of possibility of thinking and in the process releases from texts that may have become to seem too worked over to offer new promise, precisely the opening to futurity that is required for an investigation to be worthy of serious attention. In thus presenting a future from within the investigation of a prime thinker of modernity the author thus belongs squarely within the horizon of this series and this is the reason for the inclusion of this work within it.

GARY BANHAM
Series Editor
Renewing Philosophy

Acknowledgements

I am indebted to numerous individuals and institutions for the writing of this book. I would like to thank the British Academy, the Social Sciences and Humanities Research Council of Canada, which funded the doctoral thesis submitted at the University of Sussex from which the book originates, and the Arts and Humanities Research Board for a research leave. I am grateful to Geoffrey Bennington who supervised the thesis, to Paul Davies and to Malcolm Bowie, who examined it. I am greatly indebted to Malcolm Bowie for his scholarship and his generosity in helping me to reshape the thesis into a book. He read various drafts of the book and continued to provide encouraging and inspiring comments.

I would also like to express my gratitude those who helped me in invaluable ways, at various stages of the project: Thamy Ayouch, David Bate, Daniel Binswanger, Adriana Bontea, Brian Cummings, Rickie Dammann, Paul Davies, Karin de Boer, Robert Doran, Jutta Frense, Simon Gilham, Elena Gualtieri, Lamine Hamlaoui, Brigitte Hermann, Doris Hoppe, Andréa Lauterwein, Kathryn MacVarish, Serge Margel, Joëlle Menrath, Jean-Luc Nancy, Evie Neumann, William Outhwaite, Francette Pacteau, Monique Régimbald-Zeiber, Stephen Robinson, Nicholas Royle, Darrow Schecter, Philippe Sers, Pascal Sévérac, Alison Stone, Lucie Surprenant, Lisa Trahair, Martin van Gelderen, Françoise Vergès.

Finally, I would like to thank the Series Editor Gary Banham, Heather Gibson, Jennifer Nelson, Kate Schofield at Palgrave Macmillan, and Keith Povey, the copy-editor.

CÉLINE SURPRENANT

Abbreviations

GW	S. Freud, *Gesammelte Werke*, 18 vols. (London: Imago Publishing Co., 1940–52; Frankfurt am Main: S. Fisher Verlag, 1960–87)
SE	*The Standard Edition of the Complete Psychological Works*, 24 vols. (London: The Hogarth Press and the Institute of Psychoanalysis, 1953–74)

Introduction

> '. . . rien n'empêchera Dieu, s'il le veut, de faire tenir en un petit espace un nombre infini de personnes.'
>
> —Jacques de Voragine, *La Légende dorée*

In proposing the concept of mass in Freud as an object of study, one runs the risk of confusing one's reader: – 'Mass? Is that a Freudian concept? Should "mass" be understood in a physical or socio-political sense, or is it a quantitative noun?' Speaking about the 'mass' in relation to Freud's thought can be so perplexing in the sense that it may prompt the dismissive question as to whether Freud has ever written on the mass in any of these senses. Indeed 'mass' is not as such a Freudian concept. In only one essay does Freud focus on the mass but here it pertains less to the phenomenon or concept of the mass, than to the concept of identification.[1] In fact, the term 'mass' and its cognates appear sporadically in Freud's early writings onwards up to *Moses and Monotheism: Three Essays* (1939 [1937–39]). It sometimes serves as a term of classification, such as in the opposition *en masse* and *en détail* that distinguishes two kinds of paralyses and the two popular methods of interpretation.[2] It can be part of a description of the external world or of the ego as in 'The Project of a Scientific Psychology' (1895).[3] It points to human groupings whose dimensions remain unspecified, as throughout *Civilization and its Discontents* (1930). Or else, it functions as a term of comparison such as in 'My Contact with Joseph Popper Lynkeus' (1932).[4]

We will have the opportunity in the pages that follow to develop and expand on the previous examples. However, as it stands, it suffices to show that, except for the book purportedly dealing with the topic, the mass does not constitute a unified conceptual field within Freud's writing. Rather, it sends us in many directions at once. The death drive – doubtless one of the most uncertain areas of Freudian thought – does not engender as great a degree of uncertainty as the suggestion that there might be a problem around the 'mass' in Freud. The death drive may be a contentious issue, as Freud himself and commentators have repeatedly stated. Yet, it is still a precise concept that can be studied, for example, by consulting a subject index or a glossary, which will direct us to related concepts and texts.[5] It provokes disagreement concerning its speculative nature but not as to whether or not it is a Freudian concept. The same does not apply to the concept of mass. We cannot exactly say that it is polemical, as we must first show that this is in fact a problem in Freud.

This book, then, does not aim to dispel the initial bewilderment about the topic by confirming that 'mass' is not a Freudian concept. It aims, rather, to show that there is a 'problem of the mass' in Freud, which may send us to *Mass Psychology and the Analysis of the Ego* (1921), but which is nevertheless not confined to a set of agreed psychoanalytical issues or even to the occurrences of the term throughout Freud. On the one hand, we will examine how the 'mass' singularly resists conceptual identification in so far as it is attached to 'great numbers', to 'the many' in a discourse otherwise thought to be primarily concerned with the individual psyche. Given that psychoanalysis moves beyond the individual psyche only 'by analogy', on the other hand, we will see that if the 'mass' carries along with it such indeterminacy it does so in so far as it draws forth and converges with, more than any other Freudian concepts, the figurative aspect of Freud's work. Hence, the 'problem of the mass' that this book develops points to those recurring moments when the theory of psychoanalysis is grappling with the 'many', whether it be in the form of an enigmatic 'quantity', or of no less an enigmatic 'whole', which refers to 'society'.[6] We will focus on some of these points of theoretical perplexity and show how they more or less openly conflict or coincide with the basic tenets of psychoanalysis.

To suggest that we will be dealing with 'all' basic tenets would be overly ambitious. During the course of this book, we might in fact appear to be moving away from what has been recognized as Freud's most important teachings. For the two aspects upon which we will concentrate, namely, the application of psychoanalysis and Freud's mode of theorization, are, according to some, marginal concerns in comparison with, say, sexuality, or the therapeutic cure. From our perspective, however, it is precisely there that questions concerning what constitutes the fundamental stakes of psychoanalysis are most interestingly raised.

It is, on the one hand, in the application of psychoanalysis that Freud puts forward the most unthinkable hypotheses, which are judged as such not only by his contemporaries and successors, but also by him. In the texts on the application of psychoanalysis, Freud comes nearest to what has been deemed the least acceptable aspects of his thought, and which can be summarized in the idea – tinged with late nineteenth-century evolutionism – of the unconscious transmission of memory-traces. On the other hand, nowhere does the conceptual language of psychoanalysis become more problematic than in the application of psychoanalysis.[7] Some believe that the disquieting aspects of the theory can be explained away by being considered as 'figurative'. But Freud's reflections on the application of psychoanalysis show the extent to which one lacks guidance for isolating what is figurative from what is not, including when it is a question of the 'individual' and the 'mass'. The 'problem of the mass' thus points to a reflection upon the interpretation of Freud's abundant use of figures, into which the extension of psychoanalysis beyond the individual most forcefully engages us.

Whereas everyone agrees to describe metapsychology as speculative, and, to recognize the great importance that Freud gives to the unknown in that area, the application of psychoanalysis is not habitually considered as a place where Freud is battling with the unknown. Rather, the idea of 'application' evokes a mechanistic transference of concepts based on the neutralization of theoretical difficulties, on generalizations, which do not go well with the 'science of the singular' that psychoanalysis aims to be. Freud's mode of theorization and the application of psychoanalysis are therefore usually examined separately, as though conceptual difficulties stood on one side, while attempts to match psychoanalysis to questions of morality, philosophy and religion were on the other. It looks as though 'using' psychoanalytic thought meant that it no longer need worry us. The extension of psychoanalysis, however, brings us up against an indefinite quantity of psyches, of human beings, of generations (just as against an indefinite quantity of phantasies, of wishful impulses, etc.) that is no less a source of theoretical puzzlement than, say, the postulated 'quantity', which lies at the basis of the functioning of the psychical apparatus in the metapsychology. By focusing on the motif of the mass, this particular kind of 'unknown' emerges in all its complexity besides the more familiar unknowns of the theory. Our point of entry into Freud will hence be based largely on the successive recapitulations of the theory that the application of psychoanalysis obliges Freud to produce, of which *Moses and Monotheism* is one of the richest, and most decisive articulation.

The interest in this problem can be traced back, on the one hand, to the bafflement that Freud's essay on the mass provokes. There is a striking discrepancy between a certain reception of this essay and its actual content. Freud's *Mass Psychology* is seen as a significant contribution to the problem of the mass, alongside the contributions of, for example, Spinoza, Hobbes, Hegel, Marx, Gustave Le Bon, Ortega y Gasset or Elias Canetti, which one expects to find in a book on the mass. It is even said to anticipate our understanding of the historical events of the 1930s. Yet, this essay says essentially very little about the mass. Freud asks: 'What, then, is a "Mass"?'[8] The question is no sooner raised, however, than it is almost entirely dropped. Freud goes on to discuss different types of mass, following existing classifications, putting forward what has become an influential explanation of the types of bonds that unite together the members of a 'mass' and that unite them to a Leader, while seemingly leaving behind the initial disquieting concern. By the end of the essay, we have caught sight of what Freud calls the 'libidinal structure of the mass'. But is the description of the vertical and horizontal bonds that anticipate the obedience to authority that was to be increasingly observed in Europe during the 1930s in answer to the question 'what is a mass?' Does that suffice to delineate the entity that the mass represents? The chapters of *Mass Psychology* where Freud discusses the work of their wark on the subject should not deceive us. The end of Freud's survey of their work almost coincides with the disappearance of the topic from the pages of the book, which then makes room for the 'Analysis of the Ego'. By the end, then, the question 'what is a mass?' has lost nothing of its interrogative force.

The few references to the book in Freud's correspondence reinforce our doubts towards the nature of its topic. Before and after its publication in 1921, Freud mentions *Mass psychology* to various interlocutors only in passing. To one correspondent, the book is dismissed as 'verging on the banal' and to another as 'being not particularly successful'.[9] By contrast, it is presented as doing no less than 'showing the way that goes from the individual to the understanding of society'. It is not surprising if a book of which one can say at once that it 'verges on the banal' and that it leads to the 'comprehension of society', makes us ponder over its content. In raising doubts as to the exact importance of the topic, these allusions to the work suggest that Freud too had reservations about it.[10]

The critical reception has tended to minimize the exploratory nature of the book by concentrating on the explanation of the libidinal structure of the mass thus overlooking the great source of theoretical hesitations that it harbours.[11] Our initial intention was to examine more closely Freud's book on the mass and the role it plays in contemporary discussions of Freudian thought, more particularly in arguments such as, for example, those that Mikkel Borch-Jacobsen develops in *Le Sujet freudien* (1982).[12] Borch-Jacobsen's influential book raised the question as to whether (Freudian) psychoanalysis might not renew rather than radically modify the conception of subjectivity inherited from Descartes.[13] Numerous other studies have concentrated on the psychoanalytic conception of the subject before and since the publication of that book in 1982, and it is not exactly this point that directly led us into focusing on the topic of the mass, but rather the exploration, in the last section of the book, of what the author calls 'Freudian politics'. In that section, the reflection upon Freudian politics is developed explicitly from Freud's views on the mass, as though the topic were necessarily a political one. Two understandings of the term 'mass' underlie at once a condemning and a favourable interpretation of Freudian politics. First, the mass is taken as the very word of modern totalitarianism, which inserts Freud's reflection among the sociological, political and psychological analyses of the totalitarian phenomenon. On this view, Freud remains too close to some aspects of totalitarianism, notably in the role he grants to the Leader. But the most puzzling gloss of the term is the assertion that 'mass' denotes 'the necessity of thinking the other "before" the ego or, more precisely "in" the ego, *as* ego. The mass is thus at the origin (without) origin of the individual.'[14]

It is not so much what this statement says about the other or the ego that is most striking, but rather what the solicitation of the mass in that context implies for Freudian exegesis in general. If the 'origin of the ego' and the particular relation to the other from which it proceeds can be described *as a mass*, what is the status of that term (and by extension the 'ego' which is compared to it) in the commentator and in Freud? What does 'mass' mean if it helps us locate the origin of the ego in a particular relation to the other? (What is an 'ego', indeed, if it can be compared to a mass?) Once the mass no longer simply refers to 'totalitarianism' or stands as a pejorative term, which is synonymous in a conservative and reactionary lexicon with 'rabble' and 'mob', does it become an image, a model, a metaphor, in other words, what Freud calls an 'auxiliary construction'? Of what would such imprecise evocation of a grouping (of human beings or not) be the model? These questions arise in the commentator's work, but they alert us to a similar set of problems in Freud himself, and this is the point at which our inquiry begins. We are used to say that the concept of identification explains, according to Freud, 'what happens in a mass'. But does the topic of the mass in *Mass psychology* not serve an illustrative function for the theory of identification? Does the figurative possibility of the mass explain Freud's interest in it, notwithstanding the fact that, according to some descriptions of it, human masses are predisposed to 'thinking in images' and thus, raise problems of representation?

The initially localized interest in 'Freudian politics' that apparently pertained, for the most part, to one of Freud's rather discreet works, then, opens onto broader questions about the 'means of representation' at Freud's disposal for the elaboration of his theory of the unconscious. Conversely, it draws attention to the way in which Freud's theory itself comes to stand as a 'means of representation' in literary, philosophical or political discourses. Rather than providing a means of access to Freud's political thought, the mass leads to questions of interpretation, from which the almost exclusively socio-political apprehension of that topic had kept it apart.

In this respect, if we turn to one of explicit discussions of interpretation in Freud, the official rejection in the *The Interpretation of Dreams* (1900) of 'problem of the mass' can be deceptive. Let us recall Freud's provocative endorsement of lay opinion's attitude towards dreams. Whereas scientific theories exclude the problem of interpretation, popular belief has traditionally held that dreams have a meaning that can be interpreted. It has accordingly employed two methods of interpretation – the symbolic and the decoding ones – in relation to which Freud's new method is introduced.[15] The distinction between the two is well known: the symbolic technique 'considers the content of the dream *as a whole* and seeks to replace it by another content which is intelligible and in certain respects analogous to the original one' (p. 96). The decoding technique 'treats dreams as a kind of cryptography in which each sign can be translated into another sign having a known meaning, in accordance with a fixed key' (p. 97); its essence 'lies in the fact that *the work of interpretation is not brought to bear on the dream as a whole* but on each portion of the dream's content independently, as though the dream were a geological conglomerate in which each fragment of rock requires a separate assessment' (p. 99). Freud lays out the principles of the 'psychoanalytic' method of dream-interpretation against the backdrop of these two procedures.[16]

When it comes to exposing the principle of the new psychoanalytic method, Freud duplicates almost exactly the description he has given of the decoding method: 'what we must take as the object of our attention is not the dream as a whole [as the symbolic method does], but the separate portions of its content' (p. 103). The new method therefore 'approximates' the decoding one in that 'like the latter, it employs interpretation *en détail* and not *en masse*; like the latter, it regards dreams from the very first as being of a composite character, as being conglomerates of psychical formations' (p. 104). The image of a 'conglomerate' (of a geological conglomerate in the case of the decoding method) is therefore chosen pointedly, for it denotes the idea of elements 'heaped together', which nonetheless remain 'distinct'. The science of unconscious modes of thought can be a science of connections and lack of connections (of all sorts, including the more traditional logical ones) insofar as it deals with 'pieces' and 'fragments'.[17] Once however we are dealing with psychical formations, composite structures and the generally disorderly unconscious processes, are we really rid of all 'masses'?

Freud's rejection of the method of interpretation *en masse* is thus counteracted by the fact that many elements of the 'correct' method (*en détail*) are designed to deal with all types of 'masses'. Dream-interpretation encounters dream-thoughts that are 'compressed on a large scale', wishful impulses, composite structures, intermediate thoughts, associations, day-residues and so on, always in 'immense number', in large quantities.[18] Faced with these large amounts of everything, it is not surprising that condensation is said to be one of 'the most important and peculiar characteristics of the dream-work' (p. 653). What holds together these various 'sums'? We will see how 'condensation' might be the concept in Freud that is most relevant to our reflection on the problem of the mass. It would not be an exaggeration to say that, from the point of view of the notions of quantity with which it deals, *The Interpretation of Dreams* consists in a treatise on the mass, and that the many dimensions of interpretation expounded in this book constitute as many attempts at circumscribing it. So much so, that it may become impossible to evoke one of the most important texts of the twentieth century without simultaneously calling to mind a notion of the mass.

The following inquiry, then, does not bear exactly upon the traditional concept of mass. Nevertheless, we will constantly be brushing up against some of the received ideas about the 'mass', for they coincide, *mutatis mutandis*, with what has now become traditional ways of talking about the unconscious. Political, literary or historical studies of the concept of the mass typically state that it confronts the thinker with an object of study that essentially defies objectification, which, like some elements of the dream-work, defies 'conditions of representability'.[19]

There might be no concept and phenomenon more amorphous than the mass. It is not a coincidence if it figures as a paradigmatic case in influential epistemological works of the twentieth-century, or (as we will see) if it stirs up questions about the nature of scientific observation.[20] Introductions to studies on the mass suggest that, given the elusiveness of the object, the examination of the concept and of the phenomenon must apparently constantly be redone, as it can never quite be carried out, even when it is a question of the physical concept of mass.[21]

The challenge that the unconscious poses to knowledge has, however, not so much to do with its amorphous character, but rather with the fact that we can gain knowledge of it only through its effects. The latter are commonly conceived as various types of disturbances of the normal course of rational thought, everyday life, etc. Whereas amorphousness is not for the most part a positive feature of the concept of mass, the unknowability of the unconscious is its 'trademark'. Because we only ever know the unconscious through its effects, the science of the unconscious would consist in explaining the cause of their production. In this respect, one strand of the reception of Freud has repeatedly condemned what is seen as a naturalistic approach to the psyche. On this view, psychoanalysis remains on this side of the philosophical challenge to naturalism by having remained attached to an unexamined scientistic model.[22]

Another strand of Freudian studies views favourably the way in which the object of psychoanalysis presents itself an effect. Rather than seeing in that position of the object, a defective scientific stance, it finds in it a justification of Freud's *unscientific* form of rationalization, including his abundant borrowings from related domains and existing sciences. The 'false' science that thus results from Freud's independence from constituted domains of knowledge is not judged according to whether or not it fulfils naturalist intentions, but rather in relation to its affinity to unconscious processes. The eclectic mode of theorization is the proof of the existence of unconscious processes. In other words, the theory is enthusiastically seen as being itself traversed by unconscious effects. Hence, according to many commentators, Freud's mode of theorization (Freudian 'epistemology') becomes a question of style.[23]

Our examination of Freud's mode of theorization does not develop the logico-positivist vein, which the interest in metaphors, analogies and models would otherwise appear to announce. Nor does it entirely endorse the view that Freud's style is the main key to the formation of psychoanalytic concepts. Rather, the motif of the mass, yet an unlikely guiding thread in the eyes of both approaches, allows us to reflect upon the strange unity that is postulated between conceptualization and unconscious processes, which is one of the common ideas of many studies on Freud, whatever their methodological allegiances. We will therefore take up again the question of Freud's analogies, metaphors, and models, a question which, as Freud says of his book on the mass, 'verges on the banal' for having been raised on so numerous occasions. In attaching them to the problem of the mass, however, we are loosening up the habitual understanding of these terms. By being affixed to 'epistemological' questions, the traditional concept of the mass loses some of its amorphousness.[24] We will see, moreover, that Freud's offhand notations about analogies and metaphors bring them very close to the way in which he tries on several occasions to explain the process of 'conscious' thinking. For the mass directs our attention to some of the most problematic aspects of the theory, namely the idea of phylogenesis and the transmission of unconscious memory-traces. But it also directs us to other less familiar and less developed areas of the corpus, notably, to the problem of consciousness. Concentrating on the 'quantitative' motif of the mass, will therefore neither be an opportunity for taking delight in the elusiveness of the theory in its encounter with the 'many', or in the ruptures and dislocations that are still too often redeemed in the now commonplace notion of 'divided subject'.

The arguments that follow are elaborated on the basis of close readings of Freud's texts, and of some of the commentators whose work has been decisive for the reception of Freud not only in French, but for its recent Anglo-Saxon reception as well. We do not reconstitute the history of the reception of Freud's book on the mass, nor of the texts on the application of psychoanalysis, but are in dialogue with that reception. Though the term 'mass' would be a good starting point for entering into the debate about the translation of Freud, we are not for the most part focusing on that issue.[25]

The first chapter turns to Jean Laplanche and Jean-Bertrand Pontalis's influential *Vocabulaire de la psychanalyse* [*The Language of Psychoanalysis*] (1967), which consistently raises the issue of Freud's figurative language without, however, elaborating on it. Chapter 2 goes to Jacques Derrida's essay 'Freud and the Scene of Writing' (1966), which makes metaphors in Freud one of the major stakes of that thought. There would be no reason to go back once more over that essay, which has been commented upon all too often, except for considering what happens to the problem of application in it. In Derrida's reading, the latter strangely appears to be impervious to the 'metaphorical investment' that otherwise characterizes Freud's text.

Chapter 3 consists of a brief incursion in the field of 'crowd psychology' following Freud's steps, in order to show that there too, the mass partly presents itself as a problem of metaphor. With respect to the way in which late nineteenth-century 'crowd psychology', particularly that of Gustave Le Bon, relates to late nineteenth-century racist ideologies, our emphasis on metaphor might appear misguided. The following study hopes to contribute to the understanding of that discourse, but by no means pretends to cover every issue related to it, including the fact that some of the ideas that constitute 'crowd psychology' have remained disturbingly contemporary.[26]

Chapters 4 and 5 are devoted to Freud's two great texts on religion *The Future of an Illusion* (1927) and *Moses and Monotheism*. Before concentrating on them, however, chapter 4 offers what comes nearest to a survey of the term 'mass' and its cognates in Freud's writings. This survey makes us go from Freud's rather banal pejorative outlook on the mass to the several ways in which the theory depends on all types of 'largeness', which the mass partly denotes. In that context, religion is above all decried by Freud as a 'mass' illusion, despite the fact that mass phenomena 'magnify' like a microscope what might otherwise remain inaccessible to a scientific apprehension of the world. The mass thus refers us to Freud's defence of 'science' and reason in *The Future of an Illusion*.

In chapter 5, we go through the analogical argument of *Moses and Monotheism* in order to show how the problematic of the mass is precisely what obliges Freud himself to raise questions of figurative language. We will see that the application of psychoanalysis turns out to be the most theoretical and 'reflexive' aspect of psychoanalysis, in condensing all its fundamental problems.

Literary references and, as we will see, references to any domain of knowledge or of human activity in Freud's writings, have often been described and considered controversially as providing no more than a wealth of useful analogies. Hence, whenever Freud invokes a fictional character or work, the nature of the relation that he establishes between the latter and psychoanalysis is at issue.[27] We can only speculate as to why Freud ranks Émile Zola's novel *Fécondité* (1899) among the ten 'good' books that he selects, in reply to a questionnaire on reading solicited by the publisher Hugo Heller in 1907. Apart from a brief comment on how 'good books' does not mean 'magnificent works' such as Goethe's *Faust* and 'significant' ones such as Darwin's *Descent of Man*, the reply provides scarcely more than a list and does not elaborate on that particular novel by Zola, or on any other works included on the list. The reasons for appreciating *Fécondité* are all the more enigmatic since Freud had already given a lecture, of which there are no published traces, to the Society of the B'Nai B'Rith in 1900 on Zola's monumental apology of fertility, which was inspired by movements against depopulation in France at the end of the 1890s. What did Freud find intriguing in a work of fiction aimed at promoting generation in moralistic and didactic terms, and, according to literary historians, at opposing barrenness in the field of literature then dominated by symbolist ascetism?

If the reply to the questionnaire and the unpublished lecture do not tell us much about the nature of Freud's interest in *Fécondité*, his discussion of *Macbeth* in 'Some Character-Types met with in Psycho-Analytic Work' (1916), on the other hand, clearly suggests that for him the main concern of that tragedy is childlessness. *Macbeth* serves the purpose of illustrating the cases of illnesses that follow from success (consisting here in a successful murder). Freud believes that the plot is 'a demonstration of the curse of unfruitfulness and the blessings of continuous generation', for childlessness appears both as a motive and as a punishment for murder. He situates the height of the tragedy in Macduff's shattering cry concerning Macbeth: 'He has no children!'[28] According to Freud, this line constitutes the *summit* from which the whole of the play can be surveyed to reveal a host of references to father–child relations.

The succinct analysis of *Macbeth* scarcely gives us more clues about unfruitfulness than what we were able to learn about reproduction from the mere allusion to *Fécondité*. But these unequally developed literary references leave us with a striking contrast between childlessness and prolific generation, between two poles each as potentially problematic as the other for psychoanalysis. Is barrenness not a ruinous possibility for the theory of the unconscious? Does psychoanalysis not go together with individuals that procreate, that proliferate, that is, with individuals that engender father- and mother-child relations?

As we will be suggesting in relation to the mass, the presence of these two works within Freud's writings raises the question as to what is to be attributed an illustrative, figurative status within Freud. Whatever their status and, no doubt, their uneven importance as far as the elaboration of psychoanalysis is concerned, they point to an important tension within Freud that could be described as one between *abundance* and *barrenness*, between the possibility of prolific generation and the ill-fated lack of descendants.[29]

In the context of our study, and leaving aside the tension that we identified with the two works, Zola's novel can serve a loose allegorical purpose in several ways. On the one hand, the work would evoke the areas (heredity, biology, generation) that have been most problematic in the reception of Freud's thought and that continue to be so. Since the problem of the mass sends us to these areas, the novel *Fécondité* could be an allegory of our topic, the mass, the many, and the problems of transmission that are attached to it. Or else, and this is also partly our topic, Freud's interest in that novel might have been motivated by sheer *numerousness*, and we would thus be attributing to Freud a formal interest for the 'many' (for 'over-interpretation', for repetition, and all the figures of the many that one can find in his work). Finally, Freud might have had an interest in demography and the topic of the mass would lead us to the latter, alongside Zola's novel.

Historians tell us that for Zola, *Fécondité* was not only an apology of procreation in response to the danger of depopulation, as the explicit theme of the work leads us to believe, but also a defence of literary posterity, the image of biological procreation 'naturally' lending itself to the begetting of an *oeuvre*.[30] Did the novel also represent the possibility of a successful posterity for Freud who indeed links the two kinds of posterity when he deems that *Macbeth* is concerned with the topic of childlessness as well as that of ambition? Was Freud not greatly preoccupied with transmission and inheritance, beginning with that of psychoanalysis, as commentators tirelessly note?

Leaving Zola aside, Freud's work now probably stands as the very model of a prolific thinker. Every Freudian concept, text, issue having been so thoroughly considered from a clinical, institutional or biographical point of view, it is hard to imagine that there is something else to say about Freud. The following study proposes a theme that is not quite Freudian, which, while obliging us to go over the familiar grounds of Freudian thought and to immerse ourselves in it, aims to remind us of the difficulty of conceiving of the 'many', even in Freud's writings.[31]

1
Psychoanalytic Concepts

> 'I have repeatedly heard it said contemptuously that it is impossible to take a science seriously whose most general concepts are as lacking in precision as those of libido and of instinct in psycho-analysis.'
>
> —Sigmund Freud, 'An Autobiographical Study'

> Freudian thought is not a philosophy. The prejudicial difficulty that it poses to a philosophical reflection rests on the fact that, besides the concepts which it has properly created, it uses others which have long held a philosophical status (representation, unconscious, ego, subject, object, inside, outside, body, desire, etc.). These concepts however acquire their meanings in the precise theoretical structure where they function . . . and not from the variety of paradigmatic signifiers, which each of these words can evoke in philosophy. This equivocation is all the more unbearable since it is already very tricky to pick out, to respect and to interpret the often important change through time of the contents of Freudian terms. In brief, it is not possible to integrate the new contents of these concepts in its complexity, by applying them without mediation, because of their community of words, to traditional philosophical problems of the subject, of the ego, of knowledge.[1]

This statement by Michel Tort comes from an acerbic review of Paul Ricoeur's *De L'Interprétation, Essai sur Freud* (1965), which, according to the reviewer, is wrongly described as 'the first complete interpretation of Freud'.[2] It is followed by the accusation that Ricoeur, radically inattentive to the specificity of Freudian thought, carries out, in certain parts of his work, a 'brutal grafting' of philosophical – phenomenological –

problematics onto Freudian concepts (p. 1488). Pending a detailed examination of *De L'Interprétation* and of Tort's grievances against the philosopher's work on Freud, it is difficult to assess whether or not Ricoeur is renewing what Tort dismissively calls 'the play of comparisons that delights philosophers' (p. 1488), which amounts, in a somewhat simplifying formulation of the problem raised in the above passage, to 'juxtapose [*mettre en présence*] familiar philosophical concepts and Freudian corresponding ones and to observe the reaction' (ibid.). The citation suggests some degree of complexity at the level of Freudian concepts themselves (for their content is constantly changing), or more importantly, it obliges us to wonder about the relation between words and concepts (in so far as the juncture depends upon a community of words). Tort however sees in Ricoeur's endeavour a mere juxtaposition of two inassimilable series of concepts – the phenomenological and the psychoanalytical ones.

According to the reviewer, then, Ricoeur is unable to read Freud in so far as he applies to Freudian thought '*external* categories' which can be brought back to the underlying 'extrinsic problematics of "hermeneutics"' (p. 1465). What is described in this review as the 'levelling' of the theoretical scandal of Freudian thought by dominant philosophies, is expressed in less indignant terms in one of Tort's later essays. The so-called mistaken readings of Freud by philosophers is here circumscribed under the heading of 'ideologization': 'instead of the analysis of the system of Freudian concepts, what is taking place is the development of an ideological philosophical discourse that uses psychoanalytic concepts in an associative, subjective, literary and analogical manner.'[3] For the moment, it is not Ricoeur's hermeneutic reading of Freud, nor Tort's developments on it that are of interest, but rather the way in which, for the psychoanalyst, the annexation of psychoanalysis by what he calls the dominant philosophies of phenomenology and existentialism, engenders what he perceives as 'an analogical use of psychoanalytic concepts' (p. 1467).

Other commentators of Freud have formulated similar reproaches against misleading interpretations of Freud, without however speaking of the ideologization of psychoanalysis by philosophy. In fact, the excessive schematization does not issue only from philosophy's supposedly too-hasty assimilation of Freudian thought. This represents only one facet of the problem, another being the scientistic inflexion of psychoanalysis encouraged by Freud's well-known reliance on nineteenth-century scientific concepts. The psychoanalyst André Green gives expression to this problem in 1962, with particular reference to the concept of the unconscious:

> Certain contemporary trends have had the tendency to reduce so considerably the import of the unconscious that one could have been led to believe that it is not impossible to do without it. Or else interpretations posterior to Freud aimed to remodel the description of the unconscious in order to purify it from what its original form appeared to owe to nineteenth-century thought, either so as to eliminate the share of hypothetical construction, or to integrate its mechanisms to biological and psychological knowledge, or else, in a diametrically opposed manner, so as to divest the concept of all scientistic resonance, in order to raise it to the level of a genuine phenomenology of spirit. Nevertheless, in both cases, the revision did not go without some impoverishment of the letter of Freudian thought.[4]

There is no need to have explored in detail both Green and Tort's arguments against what they perceived as flawed interpretations of Freud for noticing that they both advocate the respect of the 'irreducible originality' of Freud's work, as Green puts it, or, in Tort's terms, the need to elaborate 'an epistemological theory of psychoanalysis'.[5] We could expound at much greater length on the psychoanalysts' respective formulations of the problem, notably, on Tort's suggestion that it is the absence of a proper epistemological reflection that obliges psychoanalysis, to 'beg its epistemological foundations' to other sciences.[6] However, for our purpose, what the one refers to under the heading of the irreducible originality of Freudian thought, or the other when he speaks of an epistemological theory matters less than the way in which they both recommend 'the analysis of the system of Freudian concepts themselves'. For the latter, according to these views, should not be studied by pairing them with philosophical concepts because of a community of words, as Tort suggested, but rather by following their transient contents, through the constant revisions that characterize Freud's work.[7] Many of Freud's epistemological statements underline this movement: 'the deeper we penetrate into the study of mental processes the more we recognize their abundance and complexity [*Reichhaltigkeit und Verwicklung*]. A number of simple formulas which to begin with seemed to meet our needs have later turned out to be inadequate. We do not tire of altering and improving them.'[8] Freud will in fact not be the only one to underline the difficulty of the relentless changes of psychoanalytic concepts (it has become a familiar theme of commentaries). The philosopher Jean Hyppolite, for example, seeking to explore the analogy between Freudian thought and contemporary metaphysics in 1959, expresses a shared view, probably in the manner that Tort precisely rejects. He states that if the essence of Freudian thought can only be drawn out uneasily, it is because the latter has 'never ceased to evolve, to be rectified', Freud having tirelessly 'transformed his models, modified his language, as if in quest of a foreshadowed but never definitively elaborated truth'.[9]

Faced with the *internal* complexity of Freudian thought, to which the 'transience of concepts' contributes, then one should 'practice a meticulous reading of the Freudian text at the level of the history of concepts in order to recapture their constitution and their restructuration'. For the *travail du concept* is itself sufficiently elaborate to discourage any unwarranted annexation to this or that problematic (whether it be philosophical or scientistic).[10] If we were to be guided by Tort's inveighing against 'associative, subjective, literary and analogical' uses of psychoanalytic concepts, once involved in the Freudian text, problems raised by misleading associations of psychoanalytic concepts to 'something else' would be eliminated and would leave room for the task of 'locating . . . respecting and interpreting the often important changes through time of the contents of Freudian terms'.[11]

Now, it has become banal to say that 'Freud expounds his analytic theory in borrowed concepts.'[12] Thus, if it is possible, according to Tort, to distinguish the concepts which psychoanalysis 'has properly created' from those which 'have long possessed a philosophical status', and to avoid confusing them by misguided associations, according to Jean Laplanche and numerous others, Freud's terminology is precisely characterized by the way in which concepts are *simultaneously* properly its own and borrowed. Laplanche:

> Paradoxically, indeed, the psychoanalytic terminology is marked at once by its specificity and by its borrowed, 'derivative' character. All the psychoanalytic terms have an original acceptation, precisely related to the doctrine [*corps de la doctrine*]. But at the same time, even if some of them take on the appearance of neologisms, it is easy to track down their origin in more or less closely related fields, among which psychology is far from constituting the main source: natural sciences, biology, economy, medicine.[13]

We could add to the list many other closely related fields, such as, for example, popular knowledge, strategico-military sciences, literature and poetry. On this account, the meticulous study that Tort recommends might in fact intensify the problem, which he links somewhat polemically to philosophical interpretations. For it is not only *between* philosophical and psychoanalytic concepts that a certain homonymy can prompt levelling rapprochements.[14] Rather, if we agree with Laplanche, the specificity of Freud's terms lies crucially in the fact that they are, for the most part, inextricable from a community of words, which sends us back not only to one domain of knowledge and experience but to a whole host of them, up to and including ordinary language. The problem is all the more serious that in the circulation of concepts that Freud instigates, the source concepts are unrecognizable once they are 'imported' into Freud's theoretical constructions, because in 'borrowing' concepts Freud in fact simultaneously 'invents' them.[15] It is therefore difficult to imagine how the 'analysis of the system of Freudian concepts itself' can be carried out without some minimal comparative *act*, or without the participation in one community of words or another. As we will see in chapter 5, as soon as Freud himself makes analogical a use of psychoanalytic concepts, it is difficult, as Tort and others wish to do, convincingly to condemn such a use.

Granted that Freudian thought compels us to establish various comparisons between its concepts and 'something else', the question arises as to whether the comparative activity, which the constitution of psychoanalytic concepts encourages, itself gives rise to a concept. Is the *relation* between Freudian concepts and their source the object of a theoretical elaboration? Let us not yet ask this question of Freud, but of the commentators with whom we have begun. If we refer back to Tort's pronouncement, everything leads us to believe that difficulties arising from the borrowed character of psychoanalytic concepts might be quickly brushed aside. For the latter acknowledges that psychoanalytic theory has something to do with other domains such as biology or economics, he however deems that 'models' (biological, economic, etc.) have a clear metaphorical character (p. 113). The relation of psychoanalytic concepts to their models echoes, according to this description, the so-called misuses of psychoanalytic concepts by philosophers (in so far as they are associative, subjective, literary or analogical). Following Tort's attribution of a 'metaphorical character' to the traces of various sciences in Freudian thought, the latter apparently treats biological, economical or neuro-physiological concepts as philosophers treat psychoanalytic concepts, namely, 'metaphorically' or 'analogically'.

The term 'metaphor' typically signals, in works on Freud, the latter use of borrowed scientific and non-scientific concepts. One speaks, among others, of Freud's 'linguistic, financial, political, energetic, geological metaphors'.[16] Given that all Freudian concepts may be related, to a certain extent, to another domain, it is not surprising if exegeses of Freud often comprise reflections upon metaphors, models or analogies.[17] Freud himself meditated upon the figurative nature of scientific terms, among other places, in *Beyond the Pleasure Principle* (1920), and does not shy away from describing various aspects of his research activity in terms of 'fiction' and 'mythology', or from linking his discoveries to poetic insights.[18] While commentators generally agree on the metaphorical character of the Freudian conceptuality, they also reckon, as Jean-Bertrand Pontalis states, that 'in psychoanalysis, this metaphorical character takes on a particular value, which is not reducible to that of the use of images aimed at *illustrating* notions.'[19] Not only, then, do derived concepts mark themselves out by being considered as metaphorical, but 'metaphorical' (and the interchangeable terms enumerated above) too apparently takes on a particular value as soon as it is applied to psychoanalytic concepts.

Let us turn to Laplanche and Pontalis's *Vocabulaire de la psychanalyse* (1967), and to the authors' presentation of their work, which well highlights this problem.[20] Their approach to the metaphorical character of Freudian concepts can be traced back to two interrelated ideas that underlie discussions of the peculiarities of Freudian concepts. The first one consists in claiming that its 'object of investigation' determines the singularity of psychoanalytic thought – its figurative character, its diverse registers, and its apparent incoherence. Hence, psychoanalytic language cannot relate to the conceptual language of other scientific domains other than 'metaphorically' – because, unlike the sciences, whose concepts it borrows, and, as we will see, in spite of Freud's desired alliance with them, for example, with physics, psychical processes elude conceptual language in general. The more offhandedly psychoanalytic language makes use of existing scientific language (Laplanche speaks, for instance, of Freud's 'exemplary casualness' towards anatomy), the more it would seem to deal with its *object* in all seriousness.

Such an approach asserts that the operation of the psychical processes are knit together with questions of style; that conceptual and stylistic concerns mutually influence each other, indeed that they converge. Freud himself suggested as much on numerous occasions, notably, with respect to the writing of *The Interpretation of Dreams*.[21] There are many ways to note and to qualify this potentially disruptive unity.[22] The correspondence between style and object in psychoanalytic discourse is based on the commonly held idea that the functioning of the unconscious – the object of psychoanalysis – disrupts classical norms of theorization.[23] Since the very discourse that seeks to systematize knowledge of the unconscious is, on this view, itself to be conceived of as an effect of unconscious activity, the 'originality' of Freudian thought becomes admissible.[24]

The singularity of the 'object' of psychoanalysis can also be presented in terms of the 'contradiction' that is bound to arise from the moment that the object is said to 'elude conceptual language'. In his presentation of the specificity of the *Vocabulaire*, Pontalis formulates the problem in the following manner:

> If the unconscious is posited as the object of psychoanalysis and if we admit, as Freud stated from the *Traumdeutung* onwards, that the latter obeys laws which are very distant from conceptual language, is any endeavour focused on such a language and in principle destined to remain in this sphere of intelligibility not at once struck by relative powerlessness, or at least confronted to a contradiction?[25]

For despite the fact that 'psychoanalytic experience unfolds through and through in language,' it is, Pontalis argues, 'basically a contesting of conceptual language'.[26] This idea is closely related to that of congruence between style and object in so far as it makes of an incompatibility – of a contradiction or a paradox – a 'point of agreement' by linking the contradiction to the mode of functioning of psychical processes.

It is in the context of these two positions that one wonders what exactly is at issue for these commentators under the headings of conceptual and metaphorical language. For the conceptual language of psychoanalysis both corresponds to a metaphorical language of sorts and proceeds from a certain degree of literality. For the authors, to draw out the rigour of Freudian thought consists in tracking down the 'literality of the notion', which amounts to bring out the fact that 'a notion, an hypothesis, which were part of Freud's conceptual apparatus act as *models*, and thus to restore their metaphorical function' [Pontalis's emphasis].[27] The decisively 'metaphorical character' of the language of psychoanalysis is therefore affirmed simultaneously as its singular 'realism', whereby the more metaphorical the concepts, the more adequate they are to their elusive object.[28]

Given the peculiarity of psychoanalytic language, to which the *Vocabulaire* introduces, it is not surprising if the latter should pose the question of its relation to established lexicographic and encyclopaedic traditions.[29] Nevertheless, the 'metaphorico-literal' character of psychoanalytic language, which prevents us simply from considering the *Vocabulaire* as a dictionary, is presented as an outstanding problem. While the authors state that their works 'constitute in a certain sense a calling into question of any systematic presentation, up to and including that of Freud' and that they have 'dismantled an apparatus and in doing so, have shown its internal organization and its functioning', they declare *not* having 'directly disputed on the value and the function of models (such as, for example, the biological model)' a function which is not 'purely metaphorical'.[30]

While there is indeed no entry for the term 'model' [*Modell, Vorbild, Muster*] (one of the possible forms which the omission can take), Freud's use of models is yet inextricable from the analysis of the other terms at issue. From the moment that such an exegesis records the dominance of a problematic of model (and not only under the explicit heading of model), how can the inquiry not also involve a worry about the value and function of Freud's use of models?[31] The *Vocabulaire* 'implies a certain number of choices', and many other terms, apart from *Vorbild*, are not included in it, because to have done so, according to the authors, would have been to 'produce a psychoanalytic encyclopaedia' (p. 131). One of its merits, however, is to have drawn attention to some terms 'which, without properly speaking having value as concepts, intervene at precise moments, in a sense that remain constant and which act as a point of thought reference' (p. 133).[32] If *Vorbild*, then, does not have a separate entry, it might be because it already takes too great a part in too many entries of the *Vocabulaire*. Or, if not exactly 'too many', at least in too crucial ones.

Let us examine this situation by turning to the entry for 'psychical apparatus' *psychischer or seelischer Apparat*, which 'underscores certain characteristics attributed to the psyche by the Freudian theory: its capacity to transmit and transform a specific energy and its subdivision into systems or agencies' (p. 358). The commentary introduces from the outset a problematic of 'models' by pointing out the way in which, in *The Interpretation*, 'Freud defines the psychical apparatus in terms of a comparison with optical apparatuses. His purpose in making this analogy is, as he puts it: "to assist us in our attempt to make the complications of mental functioning intelligible by dissecting the function and assigning its different constituents to different component parts of the apparatus"' (p. 359). Three remarks follow this brief explanation. First, even though in being compared to an optical apparatus, the psychical apparatus implies distinct 'psychical localities', it has nothing to do with the anatomical theory of cerebral localizations (Freud insists on this on numerous occasions). Rather, the division of the apparatus into various 'systems' should allow us to conceive of the differences between the flow of excitations in the various systems.[33]

It is not clear at this point if the possible confusion between Freud's idea of various psychical systems and 'cerebral localizations' arises from the moment that the psychical apparatus is compared to optical apparatuses. In any case, the importance or the specificity of the first comparison apparently diminishes in the second remark, which introduces a more determining one. Laplanche and Pontalis state that 'the word "apparatus" evokes the idea of a task, or even that of *work*' [the author's emphasis]. And as the complication of mental functioning could be represented by means of comparison, the idea of 'work' is also *pictured* by means of a borrowed schema, that of the reflex-arc: 'the psychical apparatus must be constructed like a reflex apparatus. Reflex processes remain the model of every psychical function' (Freud quoted by Laplanche and Pontalis, SE V, p. 538). The most important element, according to these two remarks, clearly appears to be the functional aspect of the psychical apparatus, and the various provisional ideas [*Hilfsvorstellungen*] which it calls forth, should first and foremost help us to conceive of 'the *transformations of energy* from the free to the bound state . . . and the interplay of cathexes, anticathexes and hypercathexes' (pp. 32–3). Each of these last three terms give rise to a separate entry, and the optical metaphor, the idea of *psychical locality*, as well as of the reflex-arc are developed more fully in the entry 'topography'. There are however some uncertainties concerning the status which should be ascribed to Freud's borrowings: 'à plus d'une reprise, Freud continue à chercher, *sinon des correspondances précises, du moins des analogies, ou peut-être des métaphores*, dans la structure spatiale du système nerveux' (p. 487) [my emphasis].

There remains the third remark, which deserves to be quoted at length:

> These brief remarks show that the psychical apparatus serves for Freud's purpose as a *model* – or, as he said himself [in *The Interpretation*], as a 'fiction'. This model may at times be a physical one . . . on other occasions, it is derived instead from biology (the 'protoplasmic vesicle' of *Beyond*). And thus the discussion of the notion of the psychical apparatus has led us towards an overall evaluation of Freudian metapsychology and the metaphors that it brings into play (p. 359).

Up until the last remark, the commentary does not underline the possible 'value as model' of the psychical apparatus itself, but rather suggests that, being comparable to 'something else', it is detachable from the optical 'apparatuses', from the model, which it resembles. (From the moment that Freud speaks of something like the 'seelische *Instrument*' (p. 527) is its value as model not already at issue?) The emphasis is, moreover, put on the fact that the psychical apparatus denotes first and foremost transformations of energy. The latter follows a certain order of succession, which the 'differentiation into substructures' by means of comparison to various instruments allows us to conceive (Freud underlines the usefulness of his 'spatial–temporal' schema for describing the process of regression). Once it has been demonstrated that the importance of the comparison (to optical apparatuses and the reflex-arc) lies in the fact that it enables Freud to develop a functional definition of the psychical apparatus, however, one of the functions, which the apparatus acquires is precisely that of 'model'. The entry does send us back to 'an overall evaluation of Freudian metapsychology and the metaphors that it brings into play', not only because the function of the psychical apparatus is a crucial element of the Freudian metapsychology, but also because it draws our attention to the predominance of the question of 'models' throughout Freud's writing. Supposing that we could evaluate the significance of that problem on the basis of the terms 'model', 'analogy' or 'metaphor', their regular occurrences in the various entries of the *Vocabulaire* would itself almost suffice to convince us that Freud's thought unavoidably leads on to such a problematic. Yet, despite the centrality of the question, the *Vocabulaire* does not devote an article to the terms model, analogy or metaphor. Having considered this work briefly, and bearing in mind that the authors discourage any attempt to 're-order' its elements in view of a synthesis, it is tempting to imagine what form such an article could take.

'Freud and the Scene of Writing'

In so far as Jacques Derrida's work on Freud, from the essay 'Freud and the Scene of Writing' (1966) to *Résistances de la psychanalyse* (1990) is characterized by its focus on Freud's use of 'metaphors', it could be said to constitute, *mutatis mutandis*, the entry on model (analogy or metaphor) the *Vocabulaire* incites us to write, but does not itself comprise.[34] As we saw, although its authors are everywhere concerned with the task of restoring the 'function of metaphor' of Freudian hypotheses and models, it does not directly deal with it. By contrast, Derrida's essay focuses explicitly on Freud's peculiar handling of metaphor. Whereas, the *Vocabulaire* first provides, for example, a functional definition of the psychical apparatus and only gradually attracts notice to its value as model, the essay from *Writing and Difference* suggests that the Freudian conception of the psyche cannot be approached otherwise than by examining closely the pervasive 'metaphorical investment' of Freud's text (p. 199).

These two approaches diverge at least with respect to the models and metaphors on which they lay stress. Whereas Laplanche and Pontalis draw attention to Freud's appeal to optical apparatuses or to the reflex-arc, Derrida underscores the predominance of writing. That there should be apparently as many significant metaphors as there are commentators should not surprise us given Freud's recourse to numerous and heterogeneous ones.[35] But how can one judge of their particular value and importance? Do they all equally deserve attention? Does their very abundance tell us something about their function?

In 'Freud', Derrida undoubtedly singles out a particular metaphorical network – the scriptural – among many other possible ones, and convincingly demonstrates its pervasiveness. But while the essay attracts notice to *one set* of metaphors, it simultaneously suggests that Freud 'opens up a new kind of question about metaphor [*métaphoricité*], writing and spacing in general' (p. 199). The essay foregrounds the extent to which the multiplicity of models complicates any exegesis of Freud, paradoxically, by isolating one metaphorical network, because it concurrently shows that Freud's handling of scriptural metaphors 'makes enigmatic' both writing and metaphor.[36] Although Freud has recourse to the metaphor writing, he is not using scriptural metaphors according to the traditional, didactic handling of metaphors, which consists in 'nous ménager un accès à l'inconnu et à l'indéterminé par le détour d'un familier reconnaissable.'[37] The deviation from that function must be thought jointly with the modification to which the concept of writing is submitted in his text. Writing becomes enigmatic with reference to the way in which, according to Derrida, 'from Plato and Aristotle on, scriptural images have regularly been used to *illustrate* the relationship between reason and experience, perception and memory' (p. 199). On this view, reason, experience, perception and memory stand for the unknown which writing – the known and familiar term – helps us to know. Both metaphor and writing could be said to function as 'instrument and technique of representation', employed at the service of the *unknown* or of *la parole vive*.[38] It is with respect to this traditional function that Freud 'opens up a new kind of question about metaphor, writing and spacing in general' (p. 199). The stakes of Derrida's claims around the 'labour of writing' are high since, for Derrida, 'that which in Freud's discourse opens itself to the theme of writing results in psychoanalysis being not simply psychology – nor simply psychoanalysis' (p. 212).

It might be useful, before dealing with them and with the inflexion of Freudian thought that they presuppose, to recall briefly in what respect Freud finds a place in Derrida's thinking by considering a well-known early text – 'La Différance' (1968) – which has already been commented upon extensively. What matters here are the allusions to Freud in it. A few paragraphs before the discussion of Freud, Derrida introduces the idea that in the language of metaphysics, consciousness 'ne se donne à penser . . . que comme présence à soi, perception de soi dans la présence,' that 'le privilège accordé à la conscience signifie . . . le privilège accordé au présent' (p. 17). The problematic of *différance* is presented in terms of the examination, initiated by Heidegger, of the 'privilège absolu de cette forme ou de cette époque de la présence en général qu'est la conscience comme vouloir-dire dans la présence à soi' (p. 17). Before elaborating, a few pages later, on Heidegger's solicitation of the 'value of presence', Nietzsche and Freud are invoked for having both called into question consciousness 'on the basis of the motif of différance'. In Freud, the suspicion of the primacy of presence as consciousness gives rise to a 'diaphoristique en tant qu'énergétique ou économique des forces' (p. 19). Freud can be likened to Nietzsche, Heidegger and Lévinas, for having been suspicious about the value of presence, by attempting to think 'a certain alterity'.[39] That the latter has a 'metaphysical name' in Freud – the Unconscious – does not diminish the extent to which 'the calling into question of the authority of consciousness is first of all and always differential' in Freud.

In the 1968 essay, then, Derrida mainly goes back over the conceptual themes that he developed in 'Freud': the concepts of trace, of facilitation [*frayage*], of reserve and of delaying (p. 21). Yet, the question of metaphoricity, which dominates the earlier essay, is strangely omitted from the discussion. When Derrida first elaborates on the energetics or economics of forces, it is to a large extent in order to show that such conception emerges out of the 'metaphorical transition' between the psyche and the various technical models.[40] Leaving aside the remark concerning the way in which Freud describes the opposition between primary and secondary processes as a 'theoretical fiction' (p. 203), 'La Différance' curiously invokes the conceptions on the basis of which Derrida credits Freud with a thought of *différance* independently from the 'syntax' or the 'labour' of Freudian discourse, from its 'metaphoric investment'. We are here seemingly dealing with concepts in spite of the way in which the earlier essay so emphatically demonstrated that 'a conception of difference is attached less to concepts than to discourse' (p. 198). That is, in spite of the way in which the energetics as a theory of trace is not, according to Derrida, discernible in Freud's text as an isolated concept, but rather through figurative relations that transform the terms it engages (p. 19).

The discrepancy between the two essays as regards metaphoricity raises questions around the application of psychoanalysis, that is to say, questions around the conceptual and textual concerns that issue from Freud's reservations about the speculative extension of his science. It is these problems that Derrida's work on Freud highlights, for the problematics of writing, of the trace and of metaphoricity imbed Freudian thought within figurative relations, which might be of another kind than the ones the essay describes. Is there indeed a gap between Derrida's concepts of writing and trace and what the latter calls the '*Freudian* concepts of writing and trace', which would suggest that the two sets of concepts do not quite coincide but are rather united through a 'metaphorical exchange'? (p. 198, and concerning the 'gap', see p. 215).[41] Are the latter surrounded by quotation marks, following the 'reticence to utilize Freudian concepts otherwise than in quotation marks' expressed in the introductory remarks of the essay? Are the Freudian metaphors of 'path, trace, breach' (p. 229) an 'unbelievable mythology' acting as a model for the Derridean concept of trace?[42]

Derrida, on the one hand, pushes aside 'the Freudian concept of the hereditary mnemic trace' when introducing the aims of the essay: 'it is a question neither of following Jung, nor of following the Freudian concept of the hereditary mnemic trace' (p. 197), but nevertheless sends us back to the extension of psychoanalysis to the 'collective'. After pointing to the concepts of *Nachträglichkeit* and *Verspätung* as 'Freud's discovery', Derrida indeed affirms that the latter 'exploits this discovery in its ultimate consequences, beyond the psychoanalysis of the individual' (p. 203). Such a reference to beyond the psychoanalysis of the individual is at odds with the a priori exclusion of the hereditary mnemic trace. For what is described throughout the essay in terms of traces, inscriptions and breachings, will become attached, in conclusion, to 'sociality'. How is this term to be understood? Does sociality stand as a metaphor destined to illustrate the 'labor of writing', or 'originary repetition'? Or is this concept meant to present différance, the trace and spacing, which, just as the dream with logical relations, one has 'no means at [one's] disposal for representing'?[43] That sociality enters the essay only belatedly and as if independently from Derrida's rejection of the hereditary mnenic trace is all the more striking, since, as chapter 5 will show, its theoretical elaboration could be described as the attempt precisely to think the 'sociality' of the psyche 'in its ultimate consequences'.[44]

With respect to the perplexing demarcation between metaphors and concepts, what Derrida discards under the heading of hereditary mnenic trace, thus concurring with many commentators in their rejection of the evolutionist overtones of certain aspects of Freudian thought, could indeed turn out to be a particularly rich discursive (and conceptual) element of Freud's text. Moving 'beyond the psychoanalysis of the individual' carries Freudian concepts along in an analogical transposition in the context of which in what heredity and the related hypothesis of phylogenesis consist 'remains undetermined', to borrow Derrida's epigraph concerning the enigmatic neurological 'facilitations' of 'The Project'. The extension of the validity of psychoanalytic concepts to 'human masses' indeed renders more acute problems around the 'transmission of psychical contents' that already encumber the description of 'individual' psychical processes. Hence, if the circulation, the preservation and the transmission of psychical contents and structure prompt an 'inexhaustible inventiveness and dream like renewal of mechanical models' (p. 229) as far as the individual psyche is concerned, should the inventiveness be no less striking when it is a question of conceiving of the same phenomena 'beyond the psychoanalysis of the individual'?

Let us suspend provisionally these questions and consider the arguments of the essay. With respect to the existing wealth of commentaries, we will be going back over familiar grounds. But what matters here, as we began to indicate, is the underlying association of metaphoricity and 'sociality', which runs in filigree through the essay but which is 'written and simultaneously erased' in Derrida's text (who speaks in relation to Freud's text of 'a movement unknown to classical philosophy . . . between the implicit and the explicit' (p. 199)). The four sections of 'Freud' present the '*strange* progression' that Freud's use of successive metaphorical models draw. At first sight, the commentary presents an *almost* unbroken chronological succession of textual and conceptual events up until one reaches, somewhat triumphantly, one of Freud's most elaborate 'hypothetical constructions' expounded in 'A Note upon the "Mystic Writing Pad"' (1925 [1924]):

> a problematic of [facilitation] [*Bahnung*] is elaborated *to conform increasingly* to a metaphorics of the written trace. *From a system of traces* functioning according to a model which Freud would have preferred to be a natural one, and from which writing is entirely absent [First Section: Breaching and Difference], *we proceed toward* a configuration of traces *which can no longer* be represented except by the structure and functioning of writing [Second Section: The Print and the Original Supplement]. *At the same time,* the structural model of writing, which Freud invokes immediately after the

> *Project*, will be persistently differentiated and refined in its originality. All the mechanical models will be tested and abandoned [Third Section: Dioptrics and Hieroglyphics], until the discovery of the *Wunderblock*, a writing machine of marvellous complexity into which the whole of the psychical apparatus will be projected [Fourth Section: Freud's piece of Wax and the Three Analogies of Writing] [my emphasis].[45]

But what is at stake is in fact the progress of *discontinuity*. For, if the point were simply to demonstrate the extent to which scriptural metaphors predominate in Freud, their successive replacement might well look like a denouement. Finally, after many hesitations, the commentary seems to say, 'psychical *content* will be *represented* by a text whose essence is irreducibly graphic', and 'the *structure* of the psychical *apparatus* will be *represented* by a writing machine.' But the point of tracking down this strange progression is precisely to show that no entirely congruent metaphor or technical model will in fact ever be found for picturing adequately the psychical *content*, or the *structure* of the psychical *apparatus*, not even the graphic text or the writing machine. The contesting of the primacy of consciousness in fact reaches up to the idea of *congruence* especially as far as the representation or the imitation of the content and of the functioning of the psyche are concerned. Freud's differential conception precisely undermines the possibility of such conformity and questions raised by the argumentative and figurative elements of his text must necessarily be formulated otherwise, as the well known passage states:

> *We shall not have to ask* if a writing apparatus – for example, the one described in the 'Note on the Mystic Writing Pad' – is a *good* metaphor for representing the working of the psyche, *but rather* what apparatus we must create in order to represent psychical writing; and *we shall have to ask* what the imitation, projected and liberated in a machine, of something like psychical writing might mean. *And not* if the psyche is indeed a kind of text, *but*: what is a text, and what must the psyche be if it can be represented by a text? For if there is neither machine nor text without psychical origin, there is no domain of the psychic without text. *Finally, what must be* the relationship between psyche, writing, and spacing for such a metaphoric transition to be possible, not only, nor primarily, within theoretical discourse, but within the history of the psyche, text, and technology? [my emphasis apart from *good*]. (p. 199)

The essay develops two lines of arguments at once. On the one hand, what is at stake is the stream of metaphors required by Freud's theoretical presentation of his original conceptions, but on the other hand, 'metaphor' does not point to any specific representation, but rather to 'the possibility of the representational relation [*rapport représentatif*]' (p. 228) between the psyche and technical models. It is on the basis of this understanding of 'metaphor' that the demarcation between the psychical *content* and the psychical *apparatus*, between the 'text' and the 'machine', is said to require and to generate 'two series of metaphors': one pertaining to a *content* and the other to a *machine*. Freud's instrumental view of the 'machine', and therefore of 'metaphor', is revealed by the way in which the two series are in fact kept apart, in spite of his otherwise non-instrumental and differential insights. The progression of Freud's descriptions shows a *text* ('psychical writing'), whose origin (the 'writing machine' of the Mystic Writing Pad, which alone can have produced it) is apparently *invented*, not only *on the model* of, but also *after* the text. That provides the basis of Derrida's discussion of this curious relation between the *content* and the *apparatus* (or 'writing' and 'writing machine', 'psyche' and 'system'), a relation that is closely related to Freud's earliest neurological description of memory in 'The Project for a Scientific Psychology.'[46]

The initial definition of memory in the 1895 text is that of 'the capacity for being permanently altered by single occurrences'. But the following difficulty arises: 'on the one hand . . . neurones are permanently different after an excitation from what they were before, while nevertheless it cannot be disputed that, in general, fresh excitations meet with the same conditions of reception as did the earlier ones' (*Project*, p. 299), which means, that 'neurones must be both influenced and also unaltered, unprejudiced' (*ibid.*). In Derrida's terms, one has to account for the way in which memory points simultaneously to 'the permanence of the trace' and to 'the virginity of the receiving substance' ('Freud', p. 200). The problem is circumvented by the hypothesis of the 'contact-barriers' [*Kontaktschranken*] and of 'facilitation' [*Bahnung*] as a principle of resistance. Turning to Freud will help us to explain briefly what is at issue under these headings.

'The Project' establishes that 'neuronal excitation [can be described] as quantity [*Qn*] in a state of flow' (p. 296) and that nervous activity functions according to the 'principle of *inertia*', which is to say that it aims towards the discharge of quantity, seeks to avoid 'being burdened by a *Qn*'.[47] The orientation of all nervous activity towards discharge is called the primary function. If the functioning of the nervous system is characterized by the 'trend to inertia', when it is faced with what Freud calls the *'exigencies of life'* or the 'endogenous stimuli' – which bring about 'the major needs: hunger, respiration, sexuality' – it must put up with [maintaining] a store of *Qn* sufficient to meet the demand for a specific action [an act by virtue of which the major needs can be appeased]' ('The Project', p. 297). This accumulation of *Qn* is 'the secondary function' and 'all the functions of the nervous system can be comprised either under the aspect of the primary function or of the secondary one imposed by the exigencies of life' (*ibid.*). We are not presented with an alternative. Once the 'exigencies of life' are introduced, the problem is not simply that nervous activity can no longer be said to be led by the 'trend to inertia' alone. Rather, faced with the exigencies of 'life', the primary function (the process of discharge) becomes inseparable from something that opposes itself to the discharge of excitation. The 'secondary function', the accumulation of quantity, necessitates 'the resistances [which] are all to be located in the *contacts*' between the neurones and which 'assume the value of barriers [*Schranken*]'. These necessary 'resistances' are what Freud calls 'the hypothesis of the contact-barriers' (p. 298).

This hypothesis allows Freud to assign the contradictory functions of memory to two categories of neurones: 'there are permeable neurones (offering no resistance and retaining nothing) . . . and *impermeable* ones (loaded with resistance, and holding back *Qn*)' (p. 300). Memory is situated in the latter. The need to account for a capacity of receptivity and of retention is not quite eliminated by such a distinction. Once the neurones whose permanently modified 'contact-barriers' are elected to 'represent' memory, something else must come into play. The 'contact-barriers' of these neurones thus permanently modified, are yet submitted to change in so far as 'rememoration' (repetition) gradually eases the passage of quantity, up to the point where these neurones may become more and more similar [*immer ähnlicher werden*] to the neurones 'offering no resistance and retaining nothing' ('The Project', p. 300). Freud is obliged to introduce another principle of differentiation between the *facilitation*, and describes the changing state of the contact-barriers as their 'degree of *facilitation* [*Bahnung*]' (*ibid.*). Memory, then, cannot be explained by the fact that some neurones as opposed to others, offer a capacity of resistance or of *facilitation* (Freud later says that they consist in 'the absorption of *Qn* by the contact-barriers' [p. 301]), because 'if facilitation were everywhere equal, it would not be possible to see why one pathway should be preferred.' Rather, and this is a crucial point for Derrida, memory can best be 'represented by the differences in the facilitations between the χ neurones' (*ibid.*), differences, which, for Derrida, are 'the true origin of memory, and thus of the psyche' ('Freud', p. 201). Given that the *facilitations* are produced by 'the *Qn* which passes through the neurone in the excitatory process and on the number of repetitions of the process' ('The Project', p. 300), the difference between the *facilitations* comes to depend upon the difference between quantities and upon the number of repetitions. Moreover, a *facilitation*, which results from the passage of quantity, can be added to the quantity and can itself become an 'operative factor' in their production. The *facilitation* is for Derrida both analogous to quantity, and 'other as well' ('Freud', p. 201).

So far, scriptural metaphors have not been directly at issue. But what Freud describes under the heading of 'contact-barriers', *facilitations*, or difference between *facilitations*, borrowing abundantly, even if loosely, from neurology, will become crucial to the understanding of 'writing' and 'metaphoricity'. When Derrida says that every aspect of Freud's neurological explanation proceeds from a 'principle of difference', he does not point to the numerous distinctions upon which Freud's explanation rests – between *permeable* and *impermeable* neurones, between the primary and secondary functions (discharge and accumulation), or indeed, between the receptivity and the capacity of retention of memory. Rather, he draws our attention to the fact that the functions aligned on the side of the primary (of discharge, of 'life'), of perception, or of receptivity, cannot be conceived independently from what *resists* them. Memory cannot simply be said to be *the result* of the passage of a certain quantity leaving a trace (the 'facilitation'), whereby something present (quantity, excitations) is later imprinted. If a certain quantity can at all leave a trace, it is only in so far as the nervous system offers a resistance (opposes a certain quantity to the passage of another). Memory is not the 'imprint' of a singular event.[48] Hence, if what is elaborated under the heading of memory characterizes all psychical processes, the functioning of the psyche involves what Derrida calls 'originary repetition' (p. 301) as the 'opposition of forces' of differing amounts of excitations. What stands for the origin is from the outset a duplication, or to put it in Freud's lexicon, the discharge of quantities is only conceivable in relation to the contrasting accumulation of quantities.

The idea of 'originary repetition' is not only formulated in relation to the neurological terms of 'The Project', but also to those of *Beyond the Pleasure Principle*:

> All these differences in the production of the trace may be reinterpreted as moments of deferring [*moments de la différance*]. In accordance with a motif which will continue to dominate Freud's thinking, this movement is described as the effort of life to protect itself by *deferring* a dangerous cathexis [*l'investissement dangereux*], that is, by constituting a *reserve* (*Vorrat*). [The accumulation of quantities of the secondary function]. The threatening expenditure or presence [what produces *facilitations*] are deferred with the help of breaching or repetition. Is this not already the detour (*Aufschub*, lit. delay) which institutes the relation of pleasure to reality (*Beyond*)? Is it not already death at the origin of a life which can defend itself against death only through an *economy* of death, through deferment, repetition, reserve? For repetition does not happen to an initial impression; its possibility is already there in the resistance offered *the first time* by the psychical neurones. (p. 202)

Given that Freud's conception of the psyche is marked by 'différance' – it is a 'topography of traces, a map of breaches' (p. 205) – it is not surprising if no existing type of writing can easily represent, according to the didactic function of metaphor, psychical writing. Freud 'makes of psychical writing so originary a production that the writing we believe to be designated by the proper sense of the word – a script which is coded and visible "in the world" – would only be the metaphor of psychical writing'.[49]

The second section of the essay considers how the recourse to writing from *The Interpretation* onwards still aims to enlighten what 'The Project' calls a 'difficulty' arising with memory. Shortly after having represented the potential of memory 'for indefinite preservation and an unlimited capacity for reception' (p. 222) in terms of *facilitations*, Freud elaborates on this contradictory functioning with reference to 'inscriptions (*Niederschriften*)' and memory becomes a question of differences between inscriptions. But if no existing model of writing still seems to be suitable, it is in so far as each type of inscriptions is associated with a 'psychical locality' (never to be confused with cerebral anatomy), or to a system (*Ics. Pcs. Cs.*). The interrelations of the localities cannot be conceived in terms of the simple transcription, or the translation of one type of inscription into another, from one system to another. What writing, conceived as 'an irreversible, linear consecution, moving from present point to present point' (p. 217), cannot represent is the particular 'topography', and crucially, the 'temporality' which the relation between the different types of inscription and their distribution in the various systems imply:

> The text is not conceivable in an originary or modified form of presence. The unconscious text is already a weave of pure traces, differences in which meaning and force are united – a text nowhere present, consisting of archives which are *always already* transcriptions. Originary prints. Everything begins with reproduction. Always already: repositories of a meaning which was never present, whose signified presence is always reconstituted by deferral, *nachträglich*, belatedly, *supplementarily*: for the *nachträglich* also means *supplementary*. The call of the supplement is primary, here, and it hollows out that which will be reconstituted by deferral as the present. (p. 212)

The insufficiency of the scriptural analogy does not only arise from models of writing themselves, but also from the fact that Freud is working according to the distinction between the *psychical content* and *apparatus*. Failing to discover appropriate scriptural models that correspond to psychical writing, Freud searches for mechanical (optical) ones. For Derrida, as long as metaphorical models are sought separately for the content and the apparatus, Freud will be unable to find the appropriate one. The 'constant appeal to the principle of difference' (p. 309) requires us to conceive of the content and of the apparatus (or 'the system and the psychical' p. 221) together. The introduction of the 'Mystic Writing-Pad' corresponds to the moment in Freud's discourse when the latter are jointly described, to the moment when the two components are finally brought together by means of 'a writing machine', an 'apparatus of originary recording or inscription'. It is worth recalling Freud's description of the instrument:

> The Mystic Pad is a slab of ark brown resin or wax with a paper edging; over the slab is laid a thin transparent sheet, the top end of which is firmly secured to the slab while its bottom end rests upon it without being fixed to it. This transparent sheet is the more interesting part of the little device. It itself consists of two layers which can be detached from each other except at their two ends. The upper layer is a transparent piece of celluloid; the lower layer is made of thin translucent waxed paper. When the apparatus is not in use, the lower surface of the waxed paper adheres lightly to the upper surface of the wax slab.

> To make use of the Mystic Pad, one writes upon the celluloid portion of the covering-sheet which rests on the wax slab. For this purpose no pencil or chalk is necessary, since the writing does not depend on material being deposited on the receptive surface. It is a return to the ancient method of writing on tablets of clay or wax: a pointed stylus scratches the surface, the pressions upon which constitute the 'writing'. In the case of the Mystic Pad this scratching is not effected directly, but through the medium of the covering-sheet. At the points which the stylus touches, it presses the lower surface of the waxed paper on to the wax slab, and the grooves are visible as dark writing upon the otherwise smooth whitish-grey surface of the celluloid. If one wishes to destroy what has been written, all that is necessary is to raise the double covering-sheet from the wax slab by a light pull, starting from the free lower end. The close contact between the waxed paper and the wax slab at the places which have been scratched (upon which the visibility of the writing depended) is thus brought to an end and it does not recur when the two surfaces come together once more. The Mystic Pad is now clear of writing and ready to receive fresh notes (SE XIX, p. 229).

Derrida's commentary of the 'Note upon the "Mystic Writing Pad"' is at least twofold. On the one hand, what is of interest is that the design of the *Wunderblock* combines the 'double system' which has been Freud's problem all along. Freud draws out three analogies (*Analogien*) between the various elements of the Mystic Pad and the psychical apparatus. One element can be likened to the function of perception ('the layer which receives the stimuli' which 'forms no permanent trace' (Freud quoted by Derrida, p. 224), another to the unconscious (the 'wax slab' where the 'permanent trace of what was written is retained . . . and is legible in suitable lights' (*ibid.*). These two analogies, Derrida argues, concern the 'space of writing, its extension and volume' (*ibid.*), while the third one is related to the time of writing: 'On the Mystic Pad, the writing vanishes every time the close contact is broken between the paper which receives the stimulus and the wax slab which preserves the impression' (Freud quoted by Derrida, p. 225). That discontinuous temporality corresponds to the 'functioning of the psychical apparatus' ('consciousness fades each time'; Freud says on numerous occasions that 'consciousness' is an episodic phenomenon). The explanation of the functioning of the machine recalls what was introduced under the heading of 'trace' or 'writing', in the first section of the essay. For example, referring to the way in which 'at least two hands are needed to make the apparatus function, as well as a system of gestures . . . an organized multiplicity of origins' (p. 226), but also more generally, to the functioning of the instrument as a whole. Derrida writes:

> Traces thus produce the space of their inscription only by acceding to the period of their erasure. From the beginning, in the 'present' of their first impression, they are constituted by the double force of repetition and erasure, legibility and illegibility. A two-handed machine, a multiplicity of agencies or origins – is this not the original relation to the other and the original temporality of writing, its 'primary' complication: an originary spacing, deferring, and erasure of the simple origin, and polemics on the very threshold of what we persist in calling perception? (p. 226)

We could discuss the convergence between the 'neurological fable' and the instrument at greater length. But there is another side to Derrida's examination, namely the question concerning 'the imitation, projected and liberated in a machine of something like psychical writing' (p. 199), or the *resemblance* between the psychical and the non-psychical apparatus. For 'writing' does not only point to the functioning of the psyche or of the Mystic Pad, but also to the metaphorical relation between the two, which itself forms a 'system of traces', and to which 'metaphoricity' points.

What looks like a congruent moment – the finding of a machine as original as the conception which it is meant to illustrate – reveals, according to Derrida, a more serious flaw. Although Freud grants the machine a remarkable power of resemblance, he nonetheless considers it instrumentally as a 'mechanical memory', that is, as supplementary tool, as 'death', reserving the privilege of life to 'psychical memory'. According to Derrida, then, Freud does not acknowledge the implication of his own insights concerning the economy of life and death: the machine 'still participates in Cartesian space and mechanics: *natural* wax, exteriority of the *memory aid*' (p. 227).[50]

Having sketched the argument of the essay, we can now ask whether Derrida's dismissal of the 'hereditary mnenic trace' does not suggest that his analyses of the metaphorical side of Freud's discourse spare certain areas of his thought, notably everything that has to do with the extension of psychoanalysis 'beyond the individual'. By doing so does he not leave aside what precisely engages the 'discontinuities' that mark Freud's conception of the psyche, and therefore, make the search of an adequate representation endless? It is indeed when Freud is moving away from any 'observable' phenomenon that the greatest metaphorical resources are required. The system of memory-traces already defies observation. To imagine the functioning of 'memory-traces' at the level of the masses will however put even more strain on the theoretical structure than the 'mythological neurology' of 'The Project'. The most striking 'epistemological' warnings are indeed the ones that accompany the hypothesis of phylogenesis, the transmission of an archaic heritage, those that Derrida has pushed aside. Freud says, for example in *The Ego and The Id* (1923), that to try to deal with phylogenesis produces the fear that such an attempt 'will lay bare the inadequacy of our whole effort' (in this instance, of the effort to discover whether religion and morality originate in the ego or the id).[51] The 'possibility of the inheritance of actual ancestral experiences' is at issue almost everywhere in Freud (SE XXIII, p. 102), and studying systematically its many occurrences from *The Interpretation*, to *Totem and Taboo* (1912–13) to *The Ego and the Id*, up until the 'The Outline of Psycho-Analysis' (1940 [1938]) exceeds the limits of the present work.[52] As we will see in chapter 5 when considering *Moses and Monotheism: Three Essays* (1939 [1937–39]), in the context of that hypothesis, the mass becomes the indefinite 'support' of the persistence and transmission of the 'forgotten' past. In 'The Project', the preservation of psychical contents depends upon the conflicting receptive and non-receptive functions of neurones, and in *The Interpretation* upon the topographical differentiation of agencies and inscriptions. In *Moses and Monotheism*, the preservation of psychical content depends upon the 'human masses' which condense 'the residues of the existence of countless egos', to borrow what Freud says of the id (p. 138). It is therefore peculiar that Derrida should note that 'in *Moses and Monotheism*, the efficacy of delay and of action subsequent to the event is at work over large historical intervals', and underline that the problem of latency is, in this text, 'in highly significant contact with the problem of oral and written tradition' (p. 203), given that he has fixed beforehand the (non-figurative?) status of 'heredity' in the introduction of the essay, and excluded it from the examination of metaphors in Freud. According to Derrida, Freud renews the traditional separation between memory and technical instruments – between memory and death. In formulating these reproaches against the backdrop of the a priori exclusion of the 'hereditary mnenic trace', however, Derrida appears conversely not willing to grant the status of model to the 'living' – the human masses – as he does when neurones, various metaphors of writing, or the writing machine are concerned.

'Freud' thus has a double interest for our study. On the one hand, it judiciously emphasizes the intrication between metaphor and concept in Freud. As an energetics of force, the Freudian conception of the psyche transforms, somewhat unknowingly, the representation between the psyche and its models, and if we agree with the consequences of Derrida's examination, between the psyche and 'the world' (p. 229). But on the other hand, it demonstrates that, even if one has fully acknowledged how the complex intrication of metaphors and concepts in Freud transforms what Derrida calls 'metaphysical oppositions', such as that between life and death, etc., there remains the difficulty of dealing with that of the 'individual' and the 'mass'. It is hence puzzling to see Derrida's essay merely allude to the question of 'beyond the psychoanalysis of the individual', because its 'themes' – the 'relation to the other', the 'originary spacing' that are implied in the temporality of *Nachträglichkeit* – point to the conceptual extremities towards which such a 'beyond' leads us. In the following study, one of the senses that the 'mass' has is inextricably bound up with the disquieting set of hypotheses related to the transmission of an archaic heritage.

2
Quantity, Mass and Metaphor

All commentaries of Freud's work, whether they should be carried out by analysts or non-analysts, raise the question of Freud's use of metaphors and models, but, as the article on the psychical apparatus from the *Vocabulaire* shows, what corresponds to this description poses problems of delimitation. One of Derrida's merits is to have expressly focused on this ambiguous situation, not exactly, however, in order to present the 'solution to all . . . difficulties', as the *Wunderblock* is purported to do. Far from settling rhetorical matters, 'Freud and the scene of writing' shows the extent to which the problem of metaphoricity runs right through Freud's theoretical edifice. If the essay however does not conclude on this aspect of Freud's work, it is partly because it, too, involves significant 'representational relations'.[1] When Derrida emphasizes that the origin of memory lies in the 'contact between *two* forces', that 'at least two hands are needed to make the apparatus function', or that writing points to the relation 'between the two apparatuses', one is not in fact dealing with dual relations.[2] Rather, the redoubling implied in 'two forces', 'two hands', 'two apparatuses' and which has been at issue throughout Derrida's essay, signals that the psyche is constituted by a multiplicity, of 'layers' or of 'traces'. The 'two' points to the several: to affirm that 'at least two hands are needed to write' amounts to saying that 'we must be several to write' (p. 226).[3]

The essay does not however limit itself with speaking of multiplicity by means of the 'two', it also speaks of it in terms of 'sociality'. What is puzzling is not so much that the 'many' should call to mind the question of sociality, but rather that what has been dealt with under the heading of 'writing' and 'metaphoricity' – the intrication of the psyche and its metaphors and models – should itself call forth the figure of an unspecified 'social' bond. Should 'sociality' be included among the projections of the psyche that preoccupy Derrida? Whatever one makes of the transition from metaphoricity to sociality, it suggests that there is an affinity between metaphoricity and 'the many'. This affinity cannot be reduced to the empirical proliferation of metaphors in Freud's text, or to the 'quantity' of metaphor that could be found in any text. Derrida's subsequent analyses of metaphor in the philosophical tradition focus on the 'tendency to multiply' that inhabits the concept of metaphor, beyond Freud's work. Rather than following Derrida's steps as regard metaphor and multiplicity, however, we will concentrate on the equivocations that arise in Freudian thought whenever the various figures of 'the many', the 'numerous', indeed 'quantity' – as one of the fundamental concepts of psychoanalysis – are at issue.

The hypothesis of phylogenesis, to which we alluded above, could be viewed as one such figure, in so far as the idea of an archaic heritage, of successive generations necessarily involves the 'numerous'. We will come back again throughout the book, and more particularly in chapter 5, to this contentious feature of Freudian psychoanalysis. Among many other aspects of Freud's work, those that involve 'quantities' and the economic point of view (does that not describe every aspect of the theory?) no doubt require more than any other the use of metaphors and models, as though the 'unknown' of psychoanalysis were above all of a quantitative nature. So much so that dealing with the figurative aspect of Freud's writings would seem necessarily to amount to dealing with 'the many'. In order to explore further the intrication between metaphors and 'quantity' in Freud's writings, the chapter will focus on the apparently common political metaphor of the mass and examine what kind of representations the term 'mass' can in fact provide of quantitative concerns. We will see that having recourse to the *image* of the mass aggravates the problems that metaphors are temporarily supposed to dissipate, and conversely, that simply assigning a figurative status to the mass can yet here constitute only a provisional step.

We underlined in chapter 1 two complementary attitudes towards the singularity of Freud's figurative mode of argumentation. Another common approach pertains more specifically to political metaphors and consists in affirming that the latter are not 'merely metaphorical' and in endeavouring to make systematic sense of them.[4] For example (and this is perhaps, with that of 'censorship', the most often quoted example), Freud resorts to the following political 'images' for describing the function of the ego:

> [The ego] is entrusted with important functions. By virtue of its relation to the perceptual system it gives mental processes an order in

> time and submits them to 'reality-testing'. by interposing the processes of thinking, it secures a postponement of motor discharges and controls the access to motility. This last power is, to be sure, a question more of form than of fact; in the matter of action the ego's position is like that of a constitutional monarch, without whose sanction no law can be passed but who hesitates long before imposing his veto on any measure put forward by Parliament.[5]

Many other passages in Freud involve various metaphors built upon political and conflictual situations.[6] Some commentators consider that the latter gives us access to Freud's *political thought*. Because of these dispersed comparisons, one indeed deduces Freud's conception of 'autonomy and freedom', his 'authoritarian stance' in relation to the 'liberal tradition'.[7] This interpretation seems to answer the objection that Freudian thought fails to be 'political' and to demonstrate that it might not be explicitly so, but that somewhere or other, there is a Freudian 'political truth' to be discovered. If only we interpret Freud's political metaphors accurately . . . Such an exegesis relies, on the one hand, on the idea that there is, in the 'external world', something to which Freud's metaphors conform, but reveals, on the other hand, that the conformity between the two dimensions goes without saying. From the moment, however, that Freud wrote essays whose explicit theme corresponds to what is otherwise deemed to be figurative, and conversely, can Freud's appeal to political terms, for example, when he speaks of the pleasure principle as an 'omnipotent institution' or of the 'dictatorship of reason' really give us clues about his political thought?[8] Which of Freud's abundant use of military images or his essays on the war and war neuroses, can serve as a basis for assessing Freud's thought on 'War and Death'? Are the essays on 'political' themes not 'metaphorical' in relation to the rest of Freud's therapeutic work, in the sense that they could serve the purpose of confirming or illustrating the core of psychoanalytic theory?

Among the many political terms, at least one of them slows down the typical translation of these comparisons into a political treatise, namely, the term 'mass' and its cognates. Supposing that metaphors carry the socio-political thought of a text, that of the 'mass' could not indeed teach us a great deal about Freud's. For the 'mass' is at all times a vaguely defined term that makes us oscillate between a 'socio-political' and a quantitative understanding of it (as when we speak simply of 'a mass of' something).

Were we to restrict ourselves to a socio-political understanding of the term, comparisons involving the mass would be no less ambiguous. For, according to some definitions of the term, for example, those elaborated by late nineteenth-century and early twentieth-century 'psychology of crowd' – it designates primarily a situation where imitation and contagion reign. In other words, according to what is meant to be its most obvious acceptation, the mass denotes a 'milieu of resemblance', of homogeneity. From that point of view, models and metaphors in Freud, in so far as they proceed from a certain ideal of resemblance, could be said to form a 'mass'. In what follows, the mass will point as much to a necessary component of Freud's mode of argumentation as to a certain, yet unspecified, human grouping.

Viewed from this angle, the metaphor of the mass is indeed an unyielding 'socio-political' marker in Freud's work. For the 'mass' rather reminds us of the extent to which Freudian thought is preoccupied with 'quantity', whether it be a question of a 'quantity' of human beings or of the psychical energy that flows conflictually according to antagonist principles. The figure of the mass, then, does not here so much carry a thinker's political views, as it reveals a knot of difficulty that Freud sometimes calls 'quantitative factors'. Instead of acting, then, as an index of Freud's 'authoritative stance', the term mass will indeed here stand for what makes Freud *himself* raise questions about the intrication of concepts and figures in psychoanalysis.

In dealing with the mass, we will constantly and obviously be preoccupied with *quantity*. Let us specify what 'quantity', 'quantitative factors' here mean. At the beginning of this chapter, we saw that the idea of repetition and of reproduction that is at the core of Freud's conception of the psyche, according to Derrida, comes to be linked to 'sociality', to the image of a bond presumably uniting humans. It is not clear whether the idea of a human social bond is introduced because the structure and functioning of the psyche cannot be conceived solipsistically, or whether the idea of sociality is meant to transpose figuratively the intrication of the psyche and its models in the field of human relations so as to render it more intelligible. (Could we not here be describing the passage that the first to the second topography marks as a passage from abstract 'systems' to anthropomorphic 'agencies' in almost exactly the same terms?) Whatever we make of this association, it alerts us of a bond between metaphors and what we called 'the many' and 'the numerous'.

In the context of Freud's writings, 'quantity' can of course refer to a 'quantity of' people, of dreams, of patients, etc. It however also points to 'the progenitor of one of the three fundamental factors in metapsychology', to a 'mysterious Q' of an essentially unknown nature. In his appendix to the 'Project for a Scientific Psychology' (1895), James Strachey underlines Freud's ignorance as to the basic nature of Q – to use Freud's notation – even though he could describe its essential features.[9] This fundamental ignorance justifies the use of 'auxiliary constructions', of *Hilfsvorstellungen* (or in the words we have been using so far, of models and metaphors). We find one of the earliest appearances of this 'unknown entity' at the end of 'The Neuro-Psychoses of Defence' (1894). The passage clearly shows the extent to which the concept of a 'quota' that cannot be measured has the status of a 'working hypothesis', the very status that Freud grants to models and metaphors:

> I should like, finally, to dwell for a moment on the working hypothesis [*Hilfsvorstellung*] which I have made use of in this exposition of the neuroses of defence. I refer to the concept [*die Vorstellung*] that in mental functions something is to be distinguished – a quota of affect or sum of excitation – *which possesses all the characteristics of a quantity (though we have no means of measuring it), which is capable of increase, diminution, displacement and discharge,* and which is spread over the memory-traces of ideas somewhat as an electric charge is spread over the surface of a body.[10]

According to Strachey, 'characteristics of Q survived in a transmogrified shape to the very end of Freud's writings.' In 'The Project' Q is considered to be 'something material . . . subject to the general laws of motion,' following the aim of 'The Project' to 'furnish a psychology that shall be a natural science', but it re-appears subsequently, gradually no longer as something material, 'under various aliases'. The various occurrences of the 'mass' could well turn out to be as many 'aliases' of this 'unknown entity'.[11]

The secret nature of Q, then, is closely associated with the 'principle' whereby faced with such an enigma, one must look for models and metaphors. So much so that just as the 'mysterious Q' could be said to be progenitor of later metapsychological concepts, as Strachey suggests, the passage that introduces it could be said to provide an antecedent, a 'prototype' of all subsequent recourses to 'working hypotheses' [*Hilfsvorstellung*], to provide one of the rules of formation of psychoanalytic concepts.

Freud comments on this procedure repeatedly. Concerning the 'displacement of quantities' that the functioning of the psychical apparatus entails, for example, Freud writes in *The Interpretation of Dreams*: 'The mechanics of these processes are quite unknown to me; anyone who wished to take these ideas seriously would have *to look for physical analogies to them and find a means of picturing the movements that accompany excitation of neurones'* (SE VI, p. 599).[12] Freud in fact never ceases to be preoccupied with the 'means of picturing' what cannot but remain 'unknown', beginning with the mysterious Q. His efforts to maintain the distinction between the 'means of picturing movements' and what motivates the search for analogies are never as thwarted as when the depictions involve the mass. Not only do these acceptations in any case tend to merge, but most importantly, in the context of Freud's writings, the mass can easily act as one of the names of Q. On the one hand, the notion of the mass would seem to fit in the chain of 'deficient' theoretical means that await their replacement, but on the other hand, it demarcates itself from other psychoanalytic concepts in that it would appear to stand as the concept of the unavoidable insufficiency and transitoriness of all psychoanalytic concepts.

Let us consider one of the figurative occurrences of the term 'mass', in the context of the revisions of the second topography, in order to show that the metaphor of the mass easily leads to confusing identifications between psychoanalytic concepts and 'means of picturing' employed by Freud in their elaboration. Lecture XXXI entitled 'The Dissection of the Psychical Personality' of the *New Introductory Lectures* (1933 [1932]) recapitulates changes brought about to the conception of the psychical apparatus around 1920. Freud has 'come upon something in the ego itself which is also unconscious, which *behaves exactly like* the repressed – that is, which produces powerful effects without itself being conscious [my emphasis].'[13] 'Something' disturbs previous states of the theory, that is, the 'resistances proceeding from the ego during analysis and an unconscious sense of guilt' (SE XIX, p. 4).[14] Certain ideas have previously arisen as early as in 1895 in 'The Project', notably, the idea of the ego as an 'organization', but they now form part of a structural view of the mind, whereby the emphasis lay on the interrelations between three agencies: the Id, the Ego and the Super-ego. Up until then, the 'coherent organization of mental processes', which is called the *ego* is forged in opposition to the repressed, which is the 'foreign territory to the ego' (p. 57), and which stands as 'the prototype of the unconscious' [*das Vorbild des Unbewußten*]. If 'a part of the ego too . . . is *Ucs.*', then, the *repressed* cannot coincide with the *Ucs.*, nor the ego with the system *Pcs.-Cs.* 'Unconscious' and 'conscious' need to be rethought in the context of the resemblance of the ego to the repressed. It can no longer solely be defined in terms of a conflict between the unconscious and the conscious, but rather one that involves 'conscience' [*Gewissen*] in the popular sense of a 'moral conscience'.

The innovation of the second topography thus most manifestly pertains to that unconscious part of the ego – the super-ego – as the representative of 'every moral restriction', the origin of conscience, 'the higher side of human life' (Lecture XXXI, p. 67).[15] Yet, Lecture XXXI touches on each province of the psychical personality [*Persönlichkeit*], notably the id [*Es*], about which Freud however admits that he does not 'have much to tell [us] that is new . . . apart from its new name', which he borrows from Nietzsche via Georg Groddeck.[16] Given the importance, in Freud, of 'naming' processes which have never hitherto been identified, assigning a 'new name' to a province of the *Seelenapparat* could mean telling much 'that is new': 'when we recognize' Freud writes 'that something has a separate existence we give it a name of its own'.

What has been said previously about the id in *The Ego and the id* is repeated. The id is 'the dark, inaccessible part of our personality' (p. 73) in the sense that one can gain knowledge of its functioning only through the study of substitutes such as, for example, neurotic symptoms and the dream-work. We come upon an important principle of Freudian thought. Not only is direct access to the processes which psychoanalysis seeks to know denied, but the latter precisely sets out to demonstrate the existence of (conflictual) processes that elude observation, that are unapparent, but that nonetheless produce *observable* effects.[17] These effects are most often conceived of as substitutes [*Ersatz*] or as *Repräsentanz*, whose formation and work [*Arbeit*] need to be explained. One speaks of 'substitutive formation' [*Ersatzbildung*], for example, to point to 'symptoms – or equivalent formations such as parapraxes, jokes, etc. – in so far as they stand for unconscious contents'.[18]

There are many formulations of this principle, such as for example, in *The Interpretation of Dreams*, where the physician is said not to be able to 'learn of . . . unconscious processes until they have produced some effect upon consciousness which can be communicated or observed . . . the conscious effect is only a remote psychical result of the unconscious process . . . and the latter has not become conscious as such.'[19] A passage from the *Introductory Lectures on Psycho-analysis* (1916–17) attracts particular notice: '[dreams], on the analogy [*in Analogie*] of our views on parapraxes . . . are a distorted substitute for an unknown content [*ein entstellter Ersatz für einen unbekannten Inhalt*] . . . the first thing is to trace them back to it.'[20] The idea that psychoanalysis should be, generally speaking, concerned with *substitution* – which makes

Ludwig Binswanger describes it as 'a paradoxical phenomenology of the inapparent' – is reinforced. Dreams are substitutes 'by analogy' to parapraxes, the latter having not only the function of representing the whole species of 'disturbed intentions', but also of providing a model of the functioning of 'psychical processes' in general.[21] *Substitution*, then, is not only one of psychical processes, which interest psychoanalysis.[22] At the level of theoretical elaboration and exposition, phenomena take the place of each other, just as dreams, parapraxes, or neurotic symptoms do of an 'unknown, repressed content'. Hence, Freud regularly comments upon the relation between dreams and neurotic symptoms, or between the latter and parapraxes with respect to the 'yield of knowledge' they allow. In the preface to the first edition of the *Interpretation*, for example, Freud refers to the relation between dreams and neuroses as 'points of contact' [*Kontaktstellen*], that are responsible for the gaps and deficiencies in the exposition. These missing 'points of contact' put to the test his powers of exposition: 'The broken threads which so frequently interrupt my presentation are nothing less than the many points of contact between the problem of the formation of dreams and the more comprehensive problems of psycho-pathology.'[23] This raises the question as to whether one phenomenon acts as a model for all psychical processes, both normal and pathological.

In this general context of substitution, the question arises as to whether the 'name of the id' can be thought as a substitute. It is however soon replaced by what Freud calls comparisons [*Vergleich*]:

> We approach the id with analogies: we call it a chaos, a cauldron full of seething excitations [*Wir nähern uns dem Es mit Vergleichen, nennen es ein Chaos, einen Kessel voll brodelnder Erregungen*]. We picture it as being open at its end to somatic influences, and as there taking up into itself instinctual needs which find their psychical expression in it, but we cannot say in what substratum. It is filled with energy [*Energie*] reaching it from the instincts [*Trieben*], but it has no organization, produces no collective will [*Gesamtwillen*], but only a striving to bring about the satisfaction of the instinctual needs [*Triebbedürfnisse*] subject to the observance of the pleasure principle. (p. 73)

Let us consider briefly the economic language of the passage. Freud states the basic functioning of the psychical apparatus repeatedly: '[I]t seems as though our total mental activity is directed towards achieving pleasure and avoiding unpleasure – that it is automatically regulated by the *pleasure principle*.'[24] Pleasure is initially related to 'the diminution, reduction or extinction of the amounts of stimulus [*Reizmengen*] prevailing in the mental apparatus', while 'unpleasure is connected with their increase' (*ibid.*). The economic conception of pleasure and pain is discussed from 'The Project' throughout the entire Freudian corpus, notably in *Beyond the pleasure principle* (1920), where Freud meditates upon the fact that, against what his earlier conception suggests, there can be pleasurable increases and tensions.[25] Whatever changes the notion of the pleasure principle undergoes, it introduces a conception of psychical activity based on the circulation of a 'quantifiable energy'. However, the pleasure principle may well be, with the reality principle, one of the two fundamental principles of the functioning of the psychical apparatus, Freud yet insists upon the hypothetical nature of such conceptions. In *Beyond*, Freud says of the sensations of pleasure and unpleasure that:

> this is the most obscure and inaccessible region in the mind, and, since we cannot avoid contact with it, the least rigid hypothesis [*die lockerste Annahme*], it seems to me, will be the best. We have decided to relate pleasure and unpleasure to the quantity of excitation that is present in the mind [*Quantität der im Seelenleben vorhandenen – und nicht irgendwie gebunden – Erregung*] but is not always 'bound' [*gebunden*]; and to relate them in such a manner that unpleasure corresponds to an *increase* in the quantity of excitation and pleasure to a *diminution*.[26]

If Freud recommends 'the least rigid hypothesis' for the 'most obscure and inaccessible region in the mind', in the passage just quoted, the hypothesis of the quantitative factor prompts the search for *comparisons*. That 'all there is in the id' are '[i]nstinctual cathexes [*Triebbesetzungen*] seeking discharges' (p. 74) according to 'the dominating economic pressure towards the discharge of energy' is expressed in terms of 'chaos' and 'seething excitations' which refuse organization and the ordering effect of a 'collective will' [*Gesamtwillen*]. The movement of excitations is compared to a situation of turmoil as it can be observed in a kettle, but what follows indicate that the image of turmoil is also based on some situation of disorganization which takes place among entities that can otherwise form a collective will. A page later, Freud specifies that the state of these instinctual impulses [*Triebregungen*] is 'different from other regions of the mind', they are 'far more mobile' in order to allow the processes of displacement and condensation which characterize the id, and which 'disregard the *quality* of what is cathected' (p. 75). But in so far as Lecture XXXI aims to explain 'the possibility [that] . . . portions of the ego and super-ego' should be 'unconscious', that is, the possibility of an *Ucs*. 'which is not repressed',[27] it insists upon the fact that the character of being unconscious cannot correspond only to processes characteristic of the id, which Freud now calls, as though he were ceasing to resort to comparisons, 'primitive and irrational' [*primitiv und irrationell*].

In 'My Contact with Josef Popper-Lynkeus' (1932), Freud recounts how the study of dreams became central to the study of other psychopathological formations. Among other problems of dream-life, the way in which the dream-work imposes distortion [*Entstellung*] 'upon the rational and intelligible material' is singled out as the 'profoundest and the most difficult' one.[28] Before dealing with the concept of repression thanks to which dream-distortion can be explained, Freud gives the following representation of the mind [*Seele*], which recalls that of the Lecture of the same year:

> our mind, that precious instrument by whose means we maintain ourselves in life, is no peacefully self-contained unity [*Einheit*]. It is rather to be compared with a modern State [*einem modernen Staat vergleichbar*] in which a mob, eager for enjoyment and destruction [*in dem eine genuß- und zerstörungssüchtige Masse*], has to be held down forcibly by a prudent superior class. The whole flux of our mental life and everything that finds expression in our thoughts are derivations and representatives [*Abkömmling und Vertretung*] of the multifarious instincts [*mannigfache Triebe*] that are innate in our physical constitution. But these instincts are not all equally susceptible to direction and education, or equally ready to fall in with the demands of the external world and of human society [*Gemeinschaft*]. A number of them have retained their primitive, ungovernable nature [*ursprünglich unbändige Charakter*]; if we let them have their way, they would infallibly bring us to ruin. (p. 221)[29]

In the passage from the Lecture, the excitations are described as *seething* [*brodeln*]. Even though this 'seething activity' is spoken of as if it were containable in a cauldron, the representation of the agitation of *Erregungen* seems in fact to appeal to a (social?) situation where disorganization prevails, and where a 'collective will' is lacking. *Brodeln* [seething], according to the distinction between the literal and the figurative operative in dictionaries, designates – figuratively – the agitation produced by a crowd, such as, for example, in the phrase: 'the streets were seething with people', and is – also figuratively – associated with unrest: 'there is seething unrest' (*Collins German Dictionary*).[30] But it is not so much on the basis of the possible *figurative* use of this term, but rather on the basis of the no less potentially ambiguous and negative reference to a *Gesamtwille*, that we are attributing to Freud's comparisons, a socio-political value.[31]

In the passage from 'My Contact', however, the comparisons pose apparently fewer problems. Leaving aside the description of the mind as an instrument [*Instrument*], the mind [*Seele*] is compared to a modern State. The suspicion that the form of agitation at issue in the previous passage, could be determined most of all with reference to a social or political situation is apparently confirmed. We could attempt to draw out which conception of the modern State might have led Freud to deem it suitable for representing the mind.[32] But the concept of the state was never one of Freud's direct concerns or themes, despite many allusions to Austrian and European politics in his correspondence, and throughout his work.[33] Freud's writings seemingly have no immediate relevance to the elucidation of such comparison. In view of this passage, we can at most assert that the 'modern State', to which Freud appeals, is divisible and can be comprised of heterogeneous elements, notably of the homogeneous *Masse*.[34] What was, in the previous passage, containable in a cauldron, is now *unified* under the heading of an agitated *Masse*. It is with reference to it that the *mannigfache Triebe* can be said to be 'destructive and eager for enjoyment' by contrast with the prudence of a 'superior class' [*Oberschicht*] that possesses as an *inhibiting* or *repressive* power.

Taken in isolation from the rest of the text, this extract provides an opportunity to gain some insight into Freud's conception of the *Masse*, which has, at first, nothing unusual about it. Besides showing eagerness for enjoyment and destruction [*eine genuß- und zerstörungssüchtige Masse*], what forms a mass is capable of avoiding 'direction and education' and more generally, 'the demands of the external world and of human society [*Gemeinschaft*]'. Freud is here concerned with the 'whole flux of our mental life [*Alles, was sich in unserem Seelenleben tummelt*]' but within that *swarming*, it is the *Triebe* that have 'retained their primitive and ungovernable character' [*ursprünglich unbändiger Charakter*] that are gathered under the heading of a *Masse*. When Freud writes the above passage, the mass has been determined – at least since the 1890s but obviously well before that – as being 'instinctual, irrational, primitive, destructive and seeking enjoyment'. By contrast with the new conception of psychical life that the passage presents, Freud would seem to renew a *common, popular* conception of the mass, whereby the mass is most of all a primitive and irrational phenomenon.[35] However elementary and traditional Freud's conception of the mass is, it is apparently suitable for representing the particular type of activity that takes place in the *id*, or for representing the 'quantity in a state of flow', to use the neuro-physiological lexicon of 'The Project'.

One cannot fail to notice, however, the peculiar relation that emerges from this passage between the *id* and the rudimentary 'instinctual' figure of the mass that is meant to 'picture' the obscure region of the mind. Pending further clarifications of the concepts of *Trieb* and *Erregung*, and the exploration of attributes such as 'primitive' [*ursprünglich*] throughout Freud, the choice of the figure of the mass does not appear to be a very judicious one, if the latter is meant to fulfil an illustrative function.[36] In view of the elementary 'instinctual' and 'quantitative' conception of the *Masse* that is at stake in these passages, comparing the *id* or the 'instinctual needs' to a *Masse* amounts, to comparing 'instinctual needs' to 'instincts', 'a mass of excitation' to 'a mass', indeed, 'quantity' to 'a mass'. The mass as *comparant* becomes indistinguishable from the *comparé*.

It would be mistaken, however, to brush this *tautological* moment aside as a mere defect of expression. For the *congruity* that the comparison of the id to a mass engenders could be considered as a 'complete comparison' even though Freud does not speak throughout his work as such of 'complete comparison' but rather of 'complete analogies' [*völlstandige Analogien*].[37] From this point of view, the tautology would be explainable in terms of the rudimentary theory of metaphor that transpires in Freud's numerous comments on the necessary use of analogies. In fact, even though the latter are often labelled as 'völlig kongruente' (*Die Traumdeutung*, p. 157), they appear to be so mostly in order the better to emphasize the 'points of disagreement' that eventually make them lose their 'completeness'. Freud indeed often speaks of the way in which a comparison 'fails'. What at first appeared as an 'identity' between a representation and the thing, soon reveals 'divergent paths', that makes us abandon that particular analogy, or momentarily, our search for analogy. Resemblance has a temporal character; in the order of theoretical exposition, it is interrupted and must be found again.

The completeness, the perfection and the imperfection of analogies and comparisons provide precious indications concerning Freud's idiosyncratic use of them. (They seem to be chosen because of an affinity with what has to be explained, but they equally seem to be chosen because the affinity eventually gives way to damning disparities. Freud's typical introduction and rejection of analogies recalls, mutatis mutandis, that of the process of thinking, as Freud elaborates on it in 'The Project'. The 'similarity' that is looked for and that constitutes a criterion for the adoption of analogies can indeed be drawn near the way in which the passage from thought (from judging) to action is described, in the sections on 'Cognition and Reproductive Thought' and on 'Thought and Reality' in 'The Project':

> *judging* is a ψ process which is only made possible by inhibition of the ego and which is evoked by the dissimilarity [*Unähnlichkeit*] between the *wishful cathexis* [*Wunschbesetzung*] of a memory and a perceptual cathexis that is similar to it. It can be inferred from this that the coincidence between the two cathexes becomes a biological signal for ending the act of thought and for allowing discharge to begin. Their non-coincidence gives the impetus for the activity of thought, which is terminated once more with their coincidence. (p. 328)
>
> The aim and end of all thought-processes is thus to bring about a *state of identity* [*Identitätszustandes*], the conveying of a cathexis *Qn* emanating from outside, into a neurone cathected from the ego . . . judging . . . is originally an associative process between cathexes coming from outside and arising from one's own body, an *identification* [*Identifizierung*] *of information or cathexes from* φ and from within' [Freud's emphasis]. (pp. 332, 334)

Just as judging and thinking are provoked by non-coincidence and end with the attainment of coincidence – which marks the beginning of action – in the field of psychoanalytic research, dissimilarity that eventually mars analogies ('imperfection', as Freud says) is the motor of theoretical activity. For ultimately no analogy is ever 'complete' and the degree of coincidence is never sufficiently high to make one pass from 'thought' to action, or to make one leave behind thought processes. (We are presupposing that 'theoretical activity' is of the order of 'thinking'. One could object that the passage from the latter to 'action' – clinical activity? – in psychoanalysis ought to occur according to other rules.) In other words, no analogy ever constitutes an adequate representation of the unknown, no 'state of identity' is ever permanently reached.

What appeared at first as a banal metaphor in fact reveals not so much the resemblance between the id and the mass, but rather that of thought processes and figurative techniques, in other words, the conformity of the 'mass' (as a figure of congruity) to the way in which Freud conceives of thought (and of knowledge?).[38] (We say 'banal metaphor', since it has nothing noteworthy about it, associationist psychology made an abundant use of the idea of multitude for describing the fate of ideas.) Since all analogies and metaphors bring about some degree of congruity, they all have something of the 'mass'. Rather than being limited to the few metaphorical occurrences of the term, the mass is a feature of the search for adequate representations of the unknown that runs through Freud's writings.[39]

We appear also to be saying that Freud's metaphors are not merely a rhetorical matter when relating them to processes of thought and more generally, to quantity. But, as the chapter aimed to suggest, focusing on the term 'mass' will allow us to remain with the problem of Freud's use of models and metaphors, even while apparently moving away from a 'merely metaphorical' understanding of this term.

3
Sciences of the Crowd

> 'It strikes me that, although the concept of "mass" (admittedly not a very *univocal* one!) has been persistent in contemporary thought to the point that a whole "discipline" was founded only to study "mass phenomena" and their impact on politics: namely "social psychology"), a precise and comprehensive *history* of the concept "mass" – starting with the Greek *to plethos* or *hoi polloi* and Latin *multitudo*, and extending to the modern conflicting notions of "the masses" (which is rather positive in revolutionary discourse) and "crowd" (which is rather negative in conservative discourse) – does not exist.'
>
> —Étienne Balibar, *Masses, Classes, Ideas: Studies on Politics and Philosophy Before and After Marx*

Having discussed briefly the problem of the metaphorical and thematic status of the mass in Freud, it might seem necessary, before considering Freud's work further, to turn to 'a precise and comprehensive history of the concept of "mass" – starting with the Greek . . .', during the course of which we are bound to come across examinations of Freud's singular treatment of the problem of the mass. The present study, however, does not take this path for reasons that the following chapter aims to explain.

Judging by Étienne Balibar's remark, which provides our epigraph, it would indeed be difficult to seek help in a 'comprehensive and precise history of the concept of "mass"' for the simple reason that such a history 'does not [apparently yet] exist'. However, judging from the existing literature on the 'mass', and contrary to what Balibar suggests, a precise and satisfying history might not exist, but the concept 'mass' almost invariably gives rise to *comprehensive studies*.[1] The call for comprehensiveness and for precision is therefore striking, for if such a history appears never to have been written, it might have a lot to do with the way in which studies of the 'mass' feel obliged to be *comprehensive*.

It could indeed be argued that when the concept (or the phenomenon) 'mass' is at issue, what otherwise qualifies scholarly methods – *comprehensiveness* – begins to merge with what needs to be explained. While scholars note the importance of differentiating between the various and diffuse occurrences of the concept 'mass' in European intellectual history, they nevertheless gather together conceptions of 'disorganization', however heterogeneous the social, political or intellectual circumstances that give rise to the latter appear to be. Viewed from this angle, the study of the mass (as an empirical phenomenon) can be said to amount to the study of disruptive gatherings, the analysis of which varies according to the social organization from which they emerge. Differentiations between definitions and descriptions of the 'mass' correspond, at least partly, to differentiations between that of 'social organizations'. One cannot fail to notice, however, that if, *generally speaking*, the problem that the mass poses inevitably pertains to one form or another of gathering, studies on the mass, by aiming for exhaustiveness, create yet one more problematic 'gathering', namely a host of thinkers.[2] One wonders which understanding of the concept 'mass' would be required for studying this type of *collectivity*.

Let us therefore turn to the '"discipline" [that] was founded only to study "mass phenomena"', namely, to late nineteenth-century 'psychologie des foules' (crowd, mass or collective psychology) rather than to general studies on the 'mass', given that, as we suggested above, the mass does not allow for a general treatment. As the first attempt to give to the study of the 'crowd' (or the 'mass') its autonomous discipline, crowd psychology should indeed offer precious indications concerning our topic. Focusing on a discipline devoted specifically to the 'crowd' – or in German to the *Masse* – however presents no satisfactory solution to the elusiveness of the object.[3] Whether we turn to recent historical analysis of its development among the emerging social and human sciences at the end of the nineteenth century in Europe, or to some emblematic texts of the discipline, 'psychologie des foules' sends us above all to methodological and institutional concerns.[4]

Reviewing the secondary literature on crowd psychology would itself demand a long chapter. The emerging science is either included in textbooks of 'social psychology' as a precursor of that science – a branch of psychology developed mostly in America during the 1950s – or as a prophetic science of totalitarianism. Or else, it is studied mostly by intellectual historians, who are preoccupied with its relation to psychology, anthropology and criminology, but most particularly, who study its conflictual involvement in the development of sociology at the end of the nineteenth century in Europe, and its failure to be recognized institutionally.[5] Because it has been associated almost exclusively with Gustave Le Bon's treatise *La Psychologie des foules* (1895), crowd psychology has too often been identified with the figure of Le Bon himself, whom one historian describes as a 'polygraphe étrange aux intérêts hétéroclites', and another as 'a notorious racist, political anti-semite and intellectual servitor of the French military class'.[6] Recent examination of the origins of 'crowd psychology' insists on the contribution of other authors of treatises on the crowd, such as Scipio Sighele, Gabriel Tarde, Henry Fournial.[7] They do not aim merely to diminish the exaggerated importance of Le Bon, but also to give to the discipline the intellectual importance that it otherwise lacks, as long as it remains attached to the dilettantism of a Le Bon.[8] What is at issue in these recent studies is less the 'crowd' than the role a failed 'science of the crowd' might have played in the history of human and social sciences. The concern for the crowd, both as an enigmatic phenomenon and as an elusive concept, gives way to a concern for the apparently more objectifiable questions of the institutionalization of knowledge and of the conflicts that ensue from it.[9]

These remarks on the recent literature on crowd psychology are expeditious; they should however suffice to indicate that we will not pursue our inquiry in the direction that this work suggests, however useful it might turn out to be in the context of a different study. Having indicated how both recent analyses of the discipline and of its emblematic texts send us back to methodological and institutional problems, we now need to consider the way in which the emblematic texts are themselves a source, if not directly of institutional problems, at least of methodological perplexities. For they provide a useful point of reference for the examination of the relation between the crowd (or the 'mass') and metaphor and models in Freud. We are leaving aside recent analyses of crowd psychology not so much therefore because they pertain to *methodological* and institutional problems. Rather, if studies on the crowd generate such perplexities, their relevance emerge only by considering the texts of the 'psychologues des foules' themselves.[10]

'Une foule n'a pas besoin d'être nombreuse'[11]

From the point of view of the distinction between primary and secondary texts, we will be dealing with late nineteenth-century treatises on the crowd even more expeditiously than we did when turning our attention to the secondary literature on the subject. Leaving aside the 'priority debate', we will focus mainly on Le Bon's *La Psychologie des foules*, following the tradition that Freud contributed to uphold by opening his own treatise on the mass with a discussion of Le Bon's theses on the crowd.[12] Even though our cursory examination will be almost exclusively limited to this work, it aims to draw out a feature that all contemporaneous essays on the crowd however share. Namely, the way in which studying the 'crowd' calls for a host of analogies and comparisons, to such a noticeable extent that it would be no exaggeration to say that the objective status of 'the crowd' or the 'mass' depends on their comparisons with 'something else'.

The recourse to analogies and comparisons in treatises on the crowd can be referred back to the traditional and didactic function of metaphor that we discussed briefly in chapter 1.[13] We saw above that, according to Derrida, Freud's use of the graphic metaphor cannot be assimilated to that procedure. In texts on the crowd, comparisons also point to the instrumental relation between the *unknown* and the *known*, whereby the crowd stands for the unknown, and the 'fauve innommé et monstrueux',[14] the 'mer agitée',[15] or the 'amas de poudre sèche' before the explosion stands for the known.[16] If we look closer at definitions and explanations of the crowd produced in the various late nineteenth-century treatises, the unknown – the crowd – however inflects the didactic use of analogies and comparisons. The recourse to figurative rapprochements itself comes to take on an unknown character, inasmuch as the *milieu* of similitude, of propagation and of circulation that the crowd designates, apparently pertains as much to the treatises as to the empirical gatherings that the science purports to study.[17] In other words, what is presented as a description of an empirical event simultaneously describes methodological elements of the science that seeks knowledge of it. The objective status of the crowd thus shares at least that feature with what we called earlier the 'epistemology' of Freudian psychoanalysis.

Le Bon's book itself, in raising methodological concerns around comparisons and analogies, incites us, furthermore, to consider the study of the crowd as a matter of rhetoric, even though it does not exactly reflect upon the scientific procedure that it employs. In Le Bon, the question of rhetoric is broached in relation to that of the Leader. 'As soon as a certain number of living beings are gathered together', Le Bon writes, 'whether they be animals or men, they place themselves instinctively under the authority of a chief, which is to say of a Leader [*d'un chef, c'est-à-dire, d'un meneur*]' (p. 117). One of the characteristics of the leaders is their knowledge of 'the science of employing words' (p. 107), or of the effective use of means of persuasion, namely affirmation, repetition and contagion (p. 125). Treatises on the crowd themselves seem to depend on these peculiar rhetorical figures, more particularly on the *contagious* comparison of the crowd to something else.

The crowd first becomes a topic of scientific inquiry around the question of collective responsibility in murderous acts committed by the 'many', that is, it is first a matter for the criminologists such as Scipio Sighele, the author of *La Folla delinquente* (1891) that is recognized as the first essay qualifying as a treatise on the crowd.[18] But, whatever the case may be around the delicate issue of collective responsibility, the violence of crowds, their destructive power depends, according to Le Bon, upon the 'idea, reasoning and imagination' of crowds. A great part of *La Psychologie des foules* is thus devoted to their analysis, of which the chapter on the 'The Leader and their means of persuasion' is an important part, and where Le Bon speaks of the way in which 'ideas, sentiments, emotions, and beliefs possess in crowds a contagious power as intense as that of microbes' (p. 126), or of the way in which 'it is by examples, not by arguments that crowds are guided' (p. 127). It is in this context that Le Bon affirms that 'the improbable [l'invraisemblable] does not exist for a crowd, and it is necessary to bear this circumstance well in mind to understand the facility with which are created and propagated the most improbable legends and stories' (p. 40).

Crowd psychologists do not state that the enigma of the crowd can be explained by *similitude* in general, but rather speak of the way in which, in a crowd, 'the heterogeneous is swamped by the homogeneous' (p. 29) or, as Sighele puts it, 'l'hétérogénéité est remplacée par une homogénéité presque absolue.'[19] Hence, persuasion consists in bringing about homogeneity thanks to 'a judicious employment of words and formulas'. According to Le Bon's rudimentary theory of language, 'the power of words is bound up with the images they evoke, and is quite independent of their real significance. Words whose sense is the most ill-defined are sometimes those that possess the most influence' (p. 102).[20] Since the study of the crowd significantly involves a concern for the effect of certain figures and of certain words, might the recourse to analogies and comparisons that permeates it not fall within the domain of *similitude* which preoccupies Le Bon under the heading of the crowd? This might explain why, notwithstanding their 'impulsive and mobile' tendency to compare, essays on the crowd, by contrast with their object of study, deploy a great deal of effort to avoid falling into *homogeneity*.

In this respect, Sighele's affirmation in *La Foule criminelle* whereby '*[s]e rassembler, dans le monde humain, veut . . . dire se rendre pire*' [Sighele's emphasis] (p. 176), summarizes in a particularly succinct manner most arguments developed in treatises on the crowd, regardless of the potentially competing political prescriptions to which it may lead.

From the point of view of its structure, *La Psychologie des foules* indeed constitutes a sustained attempt to establish as many differentiations as possible for dealing with the domain of the homogeneous, an approach to the topic which, in Le Bon's terms, amounts to operating 'like the naturalist' (p. 25).[21] The study comprises two books devoted to the general characteristics of crowds and a third one to the particular characters of crowds, which provides a typology of diverse multitudes. The classification of crowds that Book III presents indeed establishes a 'table of categories', but the particular features of the various types of crowd that it now describes have served as examples throughout the essay for illustrating the general characteristics of crowds. It is thus impossible to speak of a particular crowd without comparing it to 'every' crowd: '*Like all crowds*, juries are very strongly impressed by sentimental considerations, and very slightly by argument' (p. 168). Just as it is impossible to underline a feature of, for example, the 'judiciary' crowd, without assimilating it to 'every crowd': '*As in all crowds*, so in juries there are a small number of individuals who serve as guide to the rest' [my emphasis] (p. 170). On this account, each chapter of Book III devoted to a specific crowd, merely takes up again, according to the crowd at issue, the earlier part of the treatise devoted to generalities, but this time under the heading of 'street crowds', 'parliamentary assemblies', etc. When we get to 'electoral crowds' much of what has been said concerning means of persuasion is repeated, except that Le Bon now speaks of the 'candidate' as well as of the more generic term the 'orator'.[22] This feature of the treatise could well be perceived as a lack of methodological rigour on the part of Le Bon, a judgement that can be substantiated by referring to the numerous negative assessments of his work. Or else, we could say that the typology offered in Book III confirms the political (or according to some historians, 'ideological') destination of the treatise.[23] In the context of the present inquiry, however, the lack of distinction between particular and general characters of crowds draws our attention to a certain circularity which we can associate with the domain of the homogeneous that the crowd denotes. Hence, the problem does not lie only in the fact that, regardless of the actual divisions of the book, generalities are confused with particularities and vice versa, but also in the way in which the *similarity* between every crowd annihilates any effort at establishing differentiations. In spite of the fact that the treatise first rejects the 'mere gathering' of individuals from the set of its preoccupations, the latter in fact is the element most unambiguously common to every crowd. As long as one proceeds by means of comparisons – 'Such is the psychology of electoral crowds. It is identical with that of other crowds: neither better nor worse' (p. 182) – homogeneity cannot be easily averted.

Other aspects of the treatise allow us to underline further this methodological limitation. Book I devoted to 'The Mind of Crowds [*L'âme des foules*]' opens up with the distinction between the word *crowd* in its ordinary sense, which 'means a gathering of individuals of whatever nationality, profession, or sex, and whatever be the chances that have brought them together' (p. 23), and the same word used from the psychological point of view:

> Under certain given circumstances, and only under those circumstances, an agglomeration of men presents new characteristics very different from those of the individuals composing it . . . The gathering [*collectivity*] has thus become what, in the absence of a better expression, I will call an organised crowd, or, if the term is considered preferable, a psychological crowd. (p. 24)

Only the latter kind of crowd constitutes the object of study. The distinction between the two uses of the word depends upon the fact that the psychological crowd does not necessarily denote a 'great number' of individuals gathered together, but rather the formation of 'a sort of collective mind' (p. 27). Even though the psychological crowd signifies for Le Bon a return to 'barbarity', it is contrasted with a dispersed gathering, or a 'crowd' in its ordinary sense, which lacks the unity that the formation of a 'collective mind' has. Thus, if 'the psychological crowd is a provisional being formed of heteregeneous elements, which for a moment are combined, exactly as the cells which constitute a living body form by their reunion a new being which displays characteristics very different from those possessed by each of the cells singly' (p. 27), the formation of such a transient being is not determined by the number of elements composing it. This means that, 'at certain moments [of history], Le Bon states, half a dozen men might constitute a psychological crowd, which may not happen in the case of hundreds of men gathered together by accident' (p. 24). The 'factor of number' and the mere gathering of individuals are of secondary importance, because the study of the psychological crowd does not pertain to the reunion of 'many individuals' but rather to the way in which 'by the mere fact that men form part of a crowd engaged in action, their collective psychology differs essentially from their individual psychology' (p. 157). What matters with regard to the psychological crowd is the creation of new characters, and what needs to be explained are the laws and the causes of their apparition, all of which issue from Le Bon's notion of the 'unconscious'.

What Le Bon means by unconscious phenomena is stated from the outset: 'our conscious acts are the outcome of an unconscious substratum created in the mind in the main by hereditary influences. This substratum consists of the innumerable common characteristics handed down from generation to generation, which constitute the genius of a race [*l'âme de la race*]. Behind the avowed causes of our acts there undoubtedly lie secret causes that we do not avow, but behind these secret causes there are many others more secret still which we ourselves ignore' (p. 28).[24] As Freud noted, Le Bon's unconscious involves the notion of *l'âme de la race*, which becomes gradually more prominent as the treatise progresses.[25] It is this aspect of Le Bon's work that is, rightly so, most vehemently condemned by intellectual historians. Whereas 'it is more especially with respect to those unconscious elements which constitute the genius of a race that all individuals belonging to it resemble each other' (p. 28), the influence of race acts as a principle of differentiation between the multitudes of various countries that 'offer very considerable differences of beliefs and conduct and are not to be influenced in the same manner' (p. 82). Because each *peuple* differs from the point of view of its *âme*, it also differs from the point of view of the multitude that can emerge out of it. Because of these differences between multitudes, a 'multitude of peoples' just as a crowd of individuals, can be formed only in certain given circumstances (p. 115).[26]

If, at the supra-individual level, the influence of race provides a principle of differentiation between each *people*, *l'âme de la race* (the 'unconscious substratum') is conceived of as a certain configuration of instincts, sentiments, passions by which individuals (of the same race) are potentially alike. Thus men may differ through 'conscious elements' which, according to Le Bon, pertain to education or to 'exceptional hereditary conditions' (p. 28), yet they resemble each other from the point of view of the 'unconscious substratum':

> Men the most unlike [in] the matter of their intelligence possess instincts, passions, and feelings that are very similar [*parfois identiques*]. In the case of everything that belongs to the realm of senti-

> ment – religion, politics, morality, the affections and antipathies, etc. [and we could add, referring to Le Bon's *Les Opinions et les croyances*, 'scientific knowledge'] – the most eminent men seldom surpass the standard of the most ordinary individuals. From the intellectual point of view an abyss may exist between a great mathematician and his bootmaker, but from the point of view of character *the difference is most often slight or non–existent* [my emphasis]. (pp. 28–9)

As the concessive 'parfois' indicates, men are not always susceptible to resemble each other, even though the domain of 'sentiments' includes a great many elements – religion, politics, morality, affections, antipathies, etc. – up to the point where it would seem more appropriate to say that, from the point of view of their intelligence, men are sometimes not identical. This passage however serves the purpose of introducing the idea that

> It is precisely these general qualities of character, governed by forces of which we are unconscious, and possessed by the majority of the normal individuals of a race in much the same degree – it is precisely these qualities, I say, that in crowds become common property. In the collective mind [*l'âme collective*] the intellectual aptitudes of the individuals, and in consequence their individuality, are weakened . . . the unconscious qualities obtain the upper hand. (p. 29)

Faced with the apparently simple opposition between intellectual aptitudes and individuality, on the one hand, and unconscious qualities, sentiments, instincts, on the other, it is tempting to recall Freud's remark as to the way in which 'none of that author's statements brings forward anything new. Everything that he says to the detriment and depreciation of the manifestations of the group mind [*Massenseele*] had already been said by others before him with equal distinctness and equal hostility, and has been repeated in unison by thinkers, statesmen and writers since the earliest period of literature.' If we look closer, however, it is not the idea that intellectual faculties of men are overcome in certain circumstances by unconscious qualities that poses a problem. Rather, it is the fact that the circumstances in which the intellectual faculties are replaced by unconscious qualities include being part of a crowd, whereas Le Bon's conception of the unconscious would seem to render redundant any mention of a *mise en commun*. Independently of any actual empirical gathering, the unconscious substratum is that which all individuals possess 'à peu près au même degré'. The crowd, then, refers to the bringing together of something that individuals already share. This partly explains the ambiguity that marks the various uses of 'crowd', for it appears not only to denote 'empirical gatherings', or the psychological crowd, but also the unconscious substratum itself (what indeed distinguishes Le Bon's unconscious from a 'psychological crowd'?).[27]

By focusing on the psychological crowd, *La Psychologie des foules* consists in a study of how the 'conscious life of the mind [*l'esprit*] is of small importance in comparison with unconscious life', as well as a study of the fact that 'the most subtle analyst, the most acute observer, is scarcely successful in discovering more than a very small number of the unconscious motives that determine his conduct' (p. 28). On this account, 'crowd' would appear to be a term of analogy for unconscious activities that can come to dominate. Let us recall that the treatise first states that it is only the psychological crowd that is of interest, and pushes aside the word crowd in its ordinary sense, which refers to the 'mere gathering' of individuals, whether they be numerous or not. From the moment that crowd is not used in its ordinary meaning, and is presumably detached, from the mere multitude, nothing prevents us from considering it as a term of analogy.

If the crowd indeed here seems to take on an analogical value, it is, as Freud noted, inasmuch as 'observation of the changes in the individual's reactions is what provides group psychology with its material.'[28] For the changes amount to how unconscious motives come to dominate the conscious life of the individual. In this transformation of the individual, the 'crowd' both refers to an empirical occasion and a transformed state of mind. According to Freud's presentation of the problem, the crowd confronts us with a 'new task which would lie before it unachieved' (p. 126). 'Supposing that psychology had understood everything about the individual down to his actions and his relations with those who are nearest to him . . . it would be obliged to explain the surprising fact that under a certain condition this individual, whom it had come to understand, thought, felt and acted in quite a different way from what would have been expected. And this condition is his insertion into a collection of people which has acquired the characteristics of a "psychological group" [*die Einreihung in eine Menschenmenge*].'

In Le Bon's terms, the modification at issue lies in the fact that: 'by the mere fact that he forms part of an organised crowd, a man descends several rungs in the ladder of civilization. Isolated, he may be a cultivated individual, in a crowd, he is a barbarian – that, is a creature acting by instinct' (p. 32). The chapter on the general characteristics of the crowds is thus almost exclusively devoted to the description of the striking transformation of individuals entering into a crowd. This transformation consists in the fact that they 'feel, think and act' in a manner quite different from that in which each individual of them would feel, think and act were he in a state of isolation' (p. 27).[29] Almost. Since, from the moment that the characteristics of a psychological group are issued, it is no longer so easy to isolate the individual, whose modification should however be the matter of crowd psychology. Thus, Le Bon goes so far as to speak of the way in which individuals are 'transformed into a crowd' a transformation which 'puts them in possession of a sort of collective mind [*âme collective*] p. 11. If, however, individuals become indistinguishable, it does not mean that all individuality disappears. On the contrary, we could say that the first pages of *La Psychologie des foules* do not only describe the way in which individuals are transformed into a crowd, but also the way in which the crowd is simultaneously transformed into an individual, under the heading of '*the* psychological crowd'. Individuals may indeed be 'modified' – they turn into a crowd – but never as radically as the amorphous multitude when it turns into a 'psychological crowd'.[28]

It is thus difficult simply to assert that the problem of the crowd is considered *first* from the point of view of the individual, since, throughout the treatise, the problem might in fact be dealt with *only* from the point of view of the individual, as long as it is posed *only* in terms of 'the psychological crowd'. This said, there are times when the book does focus exclusively on the transformation of the individual. As we saw above, such transformation of the individual's mode of feeling, thinking and acting is explained by the possibility that the conscious personality of individuals may be led by 'unconscious motives'. The difficulty starts from the moment that such unconscious motives can apparently override the conscious personality only when the latter is no longer distinguishable from many other ones. In other words, is the fading away of individuality, that is, of the conscious personality, imputable to the way in which unconscious motives come to dominate, or to what Le Bon calls 'numerical considerations' [*le seul fait du nombre*] (p. 30)? Or, does speaking of *le seul fait du nombre* (the crowd in its ordinary sense) amount to speaking of the domination of unconscious motives? If we keep coming up against the possible rapprochement between the crowd and 'unconscious motives', it might be because, as soon as the 'group mind' is at issue, studying the modification of the individual leads us directly to it, since the group mind is formed by the disappearance of individuality before unconscious common qualities.

This said, there is an effort on Le Bon's part to continue speaking of the individual, even if only by means of various comparisons, since no 'individual' can be in principle at issue. For example, Le Bon writes that an individual in a crowd possesses 'the spontaneity, the violence, the ferocity, and also the enthusiasm and heroism of primitive beings' (p. 32), that, 'an individual in a crowd is a grain of sand amid other grains of sand, which the wind stirs up at will' (pp. 32–3). The most well known comparison of this chapter is probably that between the state of the individual in a crowd and 'the state of fascination in which the hypnotised individual finds himself in the hands of the hypnotyser' (p. 30). We say: the comparison, even if, according to Freud, 'Le Bon explains the condition of an individual in a group as being actually hypnotic, and does not merely make a comparison between the two states'. Freud's remark concerning Le Bon's 'assimilation' [*Angleichung*] of the hypnotic relation to the state of an individual in a crowd has to be viewed in the context of the discussion of 'suggestibility', which, alongside mental contagion and 'the factor of number', constitutes the three causes determining the apparition of the specific characters of crowd.[30] Here, hypnosis would seem to be too similar to suggestibility to function as a term of comparison. To paraphrase what Freud says of certain analogies to which he has recourse, and which we discussed briefly in chapter 2, the two terms 'come near identity'.[31]

When Freud's comments about hypnosis in *Mass Psychology*, he is generally suspicious of any explanation of the psychological crowd that refers either to 'suggestibility', to 'contagion' or to 'hypnosis'. From the perspective of our cursory reading of Le Bon, however, Freud's suspicions about hypnosis and suggestion are not here immediately relevant. Le Bon's comparison of what happens to an individual in a crowd to the hypnotic relation might indeed appear to be more pervasive throughout the treatise than any other comparisons, but it is nevertheless not the only term of comparison.[32] We begun by saying that the objective status of the crowd depends on its being compared to something else. We have seen how Le Bon introduces his discussion of the general features of crowds by focusing on the individual. But in attempting to describe the state of an individual in a crowd, Le Bon cannot do otherwise than to resort to 'the psychological crowd', namely to something like the *âme collective* and the 'unconscious substratum', from which it becomes difficult to isolate the individual, since each individual is apparently defined in relation to his/her potential sharing in them. Hence, the treatise might in fact approach the problem of the crowd *only* from the point of view of the individual as long as the crowd keeps being compared to an individual, and this, even if the comparison is not as explicit in Le Bon as, for example, in Sighele. Referring to the unity of action that characterizes the crowd, the Italian criminologist writes in *La Foule criminelle*: 'Le nom collectif de *foule* indique que les personnalités particulières des individus qui en font partie, se concentrent et s'identifient en une seule personnalité' (p. 33), and that in certain circumstances, 'la foule marche *comme un seul homme*' (my emphasis, p. 67). From chapter II onwards, Le Bon's treatise turns to the crowd itself, or to *l'âme collective*, notably to the detailed study of the crowd. Studying crowds in detail not only means to attribute to them a 'personality' (they have 'characters', namely, 'impulsiveness, mobility and irritability', they lack judgement, etc.), but also to compare them to the isolated individual. As we indicated above, when entering into a crowd, the individual is dominated by unconscious motives, whereby new characters, such as impulsiveness, irritability, credulity or mobility appear. Henceforth, as far as those new characters are concerned, it is more than ever difficult to know whether the point of reference is the individual (and the unconscious substratum which is shared by all individuals) or the crowd (the examination of which can only be carried out by dealing with the crowd as if one were dealing with an individual). When we introduced the 'mass' or the 'crowd' as a 'milieu of *ressemblance*' in chapter 2, we were partly referring to traditional descriptions, to which Le Bon's belong, of 'what happens in a crowd'. The profusion of comparisons that the crowd produces could now be called a 'crowd' or a 'mass', if, with this term, we refer to the way in which the *comparant* and the *comparé* mingle with each other, as the *individual* and the *crowd* do in the dusty treatises of crowd psychology.

4
On a Large Scale

The following chapter proposes to examine the conception of the mass that runs through Freud's work with particular reference to the analysis of religion that is developed in the essays on application. In *The Future of an Illusion* (1927), this reflection leads to the hope that, one day, science will take over from religious ideas. This prediction rests on a traditional apportioning whereby ignorance and superstition are the lot of the many while enlightenment through science the prerogative of the few. The psychoanalytic examination of religion does not entirely modify this view, it could even be said to reinforce it. Our purpose, however, is less to insist on the pejorative view on 'the great number' that psychoanalysis undeniably holds than to explore the way in which the scientific activity that psychoanalysis aims to constitute cannot easily make room for 'the many'. It is mostly as far as the future science at issue in *The Future* is above all the *psychoanalytic* science of the mind, whose object of study is a psychical apparatus that the incompatibility between science and 'the many' takes its full importance. An overview of the apparently only 'social' concept of the mass that runs through Freud thus leads us to the core of the psychoanalytic project, by confronting us with the 'delicate apparatus of the mind', whose operations are not easily conceivable on a large scale.

The term 'Masse' and its cognates rarely appear in Freud's writing. It is used either in a social sense, interchangeably with crowd, multitude or mob to mention but a few more or less synonymous terms [*Menge, Haufen, Pöbel*]. It is also used in a loose physical sense, such as, for example, in 'The Project for a Scientific Psychology' (1895), where Freud describes the external world in terms of 'powerful masses which are in violent motion and which transmit their motion [*heftig bewegte Massen . . . die ihre Bewegung fortpflanzen*]'. Somewhat departing from the physical sense, Freud also speaks of the ego as a 'a constantly cathected mass of neurones [*eine stetig besetzte Neuronenmasse*]' in the same work.[1] It occurs, moreover, in compound nouns such as *Massenseele, Massenphantasie, Massen-Ideal,* and it can have a quantitative sense such as *Libido-Menge, Vorstellungsmasse,* or *Empfindungsmasse.*[2]

Let us specify that the term mass 'rarely appears' for a reader of the English translation of Freud's work, since the term is often translated as 'group', most noticeably in the *Massenpsychologie und Ich-Analyse* (1921), the existing English translation of the title [*Group psychology and the Analysis of the Ego*] we have systematically avoided so far. According to the editors of a recent French translation of that essay, James Strachey and his co-translators aimed to leave any possible association with the totalitarian concept of the mass out of Freud's writing. We will not here go back over the controversy surrounding the translation of Freud's writings, and of that essay in particular. Strachey does sometimes use 'mass' in some essays where Freud unambiguously speaks of the 'mob', and of the great numbers. It is noteworthy however that whereas Strachey generally avoids 'mass' for translating *Masse* and its synonym – for translating the not obviously pejorative 'social' occurrences of the term – he does not hesitate to use the English 'mass' for rendering a number of quantitative nouns, notably in *The Interpretation of Dreams* (1900), where for example, a *Summe* of impressions becomes 'a mass'.[3] In this context, it would not be difficult, and not entirely wrong either for a reader of Freud in English to deem that the term mass in Freud is a quantitative term, and not to take any particular notice of it.

If we provisionally limit ourselves to the examples of the 'social' use of these terms, they apparently pose no serious semantic problems apart from having 'a very wide meaning'.[4] In 'Lines of Advance in Psycho-analytic Therapy' (1919 [1918]), for example, Freud speaks of the possibility of offering psychoanalytic treatment to the 'considerable mass of the population'. In *Civilization and its Discontents* (1930), he distinguishes the greatness of some men from 'the aims and ideals of the multitude' [*Ziele und Ideale der Menge*], or states that 'philosophy has no direct influence on the great mass of mankind [*die große Menge von Menschen*]; it is of interest to only a small number even of the top layers of intellectuals and is scarcely intelligible to anyone else.'[5] What is at issue in these examples is at least partly a large number of individuals, although how large a number remains unspecified.

These terms never however designate neutrally an indefinitely large quantity of people. They signal the separation of mankind into a minority and a majority whereby the 'great number' corresponds to the lowest (widest) stratum of society, and 'the minority' to the highest rarefied other one composed of exceptional individuals. Many of Freud's statements indeed more or less obliquely underscore 'the innate and ineradicable inequality among men' manifested by 'their tendency to fall into two classes of leaders and followers' and the fact that the latter constitute 'the vast majority of them'.[6] As a synonym of 'the majority', mass brings negative evaluations – lack of restraint, tendency to rebel – which act as definitions of the kind of gathering the mass represents.

If only from this perspective, Freud perpetuates negative, conservative ideas of the mass and of the masses, which he inherits and shares with many other thinkers, and which proceed from the association of the 'great number' with all manners of deficiencies.[7] In Freud's writings, the masses are just as naturally called the 'dependent masses' [*der unselbständigen Massen*], considered to be 'unintelligent', described as 'uneducated', 'engaged in exhausting work', or else, said to be 'dangerous', as 'the few' are endowed with the understanding of how 'to obtain possession of the means to power and coercion', or, have alone the ability to understand philosophy.[8] This bias strikes us in various ways. In *New Introductory Lectures* (1933), for example, as in 'The Resistances to Psychoanalysis' (1925 [1924]), the hostile attitude of Freud's contemporaries towards psychoanalysis in the early days of the movement is elucidated by ascribing 'mob-characteristics [*Pöbelhaftigkeit*]' to their deplorable behaviour.[9] Notwithstanding the physical resonance of the concept of resistance and its necessary tie to the concept of mass, the scientific community is likened to an unruly mob by virtue of its violent antagonism to psychoanalysis.

It could be objected that these examples belong to historical or expository works rather than to the heart of the theoretical edifice, and that this suffices to make us reject the idea that Freudian thought presents a traditionally negative view of the masses. Such an evaluation, however, is no less discernible in the texts devoted to the process of *Kultur* [*Kulturprozeß*] such as '"Civilized" Sexual Morality and Modern Nervous Illness' (1908), *Totem and Taboo* (1912–13), *Mass Psychology* (1921), *The Future of an Illusion* (1927), *Civilization and its Discontents* (1930), 'Why War' (1933) or *Moses and Monotheism* (1939 [1937–9]). These essays not only call upon the major concepts of psychoanalysis, but also purport to present a psychoanalytical understanding of 'society'. Even where the analysis of human grouping professes to be specifically psychoanalytical, the classical rift between the few and the many and the depreciation of the latter is perceptible.

The well-known underlying assumption of these essays is that there is a conflict between the satisfaction of 'instinctual impulses' and *Kultur*.[10] 'Generally speaking' Freud writes, 'our civilization is built up on the suppression of instincts [*Unterdrückung von Trieben*] . . . it presupposes . . . the non-satisfaction [by suppression, repression or some other means?] of instinctual impulses.'[11] Instinctual impulses are not exactly paired with the majority (that has to be controlled) and *Kultur* with the minority, an a priori antagonism between the few and the many nevertheless permeates the hypothesis of instinctual renunciation. *Kultur* imposes a sacrifice for which men seek compensation through various means. A want of compensation allows hostility against the latter to develop. The less satisfaction life seems to offer, the greater is the aversion to *Kultur*, and the tendency to let passion dominate over reason.[12] The 'masses', the 'great number' are more likely to experience instinctual renunciation in just this way. This is what *The Future* suggests by presenting the 'human masses' and the work of *Kultur* as negative counterparts, just as the 'id' is described elsewhere 'as a contrast to the ego'.[13] On the one hand, 'the two characteristics of the human masses [*Menschenmassen*]' consist in the fact that 'men are not spontaneously fond of work and that arguments are of no avail against their passions', and, on the other, *Kultur* 'rests on a compulsion to work [*Arbeitszwang*] and a renunciation of instinct'. Hatred of instinctual renunciation is not exactly the reverse of imperviousness to arguments, or the 'compulsion to work' of 'not being fond of work'. Yet, given these almost symmetrical characterizations, it comes as no surprise if 'civilization provokes opposition' on the part of the 'dangerous masses'.[14]

Freud does not focus on the opposition between the few and the many, but it is implied in the elaboration of all the familiar themes of the essays of application. In his meditations on the origin and the force of religion, of moral conscience [*Gewissen*], on the effects of oppressive sexual morality on mental health, on the difficulty of being happy, on aggressivity, or on war, the position of the 'masses' is in some respect unequivocal. Taken in isolation from the psychoanalytic content of these essays, the conception of the mass that transpires in them presents no particular interest, and we have said already almost all there is to say about it. We may even wonder if the negative view of the mass is not what Freud partly has in mind in *Civilization* when he confesses his 'strong feeling . . . that what he is describing is common knowledge' and 'self-evident'.[15] The idea of the mass in the writings on *Kultur* is certainly, at one level, 'common knowledge' (is the 'mass' not the concept of 'commonality'?). In case Freud's rejection of the idea of 'perfectibility', of man's natural goodness were too disorienting, there remains the familiar pejorative depiction of the masses.[16]

Freud's attempts to understand psychical life with reference to *Kultur* nevertheless produce a number of ambiguities pertaining to its basic concepts. In addition to the rejection of the distinction between *Kultur* and *Civilization,* which has been often commented upon, the hypothesis of instinctual renunciation makes Freud hesitate as to whether one should speak of suppression, repression, or of 'some other means', of frustration, prohibition or privation. It obliges him to spell out the meaning of super-ego, conscience, sense of guilt, need for punishment and remorse, that is, it requires him to distinguish between a critical agency, a function, a perception, an 'assessment' or an 'instinctual manifestation'.[17] These essays are far from being the only ones where equivocations are created from the fact that many terms 'all relate to the same state of affairs, but denote different aspects of it'.[18]

The 'mass' stands out within this confused lexical situation. Freud does not comment or make an apology for the imprecision, the 'wideness' of its meaning, as he does for other aspects of the theory, notably concerning the drives of which he says that they are 'mythical entities, magnificent in their indefiniteness'.[19] The nearest he comes to discussing explicitly the 'wide' meaning of the mass is in *Mass Psychology,* but here, what matters is the too undifferentiated range of problems 'mass psychology' encompasses in claiming to study 'the mass', rather than the indistinctness of the noun. 'Although group psychology is only in its infancy', writes Freud, 'it embraces an immense number of separate issues and offers to investigators countless problems which have hitherto not even been properly distinguished from one another.'[20] Countless: too many. To note the overabundance of problems is here to announce their reduction. One concept – identification – will indeed allow Freud to deal with the enigma of the mass.[21]

When Freud attempts to dispel the equivocations around terms such as 'conscience' and 'sense of guilt', he appeals to the differentiation of 'aspects' that the metapsychology calls to mind, or by ordering genetically the ambiguous elements at issue.[22] The ambiguity of the term mass, however, cannot be dissipated quite in the same way. For, to consider phenomena at the level of the 'mass' might involve nothing but a 'change of scale'. Part of the impreciseness of the term lies in the quantitative consideration that it introduces, and in the fact that quantity in Freud's writings is the place of the greatest hesitations as far as conceptual demarcations are concerned. Does what the shift of scale that 'mass' introduces not take place amidst the other (metapsychological) mode of differentiation at work throughout Freud?

We began by saying that the social occurrences of the problematic term 'mass' and its synonyms have, on the whole, pejorative overtones. As soon as these occurrences are considered as an index of scale, rather than as that of an existing type of human grouping, however, their negative resonance partly recedes. Studying some of the occurrences of the mass then becomes less an opportunity to gain knowledge about Freud's dispositions towards the empirical masses, as an opportunity to witness the extent to which the issue of 'scale' (and of measurement) intervenes in the theory of the psyche.

Among the topics raised in essays on *Kultur*, religion allows us to see how the mass can be the indicator of a change of scale, rather than solely a contemptuous term for designating great numbers. Before considering more closely the arguments that Freud develops around religion in *The Future* and in the other essays that deal with religion, and before explaining what the issue of scale has to do with the critique of religious illusions, let us specify what is meant by a 'change of scale'.[23] In the context of the essays on *Kultur*, including *The Future*, it refers to the apparently simple idea whereby one moves from 'the analysis of the individual to an understanding of society'.[24] 'What characterizes psycho-analysis as a science', Freud declares in the *Introductory Lectures on Psycho-analysis* (1916–17), 'is not the material which it handles but the technique with which it works. It can be applied to the history of civilization, to the science of religion, and to mythology, no less than to the theory of neuroses without doing violence to its essential nature.'[25] A 'change of scale' therefore signposts the main motif and the motivation of the essays on application, namely, the transposition of the findings of psychoanalysis to what Freud calls in the 'Postscript' to 'An Autobiographical Study', the 'wider stage' of *Kultur*, a transposition that is supposed to extend our understanding of the *Kulturprozeß*.[26]

The two dimensions are bridged by means of analogy, against whose danger and limitation Freud ceaselessly warns us. None of the essays on *Kultur* fails to alert us about the hazardous transfer of concepts from the sphere of the individual to that of humanity. More generally throughout his writings, Freud feels obliged to apologize for the use of analogies and to speak of their limitations. As we saw above, statements about analogies generally unfold in two steps. The first phase of the perception of identity between two domains is invariably mitigated by the gradual discovery of dissimilarity up to the point where the analogy breaks down and must be abandoned. The danger that overshadows analogical reasoning is strikingly formulated in *Civilization* by means of a comparison between concepts and men, whereby the transposition of concepts is likened to the displacement of men.[27] At the end of a reflection upon the resemblance between the development of culture and that of the individual, Freud prophesizes that 'we may expect that one day someone will venture to embark upon a pathology of cultural communities [*der kulturellen Gemeinschaften*].'[28] However, we are forewarned about the risks involved in any attempt of doing so:

> I would not say that an attempt of this kind to carry psycho-analysis over to the cultural community [*Kulturgemeinschaft*] was absurd or doomed to be fruitless. *But we should have to be very cautious and not forget that, after all, we are only dealing with analogies and that it is dangerous, not only with men but also with concepts, to tear them from the sphere in which they have originated and been evolved.* Moreover, the diagnosis of communal neurosis [*Gemeinschaftensneurosen*] is faced with a special difficulty. In an individual neurosis we take as our starting-point the contrast that distinguishes the patient from his environment, which is assumed to be 'normal'. For a group all of whose members are affected by one and the same disorder no such background could exist; it would have to be found elsewhere. And as regards the therapeutic application of our knowledge, what would be the use of the most correct analysis of social neuroses, since no one possesses authority to impose such a therapy upon the group? [*Ein solcher Hintergrund entfällt bei einer gleichartig affizierten Masse*? [my emphasis][29]

The attempt to transpose the therapeutic means developed on the basis of the individual to the analysis of *Kultur* is limited from the outset by conceptual precariousness, which is not surprising since it poses problems of *quantity*. With the 'many', the level of *Kultur* here stands as the 'unknown factor' with which psychoanalysis is forced to operate, and, most importantly, which compels Freud to borrow from *other sciences* or to resort to 'analogies', 'images', just as 'the unknown X' does in the metapsychological work. This is why the anthropomorphism of the comparison attracts notice. In order to show the danger of comparing what may turn out to be too heterogeneous spheres – the individual and the cultural spheres – Freud compares concepts to men, whereas the difficulty may lie precisely in the attempt to match concepts and human beings. Analogies too can become the motif of a comparison.[30] In chapter 5, we will go back over this transition as it can be drawn out from *Moses and Monotheism* and elaborate on the potentially ruinous complications that the 'reasoning by analogy' entails as far as the extension of psychoanalytic knowledge is concerned.

In 'Lines of Advance' Freud had raised the question of the treatment of 'mass-neurosis' less speculatively. There is no mention of the lack of 'world' that would otherwise allow us to diagnose neurosis and psychosis. He goes so far as to imagine that their treatment might include suggestion and hypnosis (the very techniques of 'mass-delusions') as means of therapeutic influence:

> I have no doubt that the validity of our psychological assumptions will make its impression on the uneducated too [*auf den Ungebildeten*], but we shall need to look for the simplest and most easily intelligible ways of expressing our theoretical doctrines. We shall probably discover that the poor are even less ready to part with their neuroses than the rich . . . Often, perhaps, we may only be able to achieve anything by combining mental assistance with some material support, in the manner of Emperor Joseph. It is very probable, too, that the large-scale application [*Massenanwendung unserer Therapie*] will compel us to alloy the pure gold of analysis freely with the copper of direct suggestion; and hypnotic influence, too, might find a place in it again, as it has in the treatment of war neuroses.[31]

This passage is doubly interesting in that it affirms, on the one hand, no doubt scandalously according to some, that psychoanalysis would go so far as to use techniques, such as hypnosis and suggestion, in other words, 'regress' towards early steps of elaboration (Freud does describe his turning towards *Kultur* in 'An Autobiographical Study' as a 'regression'). It suggests, on the other hand, that both the theoretical and practical sides of psychoanalysis must be modified to accommodate the 'great number'.[32] The extent to which concepts must be transformed is precisely the problem. How far can psychoanalysis be extended without abandoning its most basic principles? For all his respect for the anticipatory power of popular knowledge over its own discovery, Freud does not concede much power to 'living' popular knowledge, in so far it may be embodied in 'the uneducated' classes.

The transition for which the essays on *Kultur* aim is, however, not uniformly conceived in terms of a difference of scale between the individual and the mass that would be cancelled out by the application of the *same* analytic method to both regions. In *Civilization*, Freud attempts to justify the use of the 'same formula' – the struggle between Eros and the death instinct – for three different processes ('the process of civilization which mankind undergoes' (p. 139), the development of the individual, and the secret of organic life). The comparison however soon pertains mostly to the first two processes, since the vital one [*Lebensprozeß*] acts as the *tertium comparationis*:

> Starting from speculations on the beginning of life and from biological parallels, I drew the conclusion that, besides the instinct to preserve living substance and *to join it into ever larger units*, there must exist another, contrary instinct seeking to *dissolve those units and to bring them back to their primaeval, inorganic state*. That is to say, as well as Eros there was an instinct of death. The phenomena of life could be explained from the concurrent or mutually opposing action of these two instincts [my emphasis].[33]

Freud does not say that between the two regions – civilization and the individual – there is a variation of scale. Their difference is yet not precisely characterized. The process of civilization is said to be a 'modification' experienced by the vital process 'under the influence of a task that is set by Eros and instigated by Ananke'.[34] Concerning the distinction between the process of civilization and the development of the individual, Freud affirms that they are '*very similar* in nature, if not *the very same* process applied to different kinds of object'. Even though the process of civilization is said to be 'an abstraction of a higher order', it is difficult to demarcate the two processes. When Freud joins them according to their similar aim – union with the community [*Gemeinschaft*] – the *two* processes can be seriously confused: 'in the one case the integration of a separate individual into a human group [*in eine menschliche Masse*], and in the other case the creation of a unified group [*einer Massenheit*] out of many individuals'.[35] Recalling the description of the process of civilization that consists in bringing 'people together into larger unities [*die Menschen zu großen Einheiten zusammenzuballen*]' is not of much help:

> civilization is a process in the service of Eros, whose purpose is to combine single human individuals, and after that families, then races, peoples and nations, into one great unity, the unity of mankind ['*zu einer großen Einheit, der Menschheit*']. Why this has to happen, we do not know; the work of Eros is precisely this. These

> collections of men [*Menschenmengen*] are to be libidinally bound to one another.[36]

Why does Eros set the task of creating 'larger' unities? Freud does not know but that the creation of unities should be the creation of progressively *larger* unities leaves no doubt. The increasing largeness of the units created by Eros however goes together with the increasing imprecision that besets their identification. The transition from the individual to the 'unity of mankind' is one from something that is apparently distinguishable to something that is progressively less and less so. What is indeed, with respect to the people [*Völker*] and the nation, the largest unity, the 'unity of mankind' [*Menschheit*]?[37] What otherwise distinguishes the unity or unit that *Masse* and *Massenheit* stand for (or in the English and French translation respectively, 'a human group' and a 'unified group'; a 'masse humaine' and 'humanité')? How, moreover, do they compare with the unity – the group mind [*Massenseele*] – that Freud is obliged to presuppose, with perplexity, in *Totem and Taboo*? Freud's reservation in this respect are expressed in a passage from the 1912–13 essay that we quoted in relation to the concept of quantity, but that deserves to be quoted again, in relation to the 'unity' that is at issue in *Civilization* (the possibility to bridge two magnitudes by means of analogy depends upon the presumption of a *Massenpsyche*):

> No one can have failed to observe, in the first place, that I have taken as the basis of my whole position the existence of a collective mind [*wir überall die Annahme einer Massenpsyche zugrunde legen*], in which mental processes occur just as they do in the mind of an individual. In particular, I have supposed that the sense of guilt for an action has persisted for many thousands of years and has remained operative in generations which can have had no knowledge of that action. I have supposed that an emotional process, such as might have developed in generations of sons who were ill-treated by their father, has extended to new generations which were exempt from such treatment for the very reason that their father had been eliminated. It must be admitted that these are grave difficulties; and any explanation that could avoid presumptions of such a kind would seem to be preferable.[38]

Is the *Menschheit* that is at issue in *Civilization* also a 'postulate', indeed a *Hilfsvorstellung*? How, moreover, do these 'unities' relate to the *Massenbildung* of which, in the same essay, Freud regrets the *misère psychologique,* whose libidinal structure he has provided in 1921 (and perhaps well before, as he recalls in Lecture XXXIV)? We already saw that Freud deems that the resistances of his contemporaries to psychoanalysis were worthy of the 'behaviour of the crowd'. He qualifies this comparison as 'his first application of psycho-analysis' suggesting that the idea of 'application' of psychoanalysis to the mass emerge in conjunction with that of resistance.[39] Freud contrasts the manifestations of Eros to that of the death instinct with respect to the way in which the former are 'conspicuous and noisy' and the latter operate 'in silence'. We are not exactly here dealing with a difference of scale. However, since the 'two kinds of instinct seldom – perhaps never – appear in isolation from each other', and since they are not recognizable otherwise than in alloys of 'varying and very different proportions', such as for example, in sadism and masochism, pathological processes cannot but be at least partly a matter of measurement.

The change of scale can also be envisaged from the point of view of the continuity between normal and pathological mental processes that underlies psychoanalysis. This too leads us to an increasing degree of imprecision as we move closer to the 'larger scale'. The idea of continuity in fact conceals various degrees of similarity, that range from identity, as in the following passage:

> there is no reason for surprise that psycho-analysis, which was originally no more than an attempt at explaining pathological mental phenomena, should have developed into a psychology of normal mental life. The justification for this arose with the discovery that the dreams and mistakes of normal men have *the same* mechanism as neurotic symptoms.[40]

to a difference of degree, such as it is expressed in the first Encyclopedia article 'On Psycho-Analysis' (1913 [1911]), where psychoanalysis is said to have 'demonstrated that there is no fundamental difference, but only one of degree, between the mental life of normal people, of neurotics and of psychotics'. The difference of degree bears upon the ease and the level of success with which one 'pass[es] through the . . . repressions' and 'struggle[s] with the . . . substitutive structures'. 'Healthy people', Freud writes, 'have to contend with the *same* tasks of mastering their libido – they simply have succeeded better in them' for there is 'internal identity between pathological processes and what are known as normal ones'.[41] Notwithstanding the suggestion that, since there is an identity between dreams of healthy and neurotic people, 'the difference between health and neurosis holds only during the day,'[42] the following extract makes clear that there exists only a quantitative difference between health and illness:

> The distinction between nervous health and neurosis is thus reduced to a practical question and is decided by the outcome – by whether the subject is left with a sufficient amount of capacity for enjoyment and of efficiency. It probably goes back to the relative sizes of the quota of energy that remains free and of that which is bound by repression, and is of a quantitative not of a qualitative nature.[43]

It is when the 'identity' is presented in methodological terms that the postulated continuity presents the greatest interest. For the difference between the two states then appears as what we can call a 'difference of scale'. In the *New Introductory Lectures* on 'Femininity', for example, the service that pathological states and that people suffering from them can give is clearly related to their 'magnifying' property. If the portrayal 'of the abundance and strength of a *normal* little girl's sexual relations with her mother' appear 'overdrawn', it may be a good idea to turn for confirmation towards 'people in whom these processes of development [have] attained a specially clear and *even excessive degree of expansion*'. For, Freud explains, 'pathology has always done us the service of making discernible by isolation and exaggeration conditions which would remain concealed in a normal state.' This echoes, notwithstanding the idea of isolation, what Lecture XXXI already stated: 'We are familiar with the notion that pathology, *by making things larger and coarser*, can draw our attention to normal conditions which would otherwise have escaped us.'[44] This recalls, among other places, 'On Narcissism: An Introduction' (1914) where 'once more', Freud writes, 'in order to arrive at an understanding of what seems so simple in normal phenomena, we shall have to turn to the field of pathology with its distortions and its exaggerations [*Vergröberungen*]', according to the familiar tenets of Freudian thought that truth can only be found in a modified form.[45]

It is not surprising if, in this context, the influence of the 'crowd' can be said, in the manner of a pathological manifestation, to magnify 'normal conditions'. In 'Psychical (or Mental) Treatment' (1890), for example, and well before *Mass Psychology*, Freud speaks of the way in which 'the individual's pious belief is intensified by the enthusiasm of the crowd of people [*Menschenmenge*] in whose midst he makes his way as a rule to the sacred locality. All the mental impulses of an individual can be enormously magnified by group influence such as this [*die Macht der Menge*].'[46] Leaving aside the fact that the pejorative connotations attaching to the mass already associate it with 'disease', it looks as though it were the name of a pathological process, alongside the 'enlarging' ones such as omnipotence of thought, overestimation [*Überschätzung*], magnification [*Vergrößerung*].[47] From a methodological point of view, these processes have amplifying virtue, but they themselves consist in magnifying processes.

To consider the 'mass' as the index of a shift of scale, then, moves us away from the simple pejorative evaluation that otherwise runs throughout Freud. From the point of view of the 'science of the psychical unconscious', the 'mass' shares the magnifying properties of pathological mental processes and, in this sense, its understanding could contribute to the elaboration of a theory of the psyche. Is this not what *Mass Psychology* suggests by culminating in a chapter on 'A Differentiating Grade in the Ego' as if the entire study had been directed towards the clarification of the relation of the ego to the ego-ideal, introduced in 'On Narcissism'? The fact that Freud somewhat neutralizes the opposition between individual and mass psychology in the very first paragraph of *Mass Psychology* can indeed only emphasize the incongruity between the declared 'sociological' topic and the actual preoccupation of the 1921 essay. 'In the individual mental life', Freud writes, 'someone else is invariably involved, as a model, as an object, as a helper, as an opponent; and so from the very first individual psychology, in this extended but entirely justifiable sense of the words, is at the same time social psychology as well.'[48] Judging on *Mass Psychology* alone, Freud's interest in the crowd as a social phenomena is as ephemeral as are certain types of crowds discussed in that book. The latter is in fact subordinated to the elaboration of the second topography, before *The Ego and the Id*, as if the accumulation of people to which the mass refers could provide an illustration of the accumulation of sort in which the ego ideal and the super-ego partly consist.

Just as the essay on the 'mass' in fact deals with 'a grade in the Ego', 'On Narcissism' conversely points towards the study of 'mass formations', by announcing, in conclusion, the possibility of the understanding of the libidinal structure of 'groups' [*Massen*]. Having introduced the notion of the ego-ideal in that essay, Freud states that it 'opens up an important avenue for the understanding of group psychology [*Massenpsychologie*]' (p. 101). In that essay too, we are dealing with processes of enlargement. The formation of the ego ideal provoked by the inevitable loss of primary narcissism proceeds through a magnification: idealization 'is a process that concerns the *object*; by it that object, without any alteration in its nature, is aggrandized and exalted in the subject's mind.'[49] Since the setting up of the ego-ideal is related to the 'institution of conscience', it introduces measurement. Conscience, as a measuring instance (which will become the super-ego in *The Ego and the Id*), develops out of the 'task of seeing that narcissistic satisfaction from the ego-ideal is ensured and . . . with this end in view, constantly watches the actual ego and measures it by that ideal'.[50]

It is the 'social side' of the 'grade in the Ego' that is however particularly noteworthy, since it is marked by the (quantitative) indefiniteness that we noted earlier as soon as the 'social' is concerned. The account of the development of conscience through the formation of the ego-ideal indeed involves picturing a progressively larger accumulation of traces of people. As we saw with other increasing movements, such as for example, the one underlying the process of *Kultur*, it obliges us to imagine a progressively more imprecise entity. 'On Narcissism' calls attention to that indefiniteness. The 'institution of conscience' is at first 'the embodiment of parental criticism' but 'that of society' soon replaces it. Parents are replaced by an 'indefinable host of people' and eventually by 'public opinion':

> what prompted the subject to form an ego ideal, on whose behalf his conscience acts as a watchman, arose from the critical influence of his parents (conveyed to him by the medium of the voice), to whom are added, as time went on, those who trained and taught him and the innumerable and indefinable host of all the other people in his environment – his fellow-men – and public opinion [*als unübersehbarer, unbestimmbarer Schwarm alle anderen Personen des Milieus*].[51]

Since according to Freud, parental criticism takes a vocal form, one wonders to what sort of clamour that series of substitution leads. Let us recall how Freud associates 'noise' to the possibility of observation: the work of Eros is 'noisy' as opposed to the 'silent' work of the death instinct. In the chapter on the ego-ideal in *Mass Psychology*, it is the 'noisy' [*lärmende*] masses and not the 'stable and lasting group formations [*Massenbildung*]' with their 'uniform and constant effects' that are the striking ones.[52] If parental influence is 'conveyed by the medium of the voice' and if an indefinite number of people comes to take over that role, will the 'group' at issue – *society* – not be of the 'noisy' kind (and the analysis of the noisy and ephemeral *Masse* would indeed constitute an analysis of 'society')? The indeterminacy surrounding the description of the group – 'the parents are [eventually] replaced by an indefinite number of fellow-men [*an Stelle der Eltern ist später die unbestimmte Menge der Genossen getreten*]' (*ibid.*, p. 102) – is no less striking here than in the later essays on *Kultur* around the unit that the 'human masses' or the 'unity of mankind' represent.[53]

The ego-ideal moreover incites us to conceive of the 'indefinite number of fellow-men' and their influence as a 'sum', as though that 'grade in the ego' (and the super ego in its vein, in so far as we are dealing with 'two' agencies) were in fact condensations of 'numerical intensity'.[54] Bridging narcissism and mass psychology would thus appear to involve contraction, up to the point where the dream-process of condensation, in the physical sense of *Kompression* that it clearly has throughout *The Interpretation*, might in fact be the psychoanalytic concept best suited for dealing specifically with the problem of the 'mass'. (See *Mass Psychology*, pp. 130–1). The accumulative nature of the ego-ideal and of the super-ego is revealed in the way in which, under the influence of 'disease' (paranoia), 'the voices, as well as the undefined multitude [*die unbestimmt gelassene Menge*] are brought into the foreground again' and 'the evolution of conscience is reproduced regressively.'[55] Being brought to the foreground can presumably take many forms. What better way of figuring this regressive reproduction of the evolution of conscience, however, than by invoking the 'noisy' ephemeral type of mass, among the other types of undefined multitude. The possibility of witnessing the evolution of conscience is linked with the evolutionist idea that all stages of development co-exist in the present of our scientific point of view, the most primitive ones being always susceptible to become dominant. The earlier stages, as well as their accumulation, are apparently only conceivable in terms of a mass, as the undefined result of a 'condensation'.[56]

The Interpretation reinforces the genetic dimension that can be given to the issue of scale (and of the domain of the 'coarse') by relating 'largeness' and 'large quantities' with childhood: 'the appearance in dreams of things of great size and in great quantities and amounts, and of exaggeration generally, may be another childhish characteristic.' These occurrences can be attributed to the fact that children 'have no more ardent wish than to be big and grown-up and to get as much of things as grown-up people do. They are hard to satisfy, know no such words as "enough" and insist insatiably on a repetition of things which they have enjoyed or whose taste they liked.' The rest of the explanation clearly shows how the propensity to exaggerate corresponds genetically to a more ancient phase of development that children and neurotics share: 'It is only the civilizing influence of education that teaches [children] moderation and how to be content and resigned.'[57] If from the point of view of childhood, exaggeration is associated with the world of adults (of *Kultur*) – adults are 'big' – the longing for having a 'lot' of everything, for 'large quantities', in brief, the lack of moderation is clearly the domain of childhood and of the neurotics.[58]

The Ego and the Id provides a different point of view on 'scale', by raising the issue of the 'scale of value', when answering to the objection that psychoanalysis has ignored 'the higher, moral, supra-personal side of human nature'.[59] But it also sends us back to the imprecision that marks 'largeness'. For the defence against the accusation reveals the extent to which, when considered genetically, the study of the mass and of the formation of the ego-ideal pertains to the imprecise region of 'the phylogenetic acquisition of each individual', that is, with the idea of an 'archaic heritage'. 'What has belonged to the lowest part of mental life of each of us is changed, through the formation of the ideal, into what is the highest in the human mind by our scale of value . . . It contains the germ from which all religions have evolved.' The quotation continues: 'it would be vain, however, to attempt to localize the ego ideal, even in the sense in which we have localized the ego, or to work it into any of the analogies with the help of which we tried to picture the relation between the ego and the id.'[60] What makes that 'agency' defy illustration, evade the 'considerations of theoretical representability'?[61] Is it primarily because it is conceived of as the substitute of an 'indefinite number of people', just as the super-ego is the precipitate of 'countless egos'? Is it because these agencies are the result of *condensation*, of an 'economy' that they cannot be 'illustrated'? Let us recall how with the dream, 'strictly speaking, it is impossible to determine the amount of condensation.' This might be even more so concerning the amount of condensation that the mass signals.[62]

We saw that the 'lowest part of mental life' is associated with the 'larger sphere' of the id, and that the 'highest part' – consciousness and conscience [*Gewissen*] – represents but a 'smaller' sphere within it. Freud eventually wonders whether the origin of religion should be assigned to the ego or to the id, and, unable to answer directly to that question, finally suggests that 'one must not take the difference between ego and id in a too hard-and-fast-sense', nor forget 'that the ego is a differentiated part of the id'.[63] It is only the ego that has 'experiences', but the experiences of the ego become that of the id through numerous repetitions. Following the principle long expressed in 'The Project' whereby the functions of reception and retention cannot be the matter of the same system, the ego cannot inherit, the id cannot have experiences, while the id can inherit the 'harboured' residues of 'the existence of countless egos'. Standing between the two, the super-ego can be envisaged to be the 'reviving shapes of former egos'. The regressive reproduction of the evolution of conscience consists in the regression towards 'the many', towards a 'mass' of sort formed by the numerous repeated experiences of 'countless egos'.

Far from denoting simply a 'social' entity, then, the mass conceals a number of methodological problems relating to scale, quantity and measurement, that lead us to the audacious question of phylogenesis (in so far as Freud believed, as we already reported, that it may 'lay bare the inadequacy of [his] whole effort').[64] In dealing with the mass, we may be faced with a 'limit-concept' that oscillates between the social and the physical senses, with yet unexplored a kind of 'quantitative factor' that might oblige us to extend Freud's economic lexicon.

If the mass can be deemed to have an instrumental role in the understanding of the differentiation of the psyche, such as, for example, in 'On Narcissism' and in *Mass Psychology*, and if it can have the status of a manifestation that usefully amplifies normal processes and allows us to understand mental functions, the idea or the phenomena of the 'great number' nevertheless poses other methodological problems for psychoanalysis. Whereas there is an insistence throughout Freud on the continuity between normal and pathological processes, since, in principle 'a neurotic manifestation may help us understand a normal one', the continuity seems to be broken in front of the disorders that take on a mass dimension.[65] Pathological processes on a large scale (such as, for example, *Massenneurosen*) are apparently not compatible with scientific activity. An explorative value may be assigned to neurosis, but not to 'mass neurosis'. Let us recall Freud's warnings against the analogical reasoning that underlies the application of psychoanalysis for the treatment of more than one 'neurotic human being' at once. It would not be too great an extrapolation to say that he might therein also be signalling the danger of too great a degree of 'sameness' between health and illness, between the individual and the mass. The identity between 'normal and pathological' mental processes, like analogies in scientific work, should not be as 'complete' as Freud's writings may sometimes affirm, at least in so far as it engages the distinction between the individual and the 'great number'. However successfully Freud may have abolished the separation between individual and 'social' psychology, it is difficult, at a methodological level, to reconcile the idea of the 'many' with the scientific task that psychoanalysis has set itself. The idea or mass phenomena might even hinder its course.

Freud's description of the 'single aim' that has oriented his work in 'The Goethe Prize Address' (1930) gives us precious indications about it:

> I have observed the more subtle disturbances of mental function in healthy and sick people and have sought to infer – or, if you prefer it, to guess – from signs of this kind how the apparatus which serves these functions is constructed and what concurrent and mutually opposing forces are at work in it.[66]

The Postcript to 'The Question of Lay-Analysis' (1926) puts it even more one-sidedly, while highlighting well the 'instructive' role and the 'accessibility' of neurotic human beings: 'the only subject-matter of psychoanalysis is the mental processes of human beings and it is only in human beings that it can be studied . . . neurotic human beings offer far more instructive and accessible material than normal ones.'[67]

What we called a change of scale in order to designate the shift from the individual to the mass, and the various enlargement, which pathological processes constitute with respect to 'normal' ones, modifies both the possibility of observation, of inference (or of guessing), and the subject of observation that underlies psychoanalytic research. When Freud asks 'what is a mass?' at the beginning of *Mass Psychology*, it is not the notion, the concept or the term that worries him, but rather the phenomena. The inquiry, like other ones in Freud, is nevertheless based on the reading of the authorities, rather than on their observation.[68] From whence, indeed, could 'mass phenomena' be observed and what can be inferred from them? Could their observation ever allow the perception of the 'subtle disturbances of mental function in healthy and sick people' as other neurotic manifestations do? Could the mass ever let anything like *subtleties* [*Feinheit*] transpire?[69] Freud does not exactly raise these questions around the mass, but it is not a coincidence if in the early chapters of the 1921 essay, the discussion of the hypotheses of crowd psychologists is introduced by a remark on the precedence of description over explanation. The topic of the mass poses acute problems at that level. The question 'what is the nature of the mental change which [the mass] forces upon the individual?' calls for something that 'escapes observation'.[70] What requires elucidation is the 'transformation' of an individual when entering into a mass, rather than 'the mass' itself, if there such be. Freud retains from these thinkers on the crowd the supposition that 'there must be something' which binds individuals together and engenders the unity that reigns in a mass: if 'individuals combine in a unity, there must surely be something to unite them, and this bond might be precisely the thing that is characteristic of a group'.[71] In other words, there must be 'something', as Freud puts it, to observe and that we should be able to describe, even if it is 'something' that has the nature of a 'bond'.[72] Freud's formula on the constitution of a mass in *Mass Psychology* is well-known: the mass is formed by 'a number of individuals who have put one and the same object [the Leader] in the place of their ego ideal and have consequently identified themselves with one another in their ego'. It is repeated many times, for example, in 1932: 'a psychological group is a collection of individuals who have introduced the same person into their super-ego and, on the basis of this common element, have identified themselves with one another in their ego.'[73] It rests on the idea that love relationships constitute the essence of the group mind [*Massenseele*], or that libidinal ties, more precisely identifications, characterize a mass.[74]

Mass Psychology is only one of the numerous places in Freud where what there is to explain evades observation and obliges one to produce an indirect description.[75] Most of Freud's developments objecting to the 'conscientialist prejudice' affirm that the object of psychoanalysis has the nature of an 'interruption' or of a 'gap' in the chain of conscious mental events, of something that in principle cannot be 'seen'. But not everything that escapes observation has the same importance. For between the observation of *individual* interruptions and gaps from the disturbances that can be inferred from mass phenomena, and more generally, from everything that has to do with the 'great number', only the former is given an explicit role in the very construction of the science. (Even though as we saw, the mass has an instructive role in helping us to discover the mechanisms of identification, the ego-ideal.) By 'construction of the science', we are here pointing to the peculiar relation that joins the object of the science (the functioning of the psychical apparatus) and the method of obtaining knowledge about it (including the 'technique' of the psychoanalytic cure). The psychical locality, if there be, is here hard to situate, but it seems in any case to be incompatible with the idea of the mass:

> Every science is based on observations and experiences arrived at through the medium of our psychical apparatus. But since *our* science has as its subject that apparatus itself, the analogy ends here. We make our observations through the medium of the same perceptual apparatus, precisely with the help of the breaks in the sequence of 'psychical' events [*gerade mit Hilfe der Lücken im Psychischen*]: we fill

> in what is omitted by making plausible inferences and translating it into conscious material. In this way we construct, as it were, a sequence of conscious events complementary to the unconscious psychical processes. The relative certainty of our psychical science is based on the binding force of these inferences [*Verbindlichkeit dieser Schlüsse*] (SE XXIII, p. 159).

The peculiar relation between the medium through which observations are made and the subject of observation had already been hinted at in a passage of 'The Project' where Freud, after having introduced the neurological quantitative functioning of the psyche, approaches 'The Problem of Quality'. Every psychological theory, Freud writes, should 'explain to us what we are aware of, in the most puzzling fashion, through our "consciousness"'. There is nothing unusual about this requirement, it even appears to be spoken in the language of existing psychological theories. But, even notwithstanding the notorious difficulty of the neurological construction at issue, the sentence is perplexing when it concludes 'since this consciousness knows nothing of what we have so far been assuming – quantities and neurones – it should explain this lack of knowledge as well' (SE I, p. 308). The editor comes to our rescue by specifying in a note that the statement of ignorance concerns 'neuronal processes' and that Freud eventually makes 'exactly the same statement about *psychical* events' (*ibid.*, note 1). The rewriting of this statement concerning *psychical* events clarifies the problem by opening up the genetic perspective of the second topography, but it does not merely replace 'neuronal processes' with 'psychical events' as it is suggested. Still in the vein of an objection to the overvaluation of 'consciousness', and leaning on Lipps's pronouncements in *Der Begriff des Unbewußten in der Psychologie* (1897) Freud indeed writes that:

> the unconscious is the larger sphere [*der größere Kreis*], which includes within it the smaller sphere of the conscious [*das kleinere des Bewußten*]. Everything conscious has an unconscious preliminary stage; whereas what is unconscious may remain at that stage and nevertheless claim to be regarded as having the full value of a psychical process. The unconscious is the true psychical reality; *in its innermost nature it is as much unknown to us as the reality of the external world, and it is as incompletely presented by the data of consciousness as is the external world by the communications of our sense organs* (SE V, pp. 612–13)

It is strange that the editor should describe the two passages as presenting the same 'statement' upon different objects, since the one from 'The Project' stands out by raising questions about scientific activity. What consciousness appears to be ignorant of here is not the unconscious mental events but their neurological description (whether the latter be fictional or not). To affirm that consciousness ignores 'quantities' and 'neurones' is to raise a worry about the subject of science and about the enigmatic place from whence science is produced, which might be distinct from consciousness. (The second statement therefore does not necessarily, as the editor indicates, substitute psychical for physiological events. Such a substitution would help us draw a line of development through Freud's work, from 'neurology' to what is psychical proper, which would no longer, have anything to do with neurones.)[76]

Both passages, however, raise the question of what it is for consciousness, the ego, or the self (who, what exactly?) to experience 'ignorance' and of the nature and the fate of the ignored material. Ignorance is one favoured access to the unconscious, it is the condition of knowledge of the unconscious: 'we call a psychical process unconscious whose existence we are obliged to assume – for some such reason as that we infer it from its effects – but of which we know nothing.'[77] This situation is probably most intelligible when it is described with reference to the analytic cure, which seeks 'to bring to conscious recognition the things in mental which are repressed'.[78] Everyone is familiar with the fundamental rule of the treatment that asks the patient not to 'keep anything back intentionally that comes into his head'.[79] What is interesting however is that, it is not only things that one would like to hide that pose problems but those that 'one would not care to admit to *oneself*'. More importantly, the imperative to say 'everything' reveals to the patient 'a very remarkable psychological problem', namely, the patient 'notices' (how?, this is the entire problem) 'a thought of his own being kept secret from his own self [*Selbst*].' And from there, for the person undertaking the cure:

> It looks as though his own self were no longer the unity which he had always considered it to be, as though there were something else as well in him that could confront that self. He may become aware of a contrast between a self and a mental life in the wider sense [*einem Seelenleben in weiteren Sinne*]. (*Ibid.*)

Whether 'a mental life in the wider sense' refers to the 'larger' sphere of the unconscious, whereby consciousness appears as a periodical, temporally limited phenomenon, and also spatially limited, is to be ascertained. Even if what is revealed is a 'thought that is kept secret', a line nevertheless joins the initial ignorance to the newly acquired knowledge of, for example, the constitution of the 'self' or, as in the passage quoted above, the psychical apparatus. The ignorance of a thought (it is being kept secret from one's 'own self') on one level is knowledge of the conflict that constitutes *the* self on another. However secret thoughts may be, their secrecy is, according to the well-known paradoxical epistemology of psychoanalysis, the guarantee of knowledge.

It is difficult to imagine how this access to knowledge could be possible at the level of the mass. Freud's analysis of religion in fact suggests that one of the harms that religion can cause comes from the fact that it is based on a kind of ignorance that cannot be redeemed by analytic work. The science of the psychical unconscious presupposes a 'subjective' knowledge of the functioning of the psychical apparatus, but simultaneously gives us confusing clues as to how to circumscribe the subject of such knowledge. The difficulty is acute when Freud speaks of the psychical apparatus in the singular. We can never be sure, for example, if the medium of perception described as part of the psychical apparatus corresponds to a 'perceiving subject', and a fortiori, to what the postulated identity between the subject and the medium of science exactly refers. But it is even more so when we try to imagine a similar congruence at the level of the mass. How can the disorders and the ignorance of 'an undefined multitude' yield knowledge of an apparatus that would be common to all? Let us recall Freud's perplexities around the hypothesis of a *Massenseele*, which is an assumption without which he would prefer to do. Ignorance on a large scale is not quite of the same nature as that of the neurotic towards the 'thought that is secret for his own conscience'.

It is not stated explicitly in *The Future of an Illusion* or in texts that deal with religion that the injurious character of religion comes from the fact that it is 'universally accepted', that it is 'shared'.[80] Freud's negative evaluation of religion yet appears to be based on the fact that religion is a *mass*-delusion [*Massenwahn*] rather than simply a delusion. It is not so much the credulity and ignorance of those who compose the masses that worry Freud as the fact that religion binds a great number of credulous people at once. 'Construction in Analysis' (1937) and other texts teach us that delusions bear striking resemblances to the work of the analyst or to the production of phantasy in day-dreaming and in creative writing. Something however happens to the latter when they take on the dimension of the mass: they become 'incapable of correction'.[81] In spite of the postulated continuity that is the very condition of Freud's analysis of religion, pathological manifestations are apparently not comparable to normal ones in every respect. The mere difference of degree would apparently hold for the difference between health and illness but not for that between 'illness of the one' and 'of the many'.

That the objection against religion in *The Future* should be aimed at the 'scale' of religious illusion is not easily perceptible because the 'common' character of religion can be easily confused with the unifying work of *Kultur*, which makes 'communal life possible'. When Freud affirms that *Kultur* relieves man from the task of 'defending himself against the superior powers of nature, of Fate . . . *in the same way for all alike*' and that 'all civilizations act alike' in this respect (*The Future*, p. 16), it could equally be an allusion to religion or to the unifying essence of *Kultur*. The reproach that is launched at the aggregative power of religion could just as well be launched at that of *Kultur*, whence in fact religious ideas come. However, whereas men can and in fact should do without religion – the essay suggests that one way of achieving this is to understand it – men cannot do without *Kultur*.[82]

Freud's reflection upon religion combines the compensatory function that it fulfils within the *Kulturprozeß* to that of its origin in early childhood and in the 'childhood of humanity'. The two interrelated aspects are elucidated by analogy with the 'normal' development of an individual and the development of neurotic human beings (with the added complication that 'neurosis' constitutes a 'normal' stage of development that can be 'normally' overcome). The function of religion is to protect men from 'the crushingly superior force of nature'. The need for protection arises out of man's 'helplessness' and of the 'urge to rectify the shortcomings of civilization which [make] themselves painfully felt'.[83] It 'derives its strength from its readiness to fit in with our wishful impulses',[84] since it reproduces infantile wishes formed in the state of *Hilflosigkeit*:

> Biologically speaking, religiousness is to be traced to the small human child's long-drawn-out helplessness and need of help; and when at a later date he perceives how truly forlorn and weak he is when confronted with the great force of life, he feels his condition as he did in childhood, and attempts to deny his own despondency by a regressive revival of the forces which protected his infancy.[85]

The reaction helplessness provokes becomes the model of the reaction the adult forms in front of the helplessness that the pressure of *Kultur* reproduces ('faced by the world [the adult] is still a child').[86] The 'helplessness' of childhood ('the infantile prototype') is however not the ultimate point of origin (at least as far as we can assess what is the model of what), for the childhood relation with the father is, *modelled* on the relation with the primal father ('the phylogenetic one') as Freud has shown in *Totem and Taboo*.[87] Among these fathers (this various scale of fathers?), it is difficult to assess which 'father' is the *Ur*-model. The specifically psychoanalytic view on religion consists nevertheless in affirming that there is an 'intimate connection between the father-complex and belief in God' and that 'a personal God is, psychologically, nothing other than an exalted father', in brief, consists in situating 'the roots of the need for religion . . . in the parental complex'.[88]

In *Civilization and its Discontents*, Freud positions his criticism of religion developed in the 1927 within the broader question of man's general *unhappiness* in *Kultur*. What is striking, however, is the particular place that religion occupies in the series of other 'auxiliary constructions' destined to a similar sheltering role. The list of 'techniques of living' drawn up in *Civilization* for alleviating the pressure of *Kultur* proceeds from the idea that the sacrifice of instincts is exacting to everyone, but that no one is affected by it equally severely: 'from its very beginning, the community comprises elements of unequal strength', that is, elements that can withstand unequal degrees of renunciation.[89] 'Strength' and 'weakness' are the measure of the degree of tolerance of the sacrifice, which, at the level of the instincts, corresponds to the capacity of the sexual instinct to displace the satisfaction of its aim.[90] It is thus the 'economics of the libido', 'its displaceability' that determines which of the 'substitutive satisfaction' one is likely to adopt for allaying the 'almost intolerable pressure' of civilized life, even if 'the programme of becoming happy' that the pleasure principle imposes on us 'cannot be fulfilled' (p. 83). In matters of economics 'there is no golden rule which applies to everyone' and one's attitude towards the demands of the external world and how independent from it one becomes is likened to a question of choice, even if the idea of choice is mitigated by 'the decisive part' played by one's psychical constitution.[91]

The methods range from the crudest – those that modify the organism (p. 78) – to the 'finer and higher' ones. The latter consists in 'shifting the instinctual aims in such a way that they cannot come up against frustration from the external world' and in using this displaced libido in order 'to heighten the yield of pleasure from the sources of psychical and intellectual work' (p. 79). This is the kind of satisfaction the artist and the scientist respectively obtain in creating and in 'discovering truths', and of which psychoanalysis has no direct metapsychological explanation – artistic gift is 'unanalysable'.[92] Such a presentation echoes the progress in intellectuality of which Freud speaks at the end of *Moses and Monotheism*, whereby moving towards the higher spheres of mental life corresponds to moving away from the senses. Between these two extremes, there is a variety of other means: illusion and phantasy, the delusional remoulding of reality, the enjoyment of works of art and of beauty, and loving. Those who are born with a 'specially unfavourable instinctual constitution' adopt the 'flight into illness' according to the principle that 'a person becomes neurotic because he cannot tolerate the amount of frustration which society imposes on him in the service of its cultural ideals.'[93] Religion stands out from the list of 'palliative measures':

> A special importance attaches to the case in which this attempt to procure a certainty of happiness and a protection against suffering through delusional remoulding of reality is made by a considerable number of people in common [*eine größere Anzahl von Menschen*]. The religions of mankind must be classed among the mass-delusions of this kind.[94]

All the enumerated measures with the exception of religion indeed presuppose individual means of striving towards happiness. Although there is no general rule that can be applied to everyone, religion imposes 'equally on everyone its own path to the acquisition of happiness and the protection from suffering', thus restricting 'the play of choice and adaptation'.[95] To partake in a universal neurosis spares 'devout believers . . . the task of constructing a personal one' whereas 'the unbeliever has to grapple with the problem on his own.'[96]

Religion 'draws [many people] into a mass-delusion [*Massenwahn*]' (p. 85). And one of the main grievances against such delusion is that no one engaged in it 'ever recognizes it as such' [*erkennen*]: 'its technique consists in depressing the value of life and distorting the picture of the real world in a delusional manner – which presupposes an intimidation of intelligence' (p. 84). This point is not elaborated further but the lack of recognition recalls, by contrast, the importance granted to ignorance everywhere else in Freud. What is wrong with mass-delusions becomes clearer when we contrast the kind of ignorance that is attached to them with the way in which scientific activity yields knowledge. Scientific activity is the technique the furthest removed from religion and it is conceived as being the prerogative of the few.

The full importance of the 'mass' character of religious illusions emerges when considering how they are acquired. On the one hand, religious illusions are said to be the 'teachings and assertions about facts and conditions of external (and internal) reality *which tell one something one has not discovered for oneself* and which lay claim to one's belief' (*The Future*, p. 25). In addition to not having 'discovered them for oneself', and to the fact that they 'lay claim to one's belief', raising the question of their authentication is prohibited. Religious ideas are to be believed because 'they were already believed by our primal ancestors' (p. 26) even if the latter were 'far more ignorant than we are' (*ibid.*). It is astonishing to realize that the most important of our cultural assets – those which 'have the task of solving the riddle of the universe and of reconciling us to the sufferings of life [are] precisely those elements that are the least authenticated of any'. That we should believe in them because 'our forefathers' did so, takes no account of the fact that what the latter have handed down to us 'bear every mark of untrustworthiness' and are 'full of contradictions, revisions and falsifications'. Freud does not deny that religious ideas contains 'historical truths', but the 'truth contained in religious doctrines are after all so distorted and systematically disguised that the mass of humanity cannot recognize them as truth'.[97] Freud eventually grants religious 'constructions' *historical* truth as he explains in a letter to René Laforgue and as he develops at length in *Moses and Monotheism*, just as he does to 'individual' phantasy and delusions.[98] Yet, unlike the distortions and the disguises of the production of the individual psyche, those of religion are not only impervious to correction, but they do not proceed from, and do not lead back to, the *subjective* knowledge implied by the functioning of a psychical apparatus. Hence, in *The Future*, the nature of illusions is a cause for indignation, and nourishes the need to inquire further into the 'inner force' of religious doctrines.

If, on the one hand, the way in which religious ideas are handed down without examination is puzzling, Freud nevertheless dates their psychical origin to childhood (and to the childhood of humanity). That they should be received so submissively despite their obvious untrustworthiness is in fact precisely a proof that they are 'fulfilments of the oldest, strongest and most urgent wishes of mankind' (p. 30), that is, that they are illusions which derive their strength from 'human wishes'. A belief is called an illusion Freud writes, 'when a wish-fulfilment', and not its relation to the external world and reality, 'is a prominent factor in its motivation' (p. 31). In so far as they derive from such wishes, from the ambivalence of the father-complex, religious doctrines are 'insusceptible of proof'. Some of them, Freud writes, 'are so improbable, so incompatible with everything we have laboriously discovered about the reality of the world, that we may compare them . . . to delusions' (p. 31). What Freud says about illusions and delusions in *The Future* is however quite succinct, and what matters is the way in which they are sharply contrasted with scientific activity, for they are not 'precipitates of experience' nor 'the result of thinking' (p. 30).

Freud insists throughout the essay on the historical development of religious ideas since to be able to explain their origin is also to be able to predict their disappearance even if in a distant, but not '*infinitely* distant, future'.[99] According to *The Future,* religion should be replaced with 'rational arguments', and the domination of the passionate impulses replaced with that of the 'intellect', in brief, a dictatorship of reason should be established.[100] The essay suggests *in extremis* that religious doctrines and science need not however be opposed, since the former can become 'a body of ideas which science no longer contradicts and is unable to disprove.' Religious doctrine 'allows for a refinement and sublimation of ideas, which makes it possible to be divested of most of the traces which it bears of primitive and infantile thinking'. The 'antagonism' between science and religion is 'only a temporary one'.[101] While it is not clear which religious doctrine exactly could be reconciled with science, the 'scientific ideas' and the scientific activity that preside over their discovery that are more likely to welcome such religious doctrine are evidently psychoanalytic ones. For psychoanalysis alone speaks of divesting religion of the 'traces of primitive and infantile thinking', or of our 'organization' as our *seelischer Apparat.*[102] What else than psychoanalytic thinking has indeed allowed us to see the pleasure that relinquishing religious illusions could yield? Freud has already expounded on the main theses on the instinctual wishful nature of religious beliefs and on their ambivalent relation to the father when he introduces the topic of science and the dictatorship of reason. Which science has made us reach that point in our thinking on religion? In other words, which *science* other than psychoanalysis would make us understand the instinctual basis of our beliefs and therefore explain our disproportionate attachment to them?

The Future becomes more intelligible if we consider references to 'scientific activity' throughout the essay as references to psychoanalysis, and if we explore briefly the unique form that psychoanalytic knowledge takes. The hostile attitude towards mass-delusions that religion constitutes becomes a matter of incompatibility between the psychoanalytic 'scientific' method and the formation of religious ideas. The future replacement of religious ideas with science above all announces the understanding of their psychical force and origin. Science is not science in 'general', but the only one (or one of the few sciences) that take seriously the hypothesis of the unconscious.

Emphasizing only a few elements from the development on science at the end of the essay will suffice to show that the scientific activity that is at issue is psychoanalysis, and to underline features of the conception of knowledge that it upholds. It is namely at issue at the end of the essay in the defence against the attacks of the opponents concerning the harm that might be done to civilization by such a piece of writing. In reply, the text minimizes the import of psychoanalysis, and compares it to a method of research, to 'an impartial instrument', to 'infinitesimal calculus' – 'All I have done . . . is to add some psychological foundation to the criticisms of my great predecessors' (p. 35), 'nothing that I have said against the truth-value of religion needed the support of psycho-analysis' (pp. 36–7). Just as the discovery the latter can help us make about the destruction of the earth cannot be blamed on the method of calculation, the affective significance of religious doctrines cannot be blamed on psychoanalysis (it is not the only time that Freud compares psychoanalysis to an ill-fated scientific advance).[103] In *The Future,* we recognize methodological pronouncements that run through many other psychoanalytic works. For example, when discussing the prohibition against questioning the authentication of religious ideas, Freud compares the latter to other teachings that too 'demand belief in their contents'. Unlike religious ideas, these teachings

> are put forward as the epitomized result of a longer process of thought based on observation and certainly also on inferences. If anyone wants to go through this process himself instead of accepting its result, they show him how to set about it. Moreover we are always in addition given the source of the knowledge conveyed by them, where that source is not self-evident, as it is [in] the case of geographical assertions. For instance, the earth is shaped like a sphere; the proofs adduced for this are Foucault's pendulum experiment, the behaviour of the horizon. (p. 26)

Is this not an enunciation of some of the principles psychoanalysis claims to follow as far as the movement to and fro from observation to concepts is concerned? Many of Freud's descriptions of the method such as in 'Instincts and their Vicissitudes' (1915), underline the combination of 'observation and inferences': 'even at the stage of description, it is not possible to avoid applying certain abstract ideas to the material in hand, ideas derived from somewhere or other but certainly not from new observations alone.'[104] It is true that when psychoanalysis compares its procedures to that of other sciences, it seems merely to follow the injunctions of natural sciences, and one could object that such a description does not tell us anything that pertains specifically to psychoanalysis.

Against the opponent that wonders whether psychoanalysis too could be deemed an illusion, Freud reasserts the idea that 'some knowledge about the reality of the world' can only be achieved by science:

> Science has given us evidence by its numerous and important successes that it is no illusion. Science has many open enemies, and many more secret ones, among those who cannot forgive her for having weakened religious faith and for threatening to overthrow it. She is reproached for the smallness of the amount she has taught us and for the incomparably greater field she has left in obscurity. But, in this, people forget how young she is, how difficult her beginnings were and how infinitesimally small is the period of time since the human intellect has been strong enough for the tasks she sets (p. 55).

The measuring aim of science cannot be more prominent than in these lines, which reminds us of the 'impératif de mesure' that commentators attach to psychoanalysis.[105] They are followed by an affirmation concerning the need permanently to modify concepts in science that typifies the epistemological stance of psychoanalysis throughout Freud's writings: it is sometimes the case that 'a rough approximation of the truth is replaced by a more carefully adapted one, which in turn awaits further perfecting. There are fields [like psychoanalysis] were we have not yet surmounted a phase of research in which we make trial with hypotheses that soon have to be rejected as inadequate . . .' (p. 55). Faced with such a statement, it is impossible not to recall Freud's insistence on the fact that psychoanalytic concepts are still 'in the process of evolution' (p. 217). He states this, for example in 'The Resistances', but also in many other texts, a situation to which 'Instincts and their Vicissitudes' gives a scientific necessity by relating the provisional character of concepts to their initial indefiniteness (SE XIV, p. 117). Freud's *general* description of scientific concepts in *The Future*, then, visibly depicts the provisional character of the most basic concepts of psychoanalysis.[106]

The rejection of introspection as 'a means of knowledge of reality outside ourselves' may be more reliable an index of the fact that the scientific activity that is at issue in *The Future* is psychoanalysis. Such a rejection is an important element of the general distrust in which psychoanalysis holds philosophy, and appealing to science is often, for psychoanalysis, a means of differentiating itself from the latter, even though it no less needs to distinguish itself from the scientific culture in which it evolves. Negative statements about philosophy are often based on Freud's rejection of the current intrication of science and philosophy (in empirical psychology). It is the latter's limited conception of consciousness that is the only genuine target of his attacks on philosophy. With respect to this conception, there is no distinction between science and philosophy (Freud refers to 'psychology' as their common name). The description of what philosophers understand by 'consciousness' in 'The Resistances' could just as well be that of the current medical and scientific profession:

> The overwhelming majority of philosophers regard as mental only the phenomena of consciousness. For them the world of consciousness coincides with the sphere of what is mental. Everything else that may take place in the 'mind' – an entity so hard to grasp – is relegated by them to the organic determinants of mental processes or to processes parallel to mental ones.[107]

Freud summarizes this state of affairs by saying that 'more strictly speaking [for the philosophers and for the scientists alike] the mind has no contents other than the phenomena of consciousness, and consequently psychology, the science of the mind, has no other subject-matter' (*ibid.*).

The possibility of knowledge of the external world is expressed against the background of such a rejection of introspection. We saw that one of the ways in which illusions in *The Future* are defined is by having as a prominent 'factor of motivation' a wish-fulfilment. The latter takes precedence over the illusion's relation to reality and therefore illusions are 'insusceptible of proof', that is, 'of the reality value of most of them we cannot judge.' Although religious illusions are no more opaque than many questions that remain unanswered by science, scientific work is nevertheless 'the only road which can lead us to a knowledge of reality outside ourselves' (p. 31). This affirmation is repeated later: could 'our conviction that we can learn something about the external reality through the use of observation and reasoning in scientific work' be an illusion? And as if to indicate which science is formulating the criticism: 'it is once again merely an illusion to expect anything from intuition and introspection; they can give us nothing but particulars about our own mental life, which are hard to interpret, never any information about the questions which religious doctrine finds it so easy to answer' (pp. 31–2).

The relation that Freud establishes between 'self-observation' and the formation of conscience and of the ego-ideal has been mentioned earlier. Freud links disparagingly the pathologies build upon the fear of self-observation to philosophical introspection, without however explaining very clearly which philosophical thought promotes the 'bad' kind of introspection, nor explaining in what it exactly consists. Instead of elaborating on the topic, he dissociates himself from philosophical introspection by invoking his 'little disposition' towards self-observation. It would be wrong to judge Freud's relation to philosophy solely on the basis of this kind of pronouncements. In any case, they do not tell us what exactly Freud is rejecting. If what is involved in these lines is a classical form of introspection that consists in the 'observation d'une conscience individuelle par elle-même . . . en vue de connaître l'esprit individuel en tant que type immédiatement observable de l'âme humaine en général' (Lalande), then it is not surprising that Freud should reject such an activity for the knowledge of the world. Notwithstanding the obscurities around 'philosophical activity' and 'psychology' in Freud, and leaving aside the topic of intuition that would require no less attention, 'introspection' is manifestly not the matter of scientific activity. Yet, not all forms of introspection are rejected. In fact, as the extract from 'The Outline' about the identity between the medium and the subject of perception of the psychical apparatus indicated, psychoanalysis proposes a modified form of introspection, namely one that partly rests on ignorance. As the topic of reason increasingly dominates the conclusion of *The Future*, the science that will replace religion obliges us to conceive of a hitherto unheard-of type of 'self-observation'.

It is when the implication of *our* organization in the very apprehension of the world is at issue, however, that the reflection on science most evidently loses all generality. The statement about science still takes the form of a reply to the attempt to discredit science on the ground that 'being bound to the conditions of our own organization, it can yield nothing else than subjective results, whilst the real nature of things outside remains inaccessible' (p. 55). More particularly, it takes the form of a list of several decisive factors that needs to be taken into account in scientific work:

> In the first place, our organization – that is, our mental apparatus – has been developed precisely in the attempt to explore the external world, and it must therefore have realized in its structure some degree of expediency; in the second place, it is itself a constituent part of the world which we set out to investigate, and it readily admits of such an investigation; thirdly, the task of science is fully covered if we limit it to showing how the world must appear to us in consequence of the particular character of our organization; fourthly the ultimate findings of science, precisely because of the way in which they are acquired, are determined not only by our organization but by the things which have affected that organization; finally, the problem of the nature of the world without regard to our percipient mental apparatus is an empty abstraction, devoid of practical interest. (p. 55)

The general discourse on scientific method here undeniably applies to the way psychoanalysis approaches knowledge of the external world, namely through a congruence between our 'mental apparatus' and the world. The passage echoes the one from 'An Outline' that stated an identity between the medium and the subject of perception ('our science has as its object that apparatus itself'). Knowledge of the external world (that can only be achieved through science, and not through introspection) coincides (or begins?) with the understanding of that peculiar instrument ('it is itself a constituent part of the world', the passage says), of its 'expediency' [*Zweckmäßigkeit*] that makes it correspond with the way 'in which the world must appear to us'. We discussed in the first chapter the way in which the mode of exposition in which psychoanalysis presents its result is meant to converge with its object, whereby the essentially elusive nature of the psyche can be discerned in the very formulations of the results. We now see that this convergence does not merely characterize the mode of exposition but also the relation of the psychical apparatus with the world.

We are compelled to refer to Freud's earlier elaboration of the 'compound instrument' and of what the latter makes of the external world, of the way in which it is a precipitate of it. The statements surrounding the picturing of the mental apparatus in *The Interpretation of Dreams* abounds in justifications about the harmless and perhaps inadequate use of images, of comparisons, of *Hilfsvorstellungen*, and about 'the method of dissection' [*Zerlegung*], which is used in 1900 to 'investigate the way in which the mental instrument is put together'. Is the 'method of dissection' a modified form of introspection? Who or what does the dissection, who invents the *Hilfsvorstellung*? It is difficult to reconcile that 'instrument' and the idea of the self that traditional introspection implies. Or to attune the various descriptions of the psychical apparatus as being 'extended in space', of an individual as a 'psychical id' and of the ego as a 'mental projection of the surface of the body', as a 'body-ego' (*The Ego and the Id,* Part II) with an equivalent activity destined to the knowledge of the world. The 'expediency' [*Zweckmäßigkeit*] of the apparatus remains opaque and Freud's account of processes of thought might help us to understand what can make us know simultaneously the apparatus and the world.

Strangely, the dimension of pleasure is missing from the description of science at the end of *The Future*. This omission is doubly striking since, on the one hand, the pleasure principle is said to dominate the functioning of the apparatus, and we must endeavour to limit its domination. Science is, on the other hand, 'the most perfect form of renunciation of the pleasure principle of which our psychical work is capable' (SE XI, p. 165). Let us recall that scientific activity is also described as a 'technique for fending off suffering' and in that perspective, it allows the 'shifting of the instinctual aims in such a way that they cannot come up against the frustration from the external world' (*Civilization*, p. 79). The rest of the passage from *Civilization* pertaining to that particular technique well completes the depiction of scientific activity from *The Future*:

> One gains the most if one can sufficiently heighten the yield of pleasure from the sources of psychical and intellectual work . . . A satisfaction of this kind, such as an artist's joy in creating, in giving his phantasies body, or a scientist's in solving problems and discovering truths, has a special quality which we shall certainly one day be able to characterize in metapsychological terms. At present we can only say figuratively that such satisfactions seem 'finer and higher'.

These techniques (art and science) have two disadvantages in comparison with the lowest means for fending off suffering and the untypical means that have a 'mass' character, such as religion:

> Their intensity is mild as compared with that derived from the sating of crude and primary instinctual impulses. It does not convulse our physical being. [Freud is announcing the 'crudest' means that is to come in the list: intoxication] and it is not applicable generally: *it is accessible to only a few people. It presupposes the possession of special dis-*

> *positions and gifts which are far from being common to any practical degree.* (*Civilization*, pp. 79–80)[108]

The Future highlights the extent to which 'the mass' or the 'masses', which lack a 'medium of perception' cannot easily act as a 'subject of science' in a 'science of the psychical apparatus'. The scientific procedure that psychoanalysis follows in seeking to discover the laws of functioning of the psychical apparatus and the 'economics of thought' prevents it from being the matter of 'the mass'. The essay suggests that the extension of its findings, rather than signposting a useful change of scale, could merely be an 'exaggeration'. When we consider the problem of the 'mass' in Freud through the analysis of religion, it strangely leads us to the characterization of scientific thinking and more generally, to the way in which the science of the unconscious imposes a redescription of 'thinking', notably as a 'small-scale' activity. 'Strangely' for traditionally the mass is a matter of passions and not of thinking.

5
Figurative Language According to Freud

It is with respect to the difficulty of defining what should yet be basic elements of psychoanalytic theory that Freud frequently refers to 'figurative language' [*Bildersprache*]. This heading encompasses as much the use of a model [*Vorbild*], an 'intellectual scaffolding' [*Hilfskonstruktion*], a 'fiction' [*Fiktion*], an analogy [*Analogie*], a comparison [*Vergleich*], a simile [*Gleichnis*], as that of an example [*Beispiel*]. If the presence of such figures is particularly noticeable throughout the Freudian corpus, however, it is partly in so far as Freud draws our attention to it, by inserting in many theoretical developments, amidst figures themselves, pronouncements concerning the impossibility of *not* using them. In these statements, Freud turns to science in order to justify what could easily be considered as a defect of psychoanalytic theory, and underlines the no less figurative aspect of scientific language.

The justification engages the connection of psychoanalysis with sciences, and its well known borrowings from them, and reveals the effort of psychoanalysis to be 'applicable' to other fields of research. In the following chapter, we will examine more closely how the relation of psychoanalysis with 'something else' (other sciences and other fields) takes place through Freud's recourse to what he calls the *Bildersprache*. Freud's *epistemological* reflections dispersed throughout the metapsychological essays well underline that state of affairs, but it is even more evident in *Moses and Monotheism. Three Essays* (1939 [1937–39]), particularly in the recapitulation of the theory of psychoanalysis of the last essay, around the demarcation between the individual and the mass.

Statements concerning the figurative character of scientific language are found, among other places, in chapters IV and VI of *Beyond the Pleasure Principle* (1920). When discussing the metapsychological hypothesis whereby 'consciousness is a function of a particular system which it describes as *Cs.*', which, because of its localization on the surface of the brain involves a differentiation between the (pleasurable or unpleasurable) action exerted upon it by internal and external excitations (p. 24), Freud brings up the example [*Beispiel*] of physical pain (p. 30). In this passage, physical pain provides a model of effraction, of an overflow of excitations coming from the periphery, thanks to which it is possible to explain the mechanism of binding [*Bindung*] of energy by the system *Cs.* (*ibid.*). In the midst of the intricate explanation of the (differential) relation between the energies of the cathected system and its capacity to bind a flux of energies causing the effraction, Freud writes: 'we must endeavour to draw a lesson from examples such as this and use [*anzulehnen*] them as a basis for our metapsychological speculations [*Vermutungen*]' (*ibid.*). But even with the help of a *Vorbild*, conjunctures or speculations on the effects that excitations have on the different psychical systems are surrounded by indefiniteness [*Unbestimmtheit*]:

> The indefiniteness of all our discussions on what we describe as metapsychology is of course due to the fact that we know nothing of the nature of the excitatory process [*die Natur des Erregungsvorganges*] that takes place in the elements of the psychical systems, and that we do not feel justified in framing any hypothesis [*Annahme*] on the subject. We are consequently operating all the time with a large unknown factor [*mit einem großen* X], which we are obliged to carry over into every new formula. (pp. 30–1)

Figurative language, then, participates in the carrying over of this 'large unknown factor' from one formula to the other. However, not only is the unknowable character of the processes at issue not eliminated by the use of models (which are themselves more or less knowable, as the example of physical pain indicates), but the hypotheses formulated on the basis of such models generate 'words of critical reflection', as Freud qualifies them in *Beyond* (p. 59).[1]

A question arises as to the persuasive power of Freud's various hypotheses. As though he were replying to the objection that he might himself find them unconvincing, in so far as they result from the combination of 'factual material with what is purely speculative [*mit bloß Erdachtem*] and thus diverging widely from empirical observation' (p. 59), Freud attempts to justify the speculative nature of his essay:

> We need not feel greatly disturbed in judging our speculation upon the life and death instincts by the fact that so many bewildering and

> obscure processes occur in it – such as one instinct being driven out by another or an instinct turning from the ego to an object, and so on. This is merely due to our being obliged to operate with the scientific terms [*den wissenschaftlichen Termini*], that is to say with the figurative language, peculiar to psychology (or, more precisely, to depth psychology) [*die eigene Bildersprache der Psychologie (richtig: der Tiefenpsychologie) zu arbeiten*]. We could not otherwise describe the processes in question at all, and indeed we could not have become aware of them. The deficiencies in our description would probably vanish if we were already in a position to replace the psychological terms by physiological or chemical ones. It is true that they too are only part of a figurative language; but it is one with which we have longbeen familiar and which is perhaps a simpler one as well. (p. 60)

This well-known and often commented-on passage states clearly how the unknowability of the processes with which psychoanalysis is concerned finds a parallel in the figurative nature of scientific language. There is no need to dwell more on this passage. Let us simply note that to insist upon the provisional character of theories is to open up the possibility of their 'permanent replacement' – hence the passage pursues with the controversial pronouncement on the way in which biology 'will blow away the whole of [psychoanalysis's] artificial structures of hypotheses' (p. 60) – and therefore announces the permanent recourse to 'images'.

Borrowings

Figurative language, then, does not refer only to the various registers of metaphors (spatial, political, strategico-military, scriptural, etc.) dispersed throughout the corpus. Freud's comments on the use of figurative language in *Beyond* draw attention to the inevitable borrowings of concepts from other sciences. The introduction to 'Instincts and their Vicissitudes' (1915) underscores Freud's preoccupation with borrowings from other domains; it begins by raising the problem of definitions in science. The articulation at issue is that between the 'material of observation' and 'abstract ideas' which are 'applied' [*anwenden*] to it. Freud says of such definitions which have the 'character of conventions' [*Charakter von Konventionen*]:

> They must at first necessarily possess some degree of indefiniteness; there can be no question of clear delimitation of their content. So

> long as they remain in this condition, we come to an understanding about their meaning by making repeated references to the material of observation from which they appear to have been derived, but upon which, in fact, they have been imposed.[2]

Definitions are not for all that arbitrarily chosen; on the contrary, their choice is determined by 'significant relations to the empirical material'. The movement to and fro from empirical material to definitions (which appear to have been 'sensed' [*erraten vermeint*]) eventually enables one to 'confine [basic scientific concepts] in definitions' (*ibid.*). But even then, definitions will nevertheless need to be modified. The topic of *Trieb* is introduced 'as a basic concept of this kind', to which the essay will attempt to give *a content*, by adopting physiological and biological points of view (p. 118). Freud, let us note, does not appeal to other sciences in order to introduce clearer delimitations, as might have been supposed. The appeal, for example, to natural sciences, serves the purpose of authorizing an unavoidable degree of uncertainty [*Unsicherheit* or *Unbestimmtheit*]. In the passage from *Beyond* which we quoted above, this is suggested by the emphasis on the figurative nature of scientific language. But just how borrowings from natural sciences may at least partly consist in the borrowing of indeterminacy, is perhaps even more evident in 'An Outline of Psycho-Analysis' (1940 [1938]). In the chapter on 'Psychical Qualities', Freud attempts to articulate the dynamic conception of the psychical apparatus, which attributes three psychical qualities to psychical processes (*Cs. Pcs. Ucs.*), to the topographical one, which is concerned with three provinces or agencies, whose relation, says Freud, are far from straightforward, in so far as the two series do not simply overlap.

Only the passage pertaining at first, to the fact of consciousness, but which soon leads to consciousness – 'a highly fugitive state' [*ein höchst flüchtiger Zustand*] – considered as one of the three psychical qualities at issue, will concern us here.[3] The topic of consciousness is introduced as one 'without parallel' [*unvergleichlich*], one which defies 'all explanation or description', and yet as immediately knowable through experience (p. 157). But that immediate knowledge is based on 'the assumption that consciousness alone is psychical' (*ibid.*), an assumption which is held despite the fact that 'conscious processes do not form unbroken sequences which are complete in themselves.' Philosophers – who exactly? – ignore these *lacunae* or at least exclude them from the study of consciousness.[4] Psychoanalysis (Freud speaks of psychology in this essay), unlike philosophy, proposes to explain these breaks by 'assuming that there are physical or somatic processes' whose discontinuous connection with facts of consciousness is at issue: 'some of them would have conscious processes parallel to them but other would not.' Psychoanalysis sees in these processes 'the true essence of what is psychical', and as a result, the nature of conscious processes must be qualified anew (*ibid.*).

To shift the emphasis away from the fact of consciousness to somatic processes, whose connection and lack of connection with conscious processes would seem to explain the breaks in the sequence of conscious events, 'enabl[es] psychology [psychoanalysis] to take its place as a natural science' (p. 158). Once admitted that acts of consciousness form discontinuous sequences, and that this discontinuity produces observable effects, it becomes possible to postulate the existence of processes which 'are in themselves just as unknowable [*unerkennbar*] as those dealt with by other sciences, by chemistry or physics, for example' (*ibid.*).[5] We do not need to go further into the fundamental assumption of 'supposedly somatic concomitant phenomena' to notice that it allows Freud to establish a continuity between psychoanalysis and natural sciences in so far as, like them, it deals with unknowable phenomena. And just as natural sciences do, psychoanalysis can 'establish the laws which they [the unknowable phenomena] obey and . . . follow their mutual relations and interdependences . . . in short, . . . arrive at what is described as an 'understanding' [*Verständnis*] of the field of natural phenomena in question' (*ibid.*). But this cannot be achieved without adopting fresh hypotheses [*Annahmen*] and fresh concepts [*neue Begriffe*] that will not be more approximative than the concepts adopted by other natural sciences. The alliance with natural sciences does not authorize the precision but rather the *indeterminacy* of psychoanalytic hypotheses and concepts. Moreover, the unavoidable recourse to an intellectual scaffolding [*Hilfskonstruktion*] corresponds to the 'intellectual scaffolding found in other natural sciences'.[6]

Psychoanalysis, then, not only borrows concepts from science, but it also borrows from it the authorization to resort to 'intellectual scaffoldings'. As the passage from *Beyond* indicated, the latter must yet be provisional and should be replaced as one accumulates and processes further experiences. But, because the advance in knowledge, as it is stated in 'Instinct and their Vicissitudes', 'does not tolerate any rigidity even in definitions' (p. 117), Freud draws attention to the way in which scientific concepts are, in any case, unavoidably indeterminate. Some of the provisional concepts of psychoanalysis, such as, for example, drive and nervous energy [*Triebe, nervöse Energie*] become more acceptable, because they are comparable, at least from the point of view of indeterminacy, to the no less indeterminate concepts of other sciences, such as, for example, force, mass or attraction [*Kraft*, *Masse*, *Anziehung*].[7]

Commentaries of Freud that consider the various species of borrowings that permeate Freudian research, usually focus on Freud's metapsychological and expository work, or more generally, on the supposedly speculative aspect of psychoanalysis, instead of focusing on clinical writings on the basis of which one could state more or less unequivocally that 'psycho-analysis is concerned with the elucidation and removal of what are called nervous disorders'.[8] Having considered some passages from metapsychological and expository essays, where the question of the *Bildersprache* occupies a prominent place, this focus appears amply justified. These essays enable us to note the extent to which progress in understanding can only be made thanks to various comparisons, models or 'auxiliary representations' [*Hilfsvorstellungen*], when faced, as Freud stated that he was, with the task of founding a *new* science.[9] We could just as well have turned to *The Interpretation of Dreams* (1900), notably to the proto-metapsychological chapter VII on 'The Psychology of Dreams', where the reflex-processes are said to be 'the model [*Vorbild*] of every psychical function', in so far as the psyche is attributed the 'capacity to transmit and transform a specific energy'.[10] But even though stating that the 'psychical apparatus [is] constructed like a reflex apparatus [*wie ein Reflexapparat*]' seems to exclude the possibility that anything else be called a model for the psychical apparatus – how indeed could there be more than *one* model? – other domains provide models for representing the functioning of the psychical apparatus, such as, for example, writing, which, as Derrida showed, has a decisive function as model. Whichever models or 'auxiliary representations' be at issue, however, their occurrence in Freud's discourse corresponds, as we have seen, to the difficulty of having to operate with a 'large unknown factor' [*mit einem großen X*], which produces observable effects. Conceived in this way, this procedure is not specifically psychoanalytic, it would be better discussed under the heading 'the nature and justification of analogical argument in science',[11] and under this heading, psychoanalysis might be excluded, so controversial has its status as a science been among proponents of such inquiries.

Rather than attempting to make the recourse by psychoanalysis to the *Bildersprache* a particular case, even if an inadmissible one, of the general scientific, analogical procedure, let us instead examine borrowings from another angle. What we discussed so far relates to moments of Freudian thought when (let us say, for *internal* reasons), the recourse to the *Bildersprache* becomes unavoidable, in so far as the nature of psychical processes remains secretive.[12] Freud deploys a great deal of effort to justify this situation, not only by describing it as a normal, scientific operation, but also by allying psychoanalysis with science on the basis of the shared difficulty posed by the unknown. The set of justifications, which should be considered as an integral part of the *Bildersprache*, aims at establishing correspondences between psychoanalysis and 'something else' which is apparently situated on the *outside* of psychoanalysis with respect both to its methods and to its *object*. This is the position which natural sciences [neurophysiology, biology, physics] appear to occupy, but we could also have mentioned political life, photographic techniques (Galton's *Mischphotographie*), or even language *tout court*.[13] But if it is true that borrowings first and foremost point to a distortion of the borrowed material, this procedure would seem to constitute an *Arbeit* (in the sense in which Freud speaks of the *Traumarbeit*) which might not be so heterogeneous to the secretive processes at issue in Freud.[14]

Application

There is a set of psychoanalytic writings, traditionally classified as 'applied psychoanalysis', and that we considered throughout our study, which would seem to present a different kind of *Arbeit*. 'Applied psychoanalysis' refers, in an editorial sense, to psychoanalytic writings on non-medical subjects, such as, for example, literature or art (the dividing line opposes medical to non-medical subjects, and not as we did above, metapsychological and clinical subjects). But the distinction, according to Ernest Jones, Freud's biographer and the editor of a 1925 English collection of such essays, 'is necessarily not a sharp one' since 'clinical value will be found' in essays of application while 'indications of the way in which psycho-analysis can be applied to non-medical subjects' will be found in 'purely psychological and medical subjects'.[15] Thus, the distinction between medical and non-medical subjects is necessarily not a sharp one in the simple sense that any non-medical subject becomes, when psychoanalysis deals with it, a subject relevant to the study and the treatment of nervous disorders. The notion of application as a way of distinguishing, even if loosely, between medical and non-medical subjects is still too rigid, and one which Freud himself seems to invalidate whenever he comments on the way in which psychoanalysis renders the distinction between the normal and the pathological a non-pertinent one.

The notion of application in fact denotes a more general feature of psychoanalytic thought. The study of hysterical symptoms, or more generally, mental disorders soon led Freud to study manifestations of the psychical unconscious occurring in normal life. Psychoanalysis would, on this view, institute itself thanks to the continuity between pathological and normal mental events that it maintains. How can passage from one set of events to the other be described? In *The Interpretation*, Freud recalls how, at the end of a long period of work on hysteria carried out in collaboration with Joseph Breuer, he formed the idea of 'treating the dream itself as a symptom and to applying [*anwenden*] to dreams the method of interpretation that had been worked out for symptoms'.[16] Given how central the study of dreams has been for psychoanalysis, if application [*Anwendung*] can indicate a shift from the study of neurotic symptoms to that of dreams, it cannot be considered as having merely an editorial function aimed at the classification of Freud's various excursions in the field of art, literature or politics. It also establishes a relation of sorts between objects of study, which may be said to be *intrinsic* to psychoanalysis.

In 'The Question of Lay-Analysis' (1926) the extremist position Freud adopts on the problem of application in the context of a discussion between medicine and psychoanalysis supports such a generalization of application. Psychoanalysis should not, Freud argues, 'find its last resting-place in a textbook of psychiatry under the heading of 'Methods of Treatment', alongside procedures such as hypnotic suggestion, autosuggestion and persuasion, which, born from our ignorance, have to thank the laziness and cowardice of mankind for their short-lived effects' (SE XX, p. 351). In order to save psychoanalysis from a fate which it does not deserve – psychoanalysis should not be 'crystallized' in a text-book, its knowledge must be provisional – Freud even asserts that 'the use of analysis for the treatment of neuroses is only one of its applications [*Anwendungen*]' and that the 'future will perhaps show that it is not the most important one' (*ibid.*). The passage ends with the concession: 'In any case, it would be wrong to sacrifice all the other applications [*Anwendungsgebiet*] to this single one, just because it touches on the circle of medical interest' (*ibid.*). According to this passage, *all* phenomena, including neuroses, can be conceived of as domains of applications.

If application, then, is a general feature of psychoanalysis, each *Anwendungsgebiet* however imposes particular modifications of existing concepts, and is potentially a place where new concepts must be elaborated. Application refers to the mutual exchanges between concepts and empirical material, bearing in mind the way in which domains of application (such as neurosis, the dream or the *Witz*) can acquire the value of model for each other. If Freud insists on the necessary provisional character of concepts and definitions, it does not mean that concepts and definitions are purely provisional (substitutable), but rather that they are permanently being applied and therefore permanently subject to modifications. Since application sends us back to various domains of potential revisions, it would seem impossible to describe application in general. But the modification or the elaboration of concepts relies more or less explicitly on the *Bildersprache*. In this way, what we have said so far about the *Bildersprache* might enable us to approach all *Anwendungsgebieten*.

Kultur

Unlike other phenomena which constitute domains of application, but which are not usually referred to under the heading of applied psychoanalysis, *Kultur* is unequivocally considered to be a domain of application.[17] Unlike other phenomena, however, it might oblige us to modify our account of the *Bildersprache*. Freud provides numerous descriptions in the historical essays of psychoanalysis's interest in *Kultur*. Let us consider the passage of the 'Postscript' (1935) to 'An Autobiographical Study' (1925):

> My interest, after making a lifelong detour through the natural sciences, medicine and psychotherapy, returned to the cultural problems which had fascinated me long before, when I was a youth scarcely old enough for thinking. At the very climax of my psychoanalytic work, in 1912, I had already attempted in *Totem and Taboo* to make use of the newly discovered findings of analysis in order to investigate the origins of religion and morality. I now carried this work a stage further in two later essays, *The Future of an Illusion* (1927) and *Civilization and its Discontents* (1930). I perceived ever more clearly that the events of human history, the interactions between human nature, cultural development and the precipitates of primaeval experiences (the most prominent example [*Vertretung*] of which is religion) are no more than a reflection of the dynamic conflicts between the ego, the id and the super-ego, which psycho-analysis studies in the individual – are the very same processes repeated upon a wider stage.[18]

This passage spells out – even if ambiguously – what motivates the inquiry carried out in the essays on *Kultur*. What is at issue in these essays is the possibility of making 'use of the newly discovered findings of analysis in order to investigate the origins of religion and morality', in so far as the process of *Kultur* [*Kulturprozeß*] appears to reflect the 'dynamic conflicts between the ego, the id and the super-ego, which psycho-analysis studies in the individual' (*ibid.*). The *rapprochement* can be traced back to what Freud described in 'Obsessive Actions and Religious Practices' (1907), one of the earliest attempts to bring together these two order of events, as a '*striking resemblance* between what are called obsessive actions in sufferers from nervous affections and the observances by means of which believers give expression to their piety [my emphasis]'.[19] It is this resemblance that 'embolden[s] [Freud] to draw inferences by analogy about the psychological processes of religious life' (*ibid.*). The basis for the analogy is the fact that obsessive actions can be shown to be the result of 'the repression of an instinctual impulse' just as 'the formation of a religion . . . seems to be based on the suppression, the renunciation, of certain instinctual impulses'. Thus just as in obsessional neurosis, the process of repression 'is only partly successful and . . . increasingly threatens to fail' (and in this sense it can 'be compared to an unending conflict'), in religious life, 'the suppression of instinct proves to be an inadequate and interminable process.' Other similarities and analogies between the two orders of facts can be found and, *leaving aside* the 'chief difference' about the nature of the instincts which, in neurosis, are 'exclusively sexual in their origin' while in religion they spring from egoistic sources, Freud concludes his essays by describing 'neurosis as an individual religiosity and religion as a universal obsessional neurosis' (pp. 126–7.) Thanks to the reasoning by analogy, it will be possible to develop one of the main theses of Freud's theory of *Kultur*, which is formulated in the following manner in '"Civilized" Sexual Morality and Modern Nervous Illness' (1908), and which we discussed in chapter 4: '[g]enerally speaking, our civilization is built up on the suppression of instincts.'[20]

Moses and Monotheism: Three Essays

Essays on *Kultur* consist, then, as Freud puts it in *Moses and Monotheism* in 'carry[ing] over the concepts of individual psychology into group psychology [*die Begriffe der Einzelpsychologie auf die Psychologie der Massen zu übertragen*]' (p. 132).[21] But the modalities of this transposition are not so simple as the concluding formula of 'Obsessive Actions', or the passage from the 'Postscript' might lead us to believe ('I perceived ever more clearly . . .'). In the third essay of *Moses* from which we quoted above, Freud admits of the difficulty of the task:

> It is not easy for us to carry over the concepts of individual psychology into group psychology; and I do not think we gain anything by introducing the concept of a 'collective' unconscious [*Begriff eines 'kollektiven' Unbewußten*]. The content of the unconscious, indeed, is in any case a collective, universal property of mankind [*ist ja überhaupt kollektiv, allgemeiner Besitz der Menschen*]. For the moment, then, we will make shift with the use of analogies [*Wir behelfen uns also vorläufig mit dem Gebrauch von Analogien*]. The processes in the life of the peoples [*Völkerleben*] which we are studying here are very similar [*sehr ähnlich*] to those familiar to us in psychopathology, but nevertheless not quite the same [*nicht ganz die nämlichen*]. (p. 132)[22]

If we refer this passage to the other essays which we considered above, problems arising from the analysis of *Kultur* seem to have nothing unusual about them. Whatever the nature of the difficulties (which we will see in a moment) may be, the recourse to analogies presents itself once more as a provisional theoretical 'solution'. And in this sense, the analysis of *Kultur* would not seem to add a new dimension to the set of relations to which the *Bildersprache* points. When Freud refers to analogy in the essays on *Kultur*, however, it does not entail merely the borrowings of concepts from other sciences: in these essays, analogy points predominantly to the way in which psychoanalytic concepts are themselves borrowed, and treated as figurative concepts. Among Freud's writings, this is perhaps no more evident than in the last of the three essays of *Moses*, a close reading of which will allow us to underline the decisive role played by the analogical use of psychoanalytic concepts.[23]

Let us briefly sketch the aims and arguments of *Moses*. The three essays that constitute Freud's last work are not easily summarized, especially in so far as Part Two of the third essay entitled 'Moses, his People and Monotheist Religion' is itself a 'faithful (and often word-for-word) repetition [*wörtliche Wiederholung*]' as Freud puts it, of the First Part (p. 103).[24] But a letter by Freud to Arnold Zweig gives a clear indication of its theme: '[e]n face des nouvelles persécutions, on se demande de nouveau comment le Juif est devenu ce qu'il est et pourquoi il s'est attiré cette haine éternelle.'[25] In order to raise the question of the way in which 'le peuple juif a acquis les qualités particulières qui le caractérisent' (p. 243), Freud attempts a reconstruction of the origin of Jewish monotheism and of its ethical prescriptions (among others, the *Bildverbot*) with reference to contemporary scholarly work on the subject, but most importantly, following the conviction that 'les phénomènes religieux ne sont accessibles à notre compréhension que d'après le modèle [*Muster*] des symptômes bien connus de l'individu, en tant que retour de processus importants' (p. 137). To put it schematically, what must be demonstrated is that Egyptian monotheism, to which the figure of 'the Great Man [*der große Mann*]' Moses is attached by means of an investigation of the Egyptian origin of his name, has been first abandoned, and returns in the form of the Mosaic religion. The disappearance of Egyptian monotheism involves the hypothesis of the murder of Moses conceived of as a repetition of the murder of the primal Father, which Freud is able to presuppose on the basis of his earlier investigation of the murder of the primal Father in *Totem and Taboo* (1912–13).

Let us consider the third essay from the point of view of the 'analogical transposition'. One of the recurrent questions which obliges Freud to resort to analogies is the following:

> We confess the belief, therefore [writes Freud at the beginning of Section B], that the idea of a single god, as well as the rejection of magically effective ceremonial and the stress upon ethical demands made in his name, were in fact Mosaic doctrines, to which no attention was paid to begin with, but which, after a long interval had elapsed, came into operation and eventually became permanently established. How are we to explain a delayed effect [*eine solche verspätete Wirkung*] of this kind and where do we meet with a similar phenomenon [*ein ähnliches Phänomenen*]? (p. 66)

A more precise description of what Freud means by 'eine solche verspätete Wirkung' is given later in the section. When Freud speaks of the 'delayed effect', what is at issue is the distorting effect of the passage of time. Various locutions are used to designate the indeterminate duration that is at issue. For example, throughout Section B of the third essay, the passage of time is described as 'a long interval'; 'a certain length of time'; a 'considerable length of time'; 'a long period'; 'a long time'. With respect to 'traumatic neuroses', the passage of time is designated as 'incubation', or, in preparation for the discussion that follows, it is called 'latency' (pp. 66–72). Time cannot be measured with precision, but that the passage of time should remain immeasurable is necessary for the hypothesis of the 'influence of distorting purposes'

(p. 68). The following passage well highlights the connection between *Verspätung* and distortion, in addition to providing a concise exposition of one of the main preoccupations of *Moses*:

> The Jewish people [*Judenvolk*] had abandoned the Aten religion [Egyptian monotheism] brought to them by Moses and had turned to the worship of another god who differed little from the Baalim of the neighbouring peoples [*Nachbarvölker*]. All the tendentious efforts of later times failed to disguise this shameful fact. But the Mosaic religion had not vanished without leaving a trace; some sort of memory [*Erinnerung*] of it had kept it alive – a possibly obscured and distorted tradition [*eine vielleicht verdunkelte und entstellte Tradition*]. And it was this tradition of a great past [*groß Vergangenheit*] which continued to operate (from the background, as it were), which gradually acquired more and more power over people's minds and which in the end succeeded in changing the god Yahweh into the Mosaic god and in re-awakening into life the religion of Moses that had been introduced and then abandoned long centuries before. That a tradition thus sunk in oblivion should exercise such a powerful effect on the mental life of a people is an unfamiliar idea to us [*vertraute Vorstellung*]. We find ourselves here in the field of group psychology [*Massenpsychologie*], where we do not feel at home [*in dem wir uns nicht heimisch fühlen*]. We shall look about for analogies [*Analogien*], for facts that are at least of a similar nature [*ähnlicher Natur*], even though in different fields. And facts of that sort are, I believe, to be found. (pp. 69–70)

So far the quoted passages involve a noticeable appeal to analogies, to which what Freud calls a problem of *Massenpsychologie* obliges him to resort. Analogous phenomena can indeed be found which will help to enlighten [*erklären*] the enigmatic 'influence of distorting purposes' (the 'unknown phenomena'). But while Freud insistently acknowledges the provenance of analogies, he does so according to the apparently unique criterion of being found 'in the most various spheres', in spheres different from the religious enigma which needs to be explained (p. 66). The progression of the argument is of particular concern here since the 'area of provenance' of analogies soon becomes psychoanalysis itself. The argument, then, goes in two opposite directions simultaneously. On the one hand, analogies are borrowed from fields which are said to stand progressively further and further away from the history of the Mosaic religion. To move further away from this history, on the other hand, is also to move closer to the concerns of psychoanalysis, up to the point where psychoanalysis provides the best analogy, even if from 'an apparently remote field [*ein scheinbar abgelegenes Gebiet*]' (p. 72). The essay seeks to demonstrate the coincidence between two processes of development (individual and cultural). Psychoanalysis however knows about only one of these two 'corresponding' processes, and in order to make the coincidence more remarkable, it would seem to institute an *écart* between individual and cultural processes, relegating the latter to the field of 'mass psychology'.

It is the fate of mass psychology that is of particular concern here, in so far as the 'remarkable fact', which belongs to mass psychology, eventually obliges Freud to use psychoanalytic concepts, more precisely, the concept of the 'repressed', as he puts it, not 'in its proper sense [*im uneigentlichen Sinn*]' (p. 132). Earlier we saw that figurative language is called for by the unknown. But in the examples that we considered, figurative language did not seem to *originate* in psychoanalysis itself. Faced with a problem of *Massenpsychologie*, or faced with a particular type of unknown (the distorting transmission, during a certain amount of time, through 'human masses'), it is *in psychoanalysis itself* that the best figures are found. When Freud presents the contents of his interrogation in *Moses*, it is not difficult to recognize motifs considered numerous times before in various other essays. The problematic of 'the delayed effect' and of 'distortion' are elaborated, among other places, in *The Interpretation*.[26] The element that is apparently added in the formulation of the problem in *Moses*, is the way in which this process is said to happen at the level of 'the life of peoples [*Völkerleben*]' (p. 132). It would seem, then, that an important part of the work consists in 'giv[ing] a content' to the cultural process [*Kulturprozeß*], of which religion is a representative [*Vertretung*], in as much as it depends upon something which is at times called 'human masses' [*Menschenmassen*] (p. 175).[27]

The use of numerous locutions for designating 'human masses' recalls the indeterminacy that characterizes the expression of duration. In order to designate the 'groups' which are involved in the various biblical and historical accounts of the story of Moses, the following terms, among others, are used: people [*Volk*]; tribe [*Stamm*]; collectivity [*Volksgenossen*]; crowd, heap [*Haufen*]. In the third essay, when the subsequent history of Mosaic religion is at issue, the 'group' subjected to the 'influence of distorting purposes' is referred to as 'das jüdische Volk' but also, more generally, as the *Menschenmassen*, given that religion, of which Mosaic religion is only a case, is a problem of *Massenpsychologie*.

It is a problem involving an indeterminate number of individuals.[28] One way of distinguishing Freud's use of *Menschenmassen*, 'human masses', and that of the term *Massenpsyche* – which the English translation renders into 'collective mind' – in *Totem and Taboo*, might be to underline the fact that the expression 'human masses' apparently functions, in the former, as a descriptive term in the reconstitution of the story of the Exodus whereas *Massenpsyche* functions as a necessary assumption [*Annahme*] or a presupposition [*Voraussetzung*] in Freud's speculation concerning the origin of society. In the second essay of *Moses*, however, attention is drawn to the indeterminacy surrounding what Freud calls a people or a tribe. The story of the Exodus raises the question of how to designate the group involved in it. Freud speaks of 'ein Volk oder ein Stamm', but adds in a note: 'We have no notion of what numbers were concerned in the Exodus from Egypt' (p. 18 note 1). The uncertainty concerning 'numbers' is later expressed again, when Sellin's hypothesis of the murder of the Egyptian Moses by the Jews completes the story of the Exodus. But this time, it is a question of postulating that 'a considerable number of people must have left the country with Moses [*Es muß eine beträchtliche Anzahl von Personen gewesen sein*]' given that 'a small collection [*ein kleiner Haufen*] would not have seemed worth while to this ambitious man with his large aims in view' (p. 36). Moses could not be a 'Leader' [*Führer*] without a considerable number of individuals. Let us recall that the problematic of the relation between the 'Leader and the mass' runs through the three essays. It is one of the four questions that are raised in conclusion of the second essay, of which Freud says that 'to study them would be an alluring task': 'how impossible it is to dispute the personal influence upon world-history of individual great men [*den persönlichen Einfluß einzelner großer Männer*]' (p. 52). It remains to be seen whether, throughout the three essays, the indeterminacy surrounding the number of individuals involved in the various groups is dispelled. It is possible to argue, however, that what is insistently called a problem of *Massenpsychologie*, has everything to do with *the factor of number* which yet appears to be of secondary importance with respect to the overall argument, and bearing in mind Freud's rejection of the 'factor of number' in the Introduction to *Mass Psychology*. Let us recall Freud's dismissal of the factor of number: 'it seems difficult to attribute to the factor of number a significance so great as to make it capable by itself of arousing in our mental life an new instinct that is otherwise not brought into play.'[29] In any case, the indeterminacy surrounding the composition of the various 'groups' involved in the phenomenon under examination, from the story of the Exodus to the audience of Mosaic doctrines, motivates, to a large extent, the 'search for analogies'.

Having thus delimited the kind of 'unknown' that calls for analogies (namely, a compound of an indeterminate interval of time allowing processes of distortion, and involving an indeterminate number of individuals), we can now look more closely at the analogical transposition itself. Section B of the third essay is an interesting place to begin, in so far as it is clearly meant to prepare the way for the 'the possibility that the solution of our problem [that of Jewish monotheism] is to be looked for in a particular psychological situation' (p. 68), which will be the focus of the next section entitled 'The Analogy [*Die Analogie*].' What we hope to demonstrate by following the peculiar insertion of analogies in the course of the argumentation, is the way in which what Freud calls a problem of *Massenpsychologie* introduces a new element in the *Bildersprache*, namely, the figurative use of psychoanalytic terms themselves.

Analogies: a problem of *Massenpsychologie*

In order to explain the peculiar influence of distorting purposes, then, Freud first calls attention to science, notably, to Darwin's theory of evolution, despite the fact that science is a 'very different domain' from religion. The fate of a new scientific theory is no enigma:

> The new truth awoke emotional resistances [*affektive Widerstände*]; these found expression in arguments by which the evidence in favour of the unpopular theory could be disputed; the struggle of opinions [*der Kampf der Meinungen*] took up a certain length of time; from the first there were adherents and opponents; *the number as well as the weight of the former kept on increasing* till at last they gained the upper hand; during the whole time of the struggle the subject with which it was concerned was never forgotten. *We are scarcely surprised that the whole course of events took a considerable length of time*; and we probably do not sufficiently appreciate that what we are concerned with is a process in group psychology [*Massenpsychologie*] [my emphasis]. (p. 67)[30]

But not only is the fate of a scientific doctrine no enigma, but it is possible to find 'an analogy . . . corresponding precisely to this process [*eine voll entsprechende Analogie*]' to it in the psychical life [*Seelenleben*] of an individual: 'Such would be the case if a person learnt something new to him which, on the ground of certain evidence, he ought to recognize as true, but which contradicts some of his wishes and shocks a few convictions that are precious to him.' This situation however is apparently only worth noticing for reiterating the fact that 'it takes time' (p. 67) in order to overcome [*überwinden*] arguments maintained by 'strong affective cathexes' (*ibid.*). It is in any case pushed aside because of its little resemblance with the religious phenomenon at issue. To move into the domain of 'the psychical life of an individual' is indeed to move away from the phenomenon of mass psychology which has to be explained. But it is a step towards the sphere of psychoanalysis. Thus the example [*Beispiel*] of traumatic neuroses is called upon as one which has 'even less in common' (*ibid.*) with religious tradition. But the way in which psychical and motor symptoms develop only *after* the event of the accident in these types of neurosis, that is after an *Inkubationszeit*, allows us to discover that, 'in spite of the fundamental difference between the two cases' (p. 68), there exists an *Übereinstimmung* between traumatic neuroses and Jewish monotheism, namely the problem of latency.

Once posited that the solution of the problem lies in a 'remote field', in a 'particular psychological situation', it becomes clear that the main analogical move of this chapter is to establish a correspondence between the phenomenon of latency and *tradition*, the latter allowing us to conceive of a 'latency period' in the history of Jewish monotheism. Just as in traumatic neuroses it was possible to identify two events (the accident and the appearance of symptoms separated by a certain interval of time), Freud's account of tradition also entails 'two events'. What needs to be explained is how Mosaic tradition, of Egyptian origin, rather than having 'vanished without leaving a trace after the murder of Moses', has been kept alive by 'some sort of memory of it [*eine Art von Erinnerung*] . . . a possibly obscured and distorted tradition' (p. 70). As with previous examples or analogies, 'two conflictual tendencies' are at issue. Let us try to identify the elements that are involved this time. There are two groups of people that will later unite to form the Jewish people. On the one hand, those 'who had been in Egypt', who had vivid memories who still felt Egyptian and bore Egyptian names (p. 68), and, therefore, who had 'good motives for repressing [*verdrängen*] the memory of the fate with which their leader and lawgiver [*ihrem Führer und Gesetzgeber*] had met'. And, on the other hand, those who were dominated by the purpose of 'glorifying the new god and to dispute his being foreign' (p. 68). Despite these different motives, both groups had the same interest in disavowing [*verleugnen*] the existence of the earlier (Egyptian) monotheistic religion. Thanks to the fact that 'the people who had come from Egypt had brought writing and the desire to write history along with them', the common disavowal which Freud calls the first compromise 'was probably soon recorded in writing' (p. 68).

The particular Freudian account of tradition begins here. For if the first compromise eventually leads to a written narration, 'it was to be a long time' before it is recognized that historical narration 'was pledged to unswerving truthfulness'. The first narration, which ensues from the disavowal and repression of the Egyptian origin of Jewish monotheism, is done in ignorance of 'the concept of falsification [*Verfälschung*]'. As a result, the first written narratives were done in the service of the repression of the Egyptian origin of monotheism. An important lapse of time separates the first narration and knowledge of the possible link between narration and truth. Freud's account of tradition is not exactly concerned with that gap (although, tradition eventually becomes a 'conflict' between 'written records' only). Indeed, despite the written falsification of (material) truth, the latter is however not eliminated:

> [Because truth was being distorted in written narratives], a discrepancy was able to grow up between the written record [*Niederschrift*] and the oral transmission [*der mündlichen Überlieferung*] of the same material – *tradition*. What had been omitted or changed in the written record might very well have been preserved intact in tradition. Tradition was a supplement but at the same time a contradiction to historical writing. It was less subjected to the influence of distorting purposes [*Einfluß der entstellenden Tendenzen*] and perhaps at some points quite exempt from them, and it might therefore be more truthful than the account that had been recorded in writing. Its trustworthiness, however, suffered from the fact that it was less stable and definite than the written account, and exposed to numerous changes and alterations when it was handed on from one generation to another by oral communication [*von einer Generation auf die andere übertragen wurde*]. A tradition of such kind might meet with various sorts of fate. What we should most expect would be that it would be crushed by the written account [*schriftlichen Fixierung*], would be unable to stand up against it, would become more and more shadowy and would finally pass into oblivion [*Vergessenheit*]. But it might meet with other fates: one of these would be that the tradition itself would end in a written record, and we shall have to deal with yet others as we proceed. (pp. 68–9)

'Latency in Jewish religious life' refers to this *contest* between fact and contents which, despite having been distorted and obscured during a long lapse of time (in written records), can 'exercise such a powerful effect on the mental life of a people [*das Seelenleben eines Volkes*]' (p. 70).

Why does Freud insist in calling the phenomenon with which he is dealing one of *Massenpsychologie*, when, as we quoted above 'he does not feel at home with such a problem [*wir uns nicht heimisch fühlen*].' The transposition of sorts of the phenomenon of 'latency in religious life' in terms of a 'conflict' between written and oral transmission across generations reinforces the idea that the 'remarkable fact' of the history of Jewish monotheism is 'not a familiar one' for psychoanalysis, suggesting that the latter is not usually preoccupied with written or oral transmission across generations. The argumentative structure of Section B should enable one to demarcate clearly the 'known' from the 'unknown', the usual psychoanalytic sphere of interest from the problem of tradition, or the individual from the 'human masses'. When the 'unknown' takes the character of written or oral transmission [*Überlieferung*] across generations, however, are these concerns as unfamiliar to psychoanalysis as this section makes us believe? Psychoanalysis, not usually preoccupied with written and oral transmission?[31]

The insistence on the heterogeneity of the two orders of phenomenon in any case justifies the search for *more* analogies from yet other 'different domains'. Up to the end of this section, finding analogies amounts to establishing differences. The genesis both of national epics and of Mosaic religion is conditioned by the attraction the past exerts on 'men's imagination [*die Phantasie der Menschen*]' (p. 71). And since the past only subsists as 'incomplete and blurred memories which we call tradition' it provides the opportunity for the poet – just as for the Jewish people – 'to fill in the gaps in memory according to the desires of his imagination [*Gelüste seiner Phantasie*] and to picture [*zu gestalten*] the period he wishes to reproduce according to his intentions' (p. 71). At this point, the persistence of the past does not yet pose the fundamental problems which, as we will see, it will eventually do, when it becomes attached to the concept of memory-traces. Thanks to the principle whereby 'the vaguer [*unbestimmt*] a tradition has become the more serviceable it becomes for a poet', there can be an analogy between national epic poetry and Mosaic religion. The common effect of tradition on the subsistence of the past should not however make us forget that a poem is not a religion; and that, as Freud's three essays ambitiously argue, the *forgotten* and distorted tradition of Egyptian monotheism is reproduced [*reproduzieren*] by Mosaic religion more accurately than any other forgotten tradition by any national epics. The congruence, then, is still too imperfect. A more relevant analogy is needed.

Having prepared the ground more or less obviously from the first analogy onwards, by speaking here and there of 'affective resistances' or of 'distorting purposes' [*entstellende Tendenzen*], or even of 'traumatic neuroses', in the section actually entitled 'The Analogy', Freud introduces 'the only satisfying analogy to the remarkable course of events that we have found in the history of the Jewish religion' (p. 72). As previously, this analogy also originates from 'an apparently remote field', but unlike the others, 'it is very complete, and approached [*aber sie ist sehr vollständig, sie kommt der Identität nahe*]': 'This analogy is met with in psychopathology, in the genesis of human neuroses – in a field, that is to say, belonging to the psychology of individuals, while religious phenomena have of course to be reckoned as part of group psychology [*Massenpsychologie*]' (*ibid*.).

Even before having examined the analogy itself, the appeal to the latter promises to leave our problem intact. For if Freud goes so far as to say that 'this analogy is not so surprising as might at first be thought – indeed it is more like a postulate [*Postulat*]' (p. 72), according to which notion of postulat? – it clearly does not eliminate the demarcation between the psychology of the individual and that of the mass, a demarcation that Freud had earlier, however, singled out as an obstacle to his demonstration. In the case of the other analogies, fundamental differences between, for example, a man having been subjected to a railway accident and the history of the Mosaic religion, or between an epic poet and the Jewish people's use of tradition, in the case of this analogy were quickly found. Freud now seems to be saying: despite fundamental differences between individual and mass psychology that indeed keeps the two terms of the analogy irreducibly apart, the analogy is 'sehr vollständig', and 'kommt der Identität nahe'. We could go back to the previous section and ask whether differences that obliged one to move from one analogy to the other did not in fact send us back to this demarcation. What indeed differentiates a religion from a poem? National epics are not always the product of one poet just as religion cannot be formed without 'a considerable number of people'.

If we remain, then, with the progression of the analogical argument in the third essay of *Moses*, it might in fact be more helpful to look forward to the two sections following 'The Analogy', which, even if only with their titles, 'Application [*Anwendung*]' and 'Difficulties [*Schwierigkeiten*]', indicate that the 'completeness' of the analogy will soon be eroded. It is easy to see that the difficulty will first present itself as a 'dissimilarity [*Unähnlichkeit*]'. Judging by the structure of Freud's argumentation, then, the various analogies, including 'the only satisfying one', are indistinguishable from the point of view of their 'completeness', in so far as, even the most 'complete' one eventually reveals 'points of heterogeneity'.[32]

The various analogies are, however, distinguishable from the point of view of their provenance. As we said earlier, the 'only satisfying analogy' is found in the 'field of psychopathology' (the domain of psychoanalysis). Will this modify the way in which, up until now, something has forbidden analogies to bring about a theoretical *Identitätszustände*, to borrow the terminology of 'The Project'?[33] How will the analogy between the genesis of Jewish monotheism and that of human neuroses lose, if at all, some of its pertinence? Will the psychoanalytic conceptuality eventually have to be discarded for being too fundamentally 'foreign' to the history of Jewish monotheism? This is most unlikely given Freud's *belief*, which underlies all three essays, whereby 'religious phenomena are only to be understood on the pattern [*Muster*] of the individual neurotic symptoms familiar to us' (p. 58). The psychoanalytic explanation of the origin of Jewish monotheism, *by analogy* with individual neurosis, is indeed maintained up until the end of the essay. But at the same time as the concordance between mass and individual psychology becomes apparently more firmly established, what was confidently confined to individual psychology and considered well known ('the individual neurotic symptoms familiar to us', but as we will see, also 'memory-traces') begins to lose some of its individual and familiar characters. *Conversely*, the so-called phenomenon of mass psychology might be said to become more and more familiar, not, however, because it becomes more and more 'knowable', but rather, from the point of view of an examination of Freud's *Bildersprache*, in so far as the phenomenon of tradition brings us closer and closer to the 'figurative' character of Freud's argumentative strategy.[34] The rest of this chapter will aim to make this clearer.

Memory-traces

As objectionable as this might appear, we have been so far mostly concerned with the technical difficulties of Freud's argumentation in *Moses*, since they arise around the demarcation between individual and mass psychology.[35] Objectionable because we are apparently 'formalizing' a question which is otherwise so clearly polemical in its aims. In order to be convinced of this, one has only to consider the numerous prefatory sections throughout *Moses*, where Freud's ambitious and according to some commentators, 'strange project' appears unequivocally determined by the troubling events throughout Europe, contemporaneous with the writing of the essays. But, we now hope to demonstrate that in so far as concentrating on the technical aspect of Freud's theoretical exposition involves understanding the particular difficulties which 'the mass' brings into the psychoanalytic conceptual elaborations, such an approach to Freud's last book might prove a necessary preliminary to any other kind of study, including the study of its polemical aims.

We saw that the analogical argument, at least in section B, goes in two opposite directions: it was the apparent distance of psychoanalysis from the striking influence of tradition in the history of Jewish monotheism that paradoxically ensured that the latter could provide the most completely analogous phenomenon with which to compare and enlighten the enigmatic 'delayed effect' of tradition. Yet, according to the singular theory of analogy that emerges in this essay (and throughout Freud's corpus), even the most 'complete' analogy must however allow for some (necessary) degree of dissimilarity.

What seems to resist the analogical move is the demarcation between 'mass' and 'individual' psychology, to which the history of Jewish monotheism and the genesis of human neuroses belong respectively. If the essay aims to establish 'the analogy between neurotic processes and religious events' (p. 92), by attempting to 'bridg[e] the gulf between individual and group psychology [*Massenpsychologie*]' (p. 100), it does not however explain the nature of the difference between 'mass' and 'individual' psychology.[36] The analogy in fact leaves the demarcation intact, then, and appears to function as a principle of differentiation. This is why we have been following in a linear fashion the insertion of analogies in section B of the third essay of *Moses*. From the next section onwards, however, while the link between the genesis of neuroses and the effect of tradition on the Jewish religion is apparently tightened up, 'analogical moves' become more and more diffuse. It is indeed no longer simply a question of linking by analogy two distinct orders of phenomenon. The genesis of human neuroses, the process that is compared to tradition, itself generates an interlocking of analogies. Analogies are no longer called upon for expository purposes only; the neurotic processes themselves, or more generally, the genesis of the individual, appear to be, to a large extent, 'analogical processes', if by analogy we refer to two orders of events that come to be connected, but that can never be assimilated completely to each other. We will not reconstitute this interlocking as a whole, since it would amount to a reconstitution of the entire argument of *Moses*, which already consists in a recapitulation of sorts of all the fundamental concepts of psychoanalysis. The analogy between the genesis of neurosis and the phenomenon of tradition in the history of the Jewish religion nevertheless calls for an explanation of some basic elements of the theory of neuroses. On the basis of a most general definition of traumas: 'We give the name of *traumas* to those impressions, experienced early and later forgotten [*die früh erlebten, später vergessenen Eindrücke*],' and notwithstanding the distinction between traumatic and non-traumatic neuroses, the genesis of neuroses is said to go 'back to very early impressions in childhood' (pp. 72–3), and 'what we call the phenomena (symptoms) of a neurosis are the result of certain experiences [*Erlebnisse*] and impressions [*Eindrücke*]'.[37] Traumas will be explained in terms of the congruence between these two types of event.

To put it even more schematically than Freud, what needs to be explained is, on the one hand, that experiences and impressions are forgotten, but, on the other hand, that they are either remembered or repeated – the positive effect of trauma – or forbidden from being remembered or repeated – the negative effect of traumas which gives rise to 'defensive reactions' such as 'avoidances' [*Vermeidungen*], 'inhibitions' [*Hemmungen*] or 'phobias' (pp. 75–6). The way in which neurotic symptoms can be all referred back, in so far as they are 'forgotten' and 'of a sexual and aggressive nature', to 'early childhood up to about the fifth year' is explained with respect to the psychoanalytic theory of sexuality whereby

> in contrast to popular opinion, the sexual life of human beings (or what corresponds to it later on) exhibits an early efflorescence which comes to an end at about the fifth year and is followed by what is known as the period of latency (till puberty) in which there is no further development of sexuality and indeed what has been attained undergoes a retrogression. (pp. 74–5)[38]

The common characteristics of symptoms are also presented schematically:

> the symptoms . . . have a *compulsive* quality [*Zwangscharakter*]: that is to say that they have great psychical intensity and at the same time exhibit a far-reaching independence of the organization of the other mental processes, which are adjusted to the demands of the real external world and obey the laws of logical thinking. They [the

> pathological phenomena] are insufficiently or not at all influenced by external reality, pay no attention to it or to its psychical representatives [*Vertretung*], so that they may easily come into active opposition to both of them. They are, one might say, a State within a State, an inaccessible party, with which co-operation is impossible, but which may succeed in overcoming what is known as the normal party and forcing it into its service. If this happens, it implies a domination by an internal psychical reality over the reality of the external work and the path to a psychosis lies open. (p. 76)

In order to add one more element to this presentation of 'the essential features of neurosis', Freud resorts to a case history – 'From a History of an Infantile Neurosis' (1918) – whose subject-matter, Freud writes, is 'far removed from the topic' for which an analogy is sought. It provides an instance of a 'a revival of the identification with his father', whereby the male patient becomes, in his adult life, 'the faithful copy [*Kopie*] of his father' (p. 80) after having repressed the fear of castration developed on the basis of his early identification with him. There is no need to go further into the complex processes that Freud is invoking in order to see which elements will become significant for the 'analogical transposition'. Not only is the schematic character of Freud's exposition not merely circumstantial, but the transposition of concepts from one sphere to the other eminently requires a degree of schematization. It comes as no surprise, then, if Freud should describe, in the next section, the development of a neurosis in a formula: 'early trauma – defence – latency – outbreak of neurotic illness – partial return of the repressed' (p. 80).

But whereas everything has so far led us to believe that the analogy pertains to neurosis and religious phenomena, the link between the two orders of event cannot be made without reference to the myth of the primal horde, and therefore, as it would be possible to show, with reference to an already intricate 'analogical situation'.[39] The assertion that 'something occurred in the life of the human species similar to what occurs in the life of individuals', which is to say, 'phenomena similar to symptoms' (*ibid.*) depends upon the presupposition that 'the human race has a prehistory [*Vorgeschichte*], and since this is unknown [*unbekannt*] – that is forgotten [*vergessen*]' (*ibid.*).[40] Both neurotic symptoms and their equivalent at the level of the 'mass', the religious phenomena, can therefore be said to originate in the 'human family' in so far as the prehistory of the human species is conceived of (why? Freud does not say but presumably, *by analogy*) as a 'family'.

After having discussed Darwin's and Atkinson's hypotheses around the story of the primal horde for the first time in *Totem and Taboo*, and having told it again, albeit slightly modified, in the Appendix B of *Mass Psychology and the Analysis of the Ego* (1921) Freud refers once more to it in *Moses*.[41] (We should say: *twice more* since he also recounts it at the very end of the essay.) There are many reasons for bringing up this story (or myth) again here. We saw that it is an indispensable step for enabling the comparison between neurosis and religion. Let us recall that in *Totem*, Freud's reflections around the primal horde aim to contribute to the explanation of the origin of religion with respect to existing anthropological theories of totemism. In the 1912 essay, the specific psychoanalytic contribution consists in explaining events of the primal horde, notably the murder of the primal father, in relation to processes (most importantly, ambivalence) encountered, thanks to the account of neurotics, in the 'contemporary family'. In *Moses*, it is however not so much the emergence of religion out of totemism that matters, but rather the extension of the principle of substitution (from the *Urvater* to the animal, from the animal to the totem) at work in the myth to *later periods*. To bring up the myth again, in other words, should enable one to account for the 'introduction of monotheism into Judaism and its continuation in Christianity' (p. 85), even if this means having to presuppose an indeterminately long 'lapse of time' between more recent history and what is already situated in an indeterminate period of time. But Freud justifies convincingly such an extension, or perhaps more accurately, as the title of the section indicates, such an application [*Anwendung*] of the story to later periods:

> [After having noted that 'no date can be assigned' to the events that take place, but that what matters is the hypothesis whereby 'the events . . . occurred to all primitive men [*Urmenschen*] – that is, to all our ancestors, Freud writes:] The story is told in an enormously condensed form [*Verdichtung*], as though it had happened on a single occasion, while in fact it covered thousands of years and was repeated countless times during that period [*in dieser langen Zeit ungezählt oft wiederholt*]. (p. 81)

Freud might here be providing a key for understanding the difficulty of the transposition of the concepts of 'individual' to 'mass psychology': in order to conceive of processes at the level of the mass, one would need to 'undo' the *condensation* achieved by the psychoanalytic conceptuality, in relation to 'individual psychical processes'. What appears to be produced in the life of one individual in fact 'is repeated countless times' during a no less immeasurable 'lapse of time'. To work at the level of the individual psyche would seem to be to work according to 'an enormously condensed form' in order to avoid, even if only provisionally, problems arising with 'quantitative indetermination'.

The story of the primal horde itself constitutes a potential source of 'analogical difficulties' that would deserve to be examined with a great many precautions. If the search for the origin of religion proceeds from the hypothetical 'primal horde' and from the attitude towards the *Urvater* displayed in this story, and from what happens in 'contemporary families', the question soon arises as to which father exactly is the *Urvater* of the other. Not to mention the fact that the father at both extremities, considered independently from each other, stands as 'a model' [*Vorbild*] according to Freud's account of processes of identification. From the story that is told in *Moses*, let us be concerned with only those elements that will be relevant for considering the peculiar affirmation, in the very last section of *Moses*, that the concept of 'the repressed' [*Verdrängung*] is not used in its 'proper' sense, and towards which this overview of Section D leads us.

The section 'Application' is divided into four main points. First, it recalls the well-known story of the primal horde – the ancient history of the family – to which the unique *Urvater* is associated (pp. 170–3), and which Freud also calls 'the prehistoric tragedy' (p. 86). Second, it inserts religion among the succession of events (social organizations and substitutions of the Father) which the murder of the *Urvater* of the primal family triggers. But it adds to the series of substitutions 'the humanizing of the being who was worshipped' (the *Vaterersatz*), the progress which takes place from totemism onwards (p. 83). The advent of polytheism is an important element of this development, and it is linked to the emergence and the disappearance of the era of the matriarchal order. The emergence of the 'mother goddesses' does not only allow one to explain how the domination of the Father recedes. Most importantly, it permits one to explain the fact that, when the patriarchal order and its male gods are finally reinstituted, the Father-substitutes 'never achieved the omnipotence of the primal father,' presumably because, Freud suggests, 'there were many of them' (p. 83). The decreasing importance of the Father (-substitutes) is explained in terms of their replacement by the mother-goddesses, but also, even if less explicitly, in terms of their multiplication. Polytheism, the coexistence of numerous gods, then, represents one type of 'forgetting' of the *Urvater*. The third point concerns the 'the return of a single father-god of unlimited dominion' (p. 84). This gives rise to the longest development of the section, as it entails telling the story of the 'introduction of monotheism into Judaism and its continuation in Christianity' (p. 85). Finally, the fourth part of the section discusses briefly 'the people's hatred of the Jews' in the light of the Jewish religion's singular relation to the murderous events of the primal family – the particular character of which lies in the particular relation to the past (p. 90).

In the midst of the reconstitution of the *Urgeschichte* and of more recent past, 'into a whole' [*zu einem Ganzen verknüpft*], Freud inserts theoretical justifications, which pertain most importantly to the conservation of the past, despite the numerous moments of forgetting, which this genetic account of religion describes. Not surprisingly, that the past should *persist,* in particular so far as the relation to the father is concerned (which one?), can be confirmed by turning to 'popular legends and fairy tales, and the analytic study of the mental life of children' (p. 84). The recapitulation of psychoanalytic findings should remind us that in such a construction [*Konstruktion*] of the genesis of religion '[t]here is nothing wholly fabricated, nothing which could not be supported on solid foundations'. In brief, this representation of history [*Urgeschichte*] lets appear that religious doctrines comprise 'two sorts of elements':

> on the one hand fixations to the ancient history of the family and survivals of it [*Fixierungen an die alte Familiengeschichte*], and on the other hand revivals of the past and returns, after long intervals, of what has been forgotten. [*Wiederherstellungen des Vergangenen, Wiederkehren des Vergessenen nach langen Intervallen*]. (p. 84)

A state of affairs that can be generalized, as Freud then goes on to do, in the following manner:

> It is worth specially stressing the fact that each portion which returns from oblivion asserts itself with peculiar force [*mit besonderer Macht durchsetzen*], exercises an incomparably powerful influence on people in the mass [*einen unvergleichlich starken Einfluß auf die Menschenmassen übt*], and raises an irresistible claim to truth against which logical objections remain powerless: a kind of '*credo quia absurdum*'. (p. 85)

Up until then, the application seems to pose no apparent problems. It is possible to indicate potential sources of analogical difficulties, but from Freud's point of view, and up until the next section, both the 'story' itself and the theoretical adjuncts fit well together. In the next section, the 'peaceful co-existence' of the representation of the *Urgeschichte*, the psychoanalytic findings on which it is based, and the application to a problem of *Massenpsychologie* begins to be weighed down by difficulties.

Having now displayed, even if selectively, important elements of the analogical transposition, let us turn to the way in which the topic of 'memory-traces' gives expression to the complication which the transposition of concepts from individual to mass psychology brings about. Only the second among the two difficulties which are raised in this section is of particular concern here:[42]

> The second difficulty about this transference to group psychology [*Übertragung auf die Massenpsychologie*] . . . poses a fresh problem of a fundamental nature. It raises the question in what form the operative tradition in the life of people [*im Leben der Völker*] is present – a question which does not occur with individuals, since there it is solved by the existence in the unconscious of memory-traces of the past [*Erinnerungsspuren des Vergangenen*]. (p. 93)

The form which tradition takes can only be put into question if tradition is not considered merely as a phenomenon of 'oral transmission [*mündliche Mitteilungen*]'. The period of time which the history of Jewish monotheism covers obliges us to conceive of tradition well beyond oral means of 'transference' [*Übertragen*]. How has the tradition of the murder of Moses been transmitted, during the many centuries that separate Egyptian monotheism from its return in the form of Jewish monotheism? It is true, Freud argues, that a continuity can be established between the time when oral transmission was still conceivable and the time when tradition 'found expression in writing [*schriftlichen Ausdruck*]'. But even then, and this is of particular interest, tradition in a written form 'can only have been known to a few people; it was not public property [*Volksgut*]' (p. 93).[43] As Freud's earlier account of tradition in terms of competing modes of transmission had led us to believe, written records alone cannot explain the persistent and forceful influence of the returning of portions of the past. In this passage, however, it is clear that the problem of the persistence of the past and of tradition pertains to 'masses'. For if written records offer no solution, it is not so much because they cannot be conceived of in isolation from other more enigmatic modes of transmission, but rather because they constitutes a form of 'knowledge' which is 'held . . . by a few people' (p. 94). Both oral transmission and written records are associated with a small number of people, and to a certain extent, with a 'calculable' amount of time (at least in the case of 'oral transmission'). The problem of tradition pertains to 'the ignorant masses [*unwissende Masse*]' by contrast with the small number of people having access to the written record of tradition.

The apparent difficulty is reinforced by turning to 'the analogous case in primaeval times' (note that it is now the story of the primal horde which is compared to the murder of Moses):

> It is quite certain that in the course of thousands of years the fact was forgotten that there had been a primal father with the characteristics we know and what his fate had been; nor can we suppose that there was any oral tradition of it, as we can in the case of Moses. In what sense, then, does a tradition come in question at all? In what form can it have been present? (p. 94)

The answer to this question is far from simple and anticipates the results of the demonstration: '[I]n my opinion there is an almost complete conformity in this respect between the individual and the group [*die Übereinstimmung zwischen dem Individuum und der Masse ist in diesem Punkt eine fast vollkommene*]; in the group too an impression of the past is retained in the unconscious memory-traces' (p. 94). The rest of the section is indeed devoted to explaining this 'almost perfect' correspondence or conformity between the individual and the group, by considering at length memory-traces at the level of the individual, given that, as the above passage implies, in the individual, 'the impression of the past is retained in the unconscious.' The didactic task thus appears simple, even if perhaps laborious, in so far as the entire psychoanalytic conceptuality is summoned up:

> Here we have formed ideas [*Vorstellungen*] [concerning the conservation of the past in the form of memory-traces], which can be confirmed without difficulty through analysis, of how something can be forgotten and how it can reappear after a while. What is forgotten is not extinguished but only 'repressed'; its memory-traces are present in all their freshness, but isolated by 'anticathexes'. [Freud mentions

> psychoanalytic concepts in inverted commas, 'in order to make it easier for readers who do not desire or are not prepared to plunge into a complicated psychological state of affairs' (p. 94). But the inverted commas will become useful again later for more important reasons]. They cannot enter into communication with other intellectual processes; they are unconscious – inaccessible to consciousness. It may also be that certain portions of the repressed, having evaded the process [of repression], remain accessible to memory and occasionally emerge into consciousness; but even so they are isolated, like foreign bodies out of connection with the rest. (p. 94)[44]

Without repeating the development about the repressed that follows, let us indicate briefly which aspects of the theory of the unconscious are emphasized, by outlining the structure of the argument (bearing in mind, as we quoted above, that 'the repressed is the prototype [*Vorbild*] of the unconscious for us.')[45] The 'forgotten past' or the repressed is that which 'retains its upward urge [*Auftrieb*], its effort [*Streben*] to force its way to consciousness [*vordringen*]' (p. 95). This is the most important point in so far as what is at issue is 'the return of the repressed', even if Freud has not yet thus designated the problem. This happens under certain conditions, but whatever the conditions be, what comes into consciousness always 'puts up with distortions' (p. 95). This representation [*Vorstellung*] of the repressed, however, presupposes the distinction between conscious and unconscious psychical processes, which suggests that 'the repressed is unconscious'. But the qualities of *conscious* (*Cs.*) and *unconscious* (*Ucs.*) do not correspond to 'belonging to the ego' on the one hand, and to 'repressed' on the other because

> consciousness is a transient quality [*flüchtige Qualität*] which attaches to a psychical process only in passing [*vorübergehend*]. For our purposes therefore we must replace 'conscious' by 'capable of being conscious' and we call this quality 'preconscious' (*Pcs*). We then say, more correctly, that the ego is mainly preconscious (virtually conscious). (p. 96)

What is to be accounted for, then, is the *dynamic* transformation of one quality into the other, given that unconscious, the 'virtually conscious' and the conscious are not equally permanent qualities (let us recall that this theoretical exposition aims to elucidate a problem of transmission). It is easier to conceive of the transformation of psychical qualities with respect to the topographical ('spatial') conception of the psychical apparatus, which, Freud repeats, has nothing to do with cerebral anatomy (p. 97). The articulation between the two topographies of the mind is clearly at issue in this passage (See 'An Outline of Psycho-Analysis', chapter IV). Let us recall that the revision of the first topography became necessary, as analytic and theoretical work forced Freud to concede that something in the ego 'behaves exactly like the repressed'.[46] and conversely, that the repressed is not necessarily unconscious. (The need for elaborating a 'second topography' of the psychical apparatus could be said to arise with an 'analogical difficulty'.)

But what is of particular interest here is the way in which Freud emphasizes that the topographical conception of the mind is also 'genetic' [*gleichzeitig genetisch ist*], which reinforces the fact that if the various psychical localities cannot be conceived of purely in spatial terms, it is in so far as 'space' has a temporal dimension. Not only then must the three psychical qualities (*Ucs. Pcs./Cs.*) be articulated (albeit always in a disjunctive manner) to 'several agencies, districts or provinces' (id, ego, super-ego), but they must also be distinguished, from the point of view of their ancientness: '[t]he id is the older of the two; the ego has developed out of it, like a cortical layer [*Rindenschicht*], through the influence of the external world' (p. 96). But, even if only on the basis of this affirmation, it is possible to see the way in which the 'influence of the external world' might come to function, from the point of view of the *id*, as a 'delayed influence', the enigma of which the third essay of *Moses* is meant to elucidate. The id is also distinguished by the way in which: '[t]he course of events in the id, and their mutual interaction, are governed by quite other laws than those prevailing in the ego', to which the *repressed* obeys. But the id and the repressed are nevertheless not reducible to each other. The nature of the differentiation between the two is well described in the following passage:

> The differentiation is accomplished in the earliest period of life, while the ego is developing out of the id. At that time a portion of the contents of the id is taken into the ego and raised to the preconscious state; another portion is not affected by this translation and remains behind in the id as the unconscious proper [*das eigentliche Unbewußte*]. In the further course of the formation of the ego, however, certain psychical impressions and processes in the ego are excluded from it by a defensive process; the characteristic of being preconscious is withdrawn from them, so that they are once more reduced

> to being component portions of the id. Here then is the 'repressed' in the id. (p. 96)

This condensed explanation of the repressed, clearly indicates areas of potential complexities. Freud goes so far as to invoke the 'complete ignorance [*völlige Unwissenheit*]' which prevails over 'the dynamic nature of the mental processes', and to say that, in the absence of knowledge, the distinction between conscious, preconscious and unconscious representation [*Vorstellung*] is attributed to 'a modification, or perhaps a different distribution, of psychical energy': '[w]e talk of cathexes and hypercathexes, but beyond this we are without any knowledge on the subject or even any starting-point for a serviceable working hypothesis [*jeder Ansatz zu einer brauchbaren Arbeitshypothese*]' (p. 97). It would be unwise, however, to dwell for too long on this summary account of the theory of repression. For, despite the fact that the latter should first and foremost allow us to understand the 'impressions of early traumas', (*ibid.*) on the basis of which the 'application' was launched, when Freud finally comes back to the topic of traumas, he introduces 'a fresh complication' [*neue Komplikation*]. At first sight, very little distinguishes it from the initial question concerning tradition. How then does the introduction of this new element inflect the course of the argument?

Up until now, it seemed that dealing with the process of repression at the level of the individual, and from the point of view of its genesis, would help the difficult transposition of the concepts from individual to group psychology. As soon as Freud introduces the fact that 'what may be operative in an individual's psychical life may include not only what he has experienced himself' (p. 98), the possibility of demarcating the two, even if only for didactic purpose is more than ever doubtful. From then on, the process of repression, as it is supposedly understood at the level of the individual, indeed turns out to be inseparable from the 'model [*Vorbild*] of a phylogenetic event' (p. 99), not, however, because the 'existence' of phylogenetic events will have been unequivocally demonstrated.

The hypothesis of the 'archaic heritage [*archaische Erbschaft*]' and the question of phylogenesis is discussed throughout Freud's work in numerous essays; it is connected with many crucial problems, notably that of symbolism, the theory of sexuality and of 'primal phantasies'. It also raises the question of Freud's dependence upon, and dissension from, biological theories of heredity at issue in his early work on the aetiology of hysteria, to which he alludes briefly in *Moses*, by invoking the adverse 'the present attitude of biological science'. Freud's treatment of the question in our passage in any case clearly suggests the type of difficulties which arise around such hypotheses. Let us merely consider some of them. The proof of the existence of an archaic heritage cannot be found by recourse to '[innate] dispositions [*bestimmte Dispositionen*]' or to the '*constitutional* factor [*der konstitutionelle Moment*] [Freud's emphasis]' in so far as 'all human beings, at all events in their early days, have approximately the same experiences, they react to them, too, in a similar manner' (p. 98). A more powerful argument lies in 'the universality of symbolism in language' which shows up in the way in which children appear to possess, in their symbolic representation [*Vertretung*] of an object by another, 'an original knowledge [*ursprüngliches Wissen*]' which cannot have been learned, and which is later forgotten by the adult. The decisive point, however, relates to the reaction of neurotic children to early traumas:

> The behaviour of neurotic children towards their parents in the Oedipus and castration complex abounds in such reactions, which seem unjustified in the individual case and only become intelligible phylogenetically – by their connection with the experience of earlier generations . . . the archaic heritage of human beings comprises not only dispositions but also subject-matter – memory-traces of the experience of earlier generations. (p. 99)

These lapidary statements concerning the archaic heritage emphasize the fact that it cannot be explained by the effect of 'direct communication' or of the 'influence of education', just as, at another level, it cannot be explained by the idea of 'disposition' or 'constitution'. One cannot fail to notice, however, that the passage, pending the exploration of the theoretical paths to which it points, first and foremost urges us to *admit* [*annehmen*] of the conservation of 'memory-traces' in the archaic heritage. It does not exactly 'prove' their existence, as Freud indeed himself notes. At the most, the proof depends upon 'the residual phenomena [*Resterscheinungen*] of the work of analysis which call for a phylogenetic derivation' (p. 100). The claim, then, that 'we have bridged the gulf between individual and group psychology' based on the presupposition of the existence of an 'archaic heritage' must be understood on the basis of what Freud calls an 'audacity [which] cannot be avoided [*eine unvermeidliche Kühnheit*]' (*ibid.*). After all, these clarifications should only allow Freud to affirm, as he does a page later, that 'men have always known (in this special way) that they once possessed a primal father and killed him' (p. 101).

Viewed from another angle, however, the audacity corresponds to what we have so far described in terms of 'analogical difficulties'. Which psychology (that of the individual or that of the mass) can indeed enlighten the other, or to put it in other words, is the model of the other?[47] The difficulty around 'memory-traces' which is raised at the beginning of the section can be reformulated again in the following manner: if memory-traces at the level of the individual can only be conceived with reference to 'the mass' (anterior generations), how can 'memory-traces' at the level of 'the mass' be at all conceivable? In other words, to 'deal with peoples as we do with an individual neurotic' (p. 100) obliges us to conceive of an equivalent, at the level of the masses, to what, at the level of the individual, is thought of as a 'mass' (a coefficient of the mass?). Or still, given that phylogenetic events (those associated with anterior generations) become manifest through the 'residual material' of analytic work, and that no analytic work goes without it, how are we to conceive of the 'residual material' at the level of the mass? Faced with this 'unknown', it is indeed tempting to invoke the concept of 'quantity', not exactly in its 'proper' metapsychological sense, but rather from the point of view of at least one of its characteristic features: namely, that it points to something (an hypothetical amount of or, number of) that is above all incalculable.

Throughout the chapter, we stated on numerous occasions the principle whereby, faced with the 'unknown', Freud resorts to the *Bildersprache*, which includes the borrowing of concepts from other sciences. We dwelt at length on parts of the third essay of *Moses* in order to show how essays usually referred to as 'applied psychoanalysis' introduce a new 'category' of figures, from the moment that psychoanalytic concepts are themselves treated as 'borrowed' concepts. This is possible thanks to the transposition by analogy of concepts of individual psychology into group psychology from which most essays on *Kultur* proceed. This passage is given particular prominence in *Moses*, beginning with the fact that two crucial sections of the third essay are entitled 'Die Analogie' and 'Anwendung'. Freud indeed presents the analogical reasoning by first stating that between the individual and mass phenomena, there exists a 'complete analogy'. But, in the course of the demonstration, there soon emerges dissimilarities, of which it is difficult to say if they support or undermine the argument. Divergences however would seem mostly to amount, and somewhat tautologically, to the demarcation between the individual and the mass.

In the other sections of *Moses* that we examined, however, Freud spoke of an 'almost complete' analogy between the conservation of the past in the form of memory-traces at the level of the individual and at that of the mass. What cuts into the 'completeness' of the analogy is the way in which the domain of mass psychology, by contrast with that of the individual, lacks a notion of 'the mass'. And the latter – which takes the indefinite form of 'residual material' – supports the hypothesis of phylogenesis and of an 'archaic heritage', thanks to which alone the existence of memory-traces *at the level of the individual* can be conceived. On this account, it might be easier to understand why Freud says that, faced with the difficult displacement of concepts from the individual to the mass, the concept of a 'collektive Unbewußt' can be of no help, given that 'the content of the unconscious, indeed, is in any case a collective, universal property of mankind' (p. 132). This is one way of handling the 'almost' in the affirmation whereby 'there is an almost complete conformity [*Übereinstimmung*] in this respect between the individual and the group [*Masse*]' from the point of view of the conservation of the past (p. 94).

If we turn, however, to the very last section of part II of the third essay of *Moses*, where Freud rejects the concept of a 'collective unconscious', the unyielding dissimilarity between individual and mass psychology takes on another significance. We mentioned earlier that the repetition of the story of the primal horde in *Moses* is justified by postulating an epoch even more remote than the distant Egyptian origin of Jewish monotheism, which makes the hypothetical link between the Egyptian and Jewish monotheisms somewhat more acceptable. But the numerous centuries that separate the two still leave room for a great degree of indeterminacy. This 'lapse of time' provisionally hinders the explanation of the 'return of the repressed'. In the section 'Difficulties', after having discussed the archaic heritage, Freud affirms, as we quoted above that 'men have always known . . . that they once possessed a primal father and killed him' (p. 101). That knowledge is 'repressed' but 'returns', as the individual analytic situation and Jewish monotheism show. Two questions arose: 'under what conditions does a memory of this kind enter the archaic heritage? And, secondly, in what circumstances can it become active – that is, can it advance to consciousness from its unconscious state in the id, even though in an altered and distorted shape? . . . if the event was important enough, or repeated often enough [*sich oft genug wiederholt hat*], or both' (p. 101).

While the hypothesis of numerous repetitions is *mutatis mutandis* maintained in the last section of part II, Freud however here adds another element to the discussion. The 'long stretch between that hypothetical primaeval period and the victory of monotheism in historical times' (p. 132), which has to be accounted for, and which remains indeterminate, is described as the time when a development began which must be described as a slow 'return of the repressed'. What however differs from the earlier part of the exposition is that Freud now notes:

> Here I am not using the term 'the repressed' in its proper sense [*den Terminus 'das Verdrängte' gebrauchen wir hier im uneigentlichen Sinn*]. What is in question is something in a people's life which is past, lost to view, superseded and which we venture to compare with [*gleichzustellen wagen*] what is repressed in the mental life of an individual. We cannot at first sight say in what form this past existed during the time of its eclipse. (p. 132)

We already quoted the rest of the passage, which goes on to state that the transposition from individual to mass psychology can only be made with the provisional recourse to analogies. But it now becomes clear that what is to be joined *by analogy* crucially involves, apart from the processes at issue, psychoanalytic concepts themselves, in this instance, the 'repressed' proper and the 'repressed' not used 'in its proper sense', which, as we said earlier, yet functions as the prototype [*Vorbild*] of the unconscious.[48]

In all essays of 'applied psychoanalysis' there reigns confusion over what Freud is exactly comparing: are comparisons linking individual phenomenon (neurosis) and mass phenomenon (religion), or analytic findings (the *theory of neurosis*) and the phenomenon of religion (let us recall that religion is a 'representative' [*Vertretung*] of the cultural process)? The 'analogical passage' from the individual to the mass highlights the difficulties around how psychoanalytic concepts relate to the 'processes' which they seek to enlighten. And as we already said, this crucially engages the *Bildersprache*.

One way of pursuing the inquiry further would be to consider how, in addition to being a question of a hypothetical transmission without 'support', the elaboration of the concept of memory-traces relies, from 'The Project for a Scientific Psychology' onwards, on a problematic of the written trace, as Derrida showed in 'Freud and the Scene of Writing' (see chapter 1). Freud's appeal to the written trace recalls the complexities that characterize his description of tradition, in so far as the latter involves a conflict between heterogeneous order of traces. (In both cases, there is a 'conflict of forces' involving a trace which must not be permanent if 'inscription' is to be possible.) Thus, it is difficult to know exactly what Freud has in mind when he contrasts memory-traces at the level of the individual with 'memory-traces' at the level of the 'human masses' from the point of view of their 'form'. For this concept leaves one generally uncertain, but perhaps especially as far as 'the form which memory-traces take' is concerned. Not only, then, is it difficult to know exactly how memory-traces *of* the 'human masses' differ from those *of* the 'individual' from the point of view of their 'form', but it is also difficult to separate 'memory-traces' from the 'intellectual scaffolding' without which such hypothesis could not be formulated (the written trace and the 'trace'). In the discussion of memory-traces in *Moses*, the *Hilfskonstruktion* at issue in the elaboration of the concept send us back, even if indirectly, to the phenomenon of *tradition* which is yet explained in terms of memory-traces. In its most crucial aspects, the psychoanalytic conceptuality is figurative, which is also, as Freud believes, a normal feature of 'scientific language'. It is not difficult to verify this throughout the whole of Freud's work. But the shift of its concepts to the domain of 'mass psychology', which confronts psychoanalysis with the question 'What is a mass?' reveals that the figurative elaboration of concepts cannot simply be left at that. Freud constantly asserts that analogies, comparisons, hypotheses, indeed concepts are provisional. One way of conceiving of the effect of their permanent replacement might be to emphasize, as we tried to do, that from the moment that one uses analogies and comparisons, intellectual scaffoldings, and so on, analogical difficulties proliferate, up to the point where it becomes uneasy to identify what properly stands in psychoanalysis, not so much for the 'unknown', but perhaps more crucially, for the 'known'.

6
Conclusion: 'On Transience'

According to the *Standard Edition*'s introduction to the essay, 'On Transience' [*Vergänglichkeit*] (1916 [1915]) gives 'a picture of Freud's feeling about the war'.[1] It is however difficult to assess whether or not the theme of the essay – transience – only pertains to the particular kind of destruction associated with the war. By the end of the essay, the brief reflection upon 'the transience of all things' indeed appears to serve the purpose of saving 'our high opinion of the riches of civilization' (p. 307) from the harm war may have done to it. War acts as a disclosing agent of the transience of all things, but it is only one instance of destruction among many others invoked by Freud, despite its incomparable brutality. It is the transience of all things that may have motivated Freud to speak about the war, rather than the reverse. Freud's statement on the destructive character of the war seems, at first sight, the furthest removed from the idea of transience that he discusses throughout the essay. He writes in conclusion:

> When once the mourning is over, it will be found that our high opinion of the riches of civilization has lost nothing from our discovery of their fragility [*Gebrechlichkeit*]. We shall build up [*aufbauen*] again all that war has destroyed, and perhaps on firmer ground [*auf festerem Grund*] and more lastingly [*dauerhafter*] than before. (*Ibid.*)

We will consider below why Freud speaks of mourning in relation to the war. What matters here is that by speaking of 'build[ing] up again . . . on firmer ground and more lastingly', Freud seems to go against his own argument, which the following statement well summarizes: 'all things (but especially libido) *must* be transient', because transience (destruction) is the condition of renewal. If the character of transience comes to characterize all things, does it not describe transience itself? Thus, in so far as Freud's concern for transience seems, at the term of the essay, to have been *replaced* by a concern for solidity and permanence, the apology of transience might be best served by Freud's allusion to the destruction caused by the war.

The question however is not whether Freud coherently argues for transience or for permanence (for the 'demand for immortality [*Ewigskeitforderung*]' p. 305). The discussion in fact obliges us to conceive of transience and permanence simultaneously. This can only be done if transience is understood as a principle of substitution rather than as a 'temporal limitation'. Given that the essay involves various modalities of transience (that of Beauty, Nature, Art [pictures and statues], of the human form, the human face, of intellectual achievement, animate life and of the 'binding' of libido to objects), one indeed wonders how the idea of temporal limitation could qualify all of them at once.

The progression of Freud's argument itself makes of transience a principle of substitution. From the outset, what would otherwise refer to a temporal limitation (the 'transience of all things') is discussed in economic terms. For the topic of Beauty and aesthetic pleasure, with which the essay opens up, is first an economic problem. The truth of 'the transience of all things' emerges on a 'summer walk through a smiling countryside' (p. 305), during which Freud and two of his friends are admiring the beauty of Nature. One of them, a poet, is however feeling 'no joy'; he is disturbed by the *thought* that the beauty before them is 'fated to extinction [*dem Vergehen geweiht war*]' (*ibid.*). Freud attempts to understand the poet's loss of enjoyment, and to refute the idea that the transience of all things should diminish in any way the value or the enjoyment of Beauty and Art. The main point of the essay is apparently to provide a psychoanalytic explanation of 'loss', with reference to the process of mourning. This is what the economic explanation prepares: '[t]he proneness to decay of all that is beautiful and perfect can, as we know, give rise to two different impulses in the mind [*seelische Regungen*]' (p. 305). One of them 'leads to the aching despondency felt by the young poet', while the other 'leads to rebellion against the fact asserted':

> No! it is impossible that all this loveliness of Nature and Art, of the world of our sensations [*Empfindungswelt]* and of the world outside, will really fade away into nothing. It would be too senseless [*unsinnig*] and too presumptuous to believe it. Somehow or other this loveliness must be able to persist [*fortbestehen*] and to escape all the powers of destruction. (p. 305)

What needs to be demonstrated is that the demand for immortality is a product of our wishes [*Wunschleben*] and 'cannot lay claim to reality'. The poet's loss of enjoyment, his 'clinging' to eternity, has to be dealt with in the economic register of the *Wunschleben*. On this economic account, not only does limitation entail no loss, but it brings about an increase of enjoyment according to the principle that '[l]imitation [*Beschränkung*] in the possibility of an enjoyment raises the value of the enjoyment' (p. 305). Freud then provides various examples of how transience should in fact bring about a gain of enjoyment. Even though these considerations appear incontestable to Freud, they make no impression on either of his friends, and Freud surmizes that 'some powerful emotional factor [*starker affektiver Moment*]' (*ibid.*) must be disturbing their judgments, namely, 'a revolt in their minds against mourning':

> the idea [*Vorstellung*] that beauty was transient was giving these two sensitive minds [*Empfindsamen*] a foretaste [*Vorgeschmack*] of mourning over its decease; and, since the mind instinctively recoils from anything that is painful, they felt their enjoyment of beauty interfered with by thoughts of its transience. (p. 306)

This is what Freud earlier described as the impulse of 'a rebellion against the fact asserted' (*ibid.*). But it is now explained with reference to mourning, whereby 'the rebellion against the fact [of the transience of all things] asserted' is likened to the 'clinging [*klammern*]'[2] of the libido to its lost objects in the process of mourning. Freud gives a succinct account of mourning:

> mourning is a great riddle, one of those phenomena which cannot themselves be explained but to which other obscurities can be traced back. We possess, as it seems, a certain amount of capacity for love [*Liebesfähigkeit*] – what we call libido – which in the earliest stages of development is directed towards our own ego. Later, though still at a very early time, this libido is diverted [*abwenden*] from the ego on to objects, which are thus in a sense taken into our ego. If the objects are destroyed or if they are lost to us, our capacity for love (our libido) is once more liberated; and it can either take over other objects instead or can temporarily return to the ego. But why it is that this detachment of libido from its objects should be such a painful process is a mystery to us and we have not hitherto been able to frame any hypothesis to account for it. We only see that libido clings

> [*klammert*] to its objects and will not renounce those that are lost even when a substitute [*Ersatz*] lies ready to hand. Such then is mourning. (pp. 306–7)

As long as one remains in a state of mourning, as long as the libido 'clings' to its lost objects, no substitution will ever take place. Freud seems to introduce the topic of mourning in order to liken the necessary substitution of objects to the transient characters of 'all things', and that any type of loss should be referred back to a libidinal explanation. This is partly what happens in the essay. However, the argument runs also slightly differently. In fact, if the account which psychoanalysis gives of mourning is to be of any help for understanding the despondency of the poet towards the provisional beauty of Nature, it might be because what characterizes the process described under this heading is its transience:

> Mourning, as we know, however painful it may be, comes to a spontaneous end. When it has renounced everything that has been lost, then it has consumed itself [*sich selbst aufgezehrt*], and our libido is once more free (in so far as we are still young and active) to replace [*zu ersetzen*] the lost objects by fresh ones equally or still more precious. (p. 307)

Thanks to the knowledge of the obscurities which can be traced back to mourning, the psychical impulses arising with transience can be understood. In the context of this discussion, however, mourning seems to be called upon partly in so far as it comes to 'a spontaneous end'. Freud's refutation of the idea that the 'perishable and unresistant [*hinfällig und widerstandsunfähig*]' (p. 307) character of things should make them lose their worth is based on the affirmation that mourning should 'consume itself', and free the libido to attach itself to 'fresh objects'. The libido that the end of mourning liberates, must itself be transient, mobile, it must be able to find 'fresh objects'. It is therefore wrong to adopt a permanent mournful attitude (Freud speaks of a 'permanent renunciation') towards the transience of 'the riches of civilization', because 'mourning' must itself be a 'transient state'. It is by not recognizing the transient character of mourning that one most runs the risk of ceasing to experience enjoyment.

The significance of the theme of *Vergänglichkeit* extends well beyond the topic of war. This does not mean that one could not attempt to systematize Freud's pronouncements on the war and seek to understand what his position towards this event might have been. But we are not invoking the essay 'On Transience' in order to launch, rather belatedly, a detailed discussion of mourning, either.

At first, it is not clear whether the topic of transience motivates the introduction of the topic of war, or the reverse. As far as Freud speaks of the war in terms of mourning, however, we can now say that it is not clear whether transience introduces mourning, or the reverse. For, in discussing transience as an emotional state caused by loss, mourning provides an explanation of loss (of any type of loss?). However, in discussing the topic of mourning in the context of a meditation on transience, Freud emphasizes one important aspect of mourning, namely its provisional character.

We pointed out, throughout the book, the way in which, in Freud's work, the object and the *method* of investigation (notably, the various *Hilfskonstruktionen* which supports hypotheses) readily exchange position, up to the point where one phenomenon may take on the value of an 'auxiliary construction' in relation to another one. This situation can be detected by paying attention not only to what Freud calls the *Bildersprache*, but also to Freud's regular comments on the difficulties that are attached to the recourse to analogies, comparisons or models. One of the hypotheses which we attempted to verify is that the difficulties brought about by the necessity of something like the *Bildersprache* arise no more sharply than with what we called the problem of the many.

In 'Mourning and Melancholia' (1917), mourning provides a term of comparison for the understanding of the pathological state of melancholia: 'we will now try to throw some light on the nature of melancholia by comparing it with the normal affect of mourning.'[3] The relation between transience and mourning in 'On Transience' also corresponds to a relation of this kind, even though it is nowhere described as such, since both mourning and transience share the character of the provisional. On this account and referring to our hesitation over the theme of the essay (is it war, transience, or mourning?), it is tempting to settle the difficulty by claiming that the essay in fact sends us back to the *Bildersprache*, notably to Freud's many pronouncements on the way in which the validity of the hypotheses of psychoanalysis 'is only provisional',[4] and on the fact that, as Freud puts it at the end of 'Mourning': 'the interdependance of the complicated problems of the mind forces us to break every inquiry before it is completed – till the outcome of some other inquiry can come to its assistance [*zu Hilfe kommen können*]' (p. 258).

We have noted on numerous occasions the provisional aspect of Freud's *Bildersprache*. One of the characters of the mass, according to definitions that we have invoked at various moments of the book, is to be ephemeral, as Freud states in *Mass Psychology*: 'the assertions of Sighele, Le Bon and the rest relate to groups of a short-lived character [*kurzlebiger Art*], which some passing interest [*vorübergehendes Interesse*] has hastily agglomerated out of various sorts of individuals.' 'On Transience' could thus provide a guiding thread for pursuing further the interrogation of the *Bildersprache*. And given that as we indicated above, the problem of the 'many' becomes attached, for Freud, to a question of time (see above 'memory-traces'), we would not be leaving the problem of the mass very far behind. In pursuing the idea of transience in Freud, we would however soon come up against the way in which like certain types of masses, consciousness is transitory:

> [s]ome processes become conscious easily; they may even then cease to be conscious, but can become conscious one more without any trouble: as people say, they can be reproduced or remembered. This reminds us that consciousness is in general a highly fugitive state [*ein höchst flüchtiger Zustand*]. What is conscious is conscious only for a moment.[5]

A study of the mass does not lead us, as might have been thought at the outset, to a supposedly concrete political result, nor even to the unconscious, as has been traditional when something like the mass is at issue, but to the status, in psychoanalysis, of the concept of consciousness itself.

Notes

Introduction

1. *Massenpsychologie und Ich-Analyse* (1921) is translated into *Group Psychology and the Analysis of the Ego* in the *Standard Edition of the Complete Psychological Works of Sigmund Freud*, XVIII. In the pages that follow, we will refer to that book as *Mass Psychology and the Analysis of the Ego* (abbreviated as *Mass psychology*, to remain closer to the German title). The history of the French translation of this essay is worth recalling as an illustration of the semantic confusion that surrounds the term mass. S. Jankélévitch, the first French translator of the essay, rendered *Massenpsychologie* into *psychologie collective* (*Psychologie collective et analyse du moi*, Payot [1924], 1950). In the two subsequent French versions of the essay, *Massenpsychologie* is turned into *psychologie des foules* (in S. Freud, *Essais de psychanalyse*, trans. by J. Altounian, A. Bourguignon, O. Bourguignon, P. Cotet and A. Rauzy, Payot, 1981) and into *psychologie des masses* (*Oeuvres complètes*, Vol. XVI, 1921–3, ed. by A. Bourguignon, P. Cotet and J. Laplanche, Presses universitaires de France, 1991). The translator's note of the 1981 publication expounds on the problems that the translation of the words *Masse* and *Massenpsychologie* pose in relation to the other terms used by Freud, such as, for example, *Gruppe*, *Menge* and *kollectiv* in the 1921 essay, but also throughout his work. They refer their choice of the word *foule* to G. Le Bon's *La Psychologie des foules* (Alcan, 1895), which Freud discusses at the beginning of his book. It is interesting to note that they rule out the rendering of *Massenpsychologie* into *psychologie des masses*, because they associate the latter with the French translation of W. Reich's *Massenpsychologie des Faschismus* and consequently argue that the 'word masse [in French] has socio-political connotations which are absent in Freud' (p. 122). The problem is taken up again in *Traduire Freud*, the first volume of the *Oeuvres complètes*, this time, in order to justify the translation of *Massenpsychologie* into *psychologie des masses* (pp. 112–13). There, in addition to recalling the socio-political connotations to the term mass, the question arises as one of retranslation or 'trilinguisme'. Indeed, in *Massenpsychologie*, Freud refers to the 2nd edition of R. Eisler's translation of Le Bon's book, *Psychologie der Massen* ([1908], 1912), but also to William McDougall, *The Group Mind* (Cambridge University Press, 1920). The term *Masse* is thus, according to the editors, 'from the outset, an hybrid of two erroneous translations' of *foule* and 'group'. The editor of *The Standard Edition* justifies the use of the term 'group' in the title and throughout Freud's essay, in terms of uniformity. It is also the best English equivalent to the 'more comprehensive German Masse', even if, according to the editor, the English equivalent of foule is crowd (see the English translation of Le Bon's *The Crowd: A Study of the Popular Mind*, London, 1920).
2. 'Some Points for a Comparative Study of Organic and Hysterical Motor Paralyses', SE I, p. 160; *The Interpretation of Dreams*, SE IV, p. 104.

3. 'Project of a Scientific Psychology' (1950 [1895]), pp. 304, 361.
4. SE XXII, p. 221.
5. See, for example, T. Dufresne, *Tales from the Freudian Crypt: The Death Drive in Text and in Context* (Stanford University Press, 2000).
6. See 'Constructions in Analysis' (1937) (SE XXIII, p. 269)
7. As Jean-Luc Nancy and Philippe Lacoue-Labarthe well indicated in 'La Panique politique', the implicit theme of which is the mass as a 'limit-concept of the social'. *Cahier Confrontations*, 2 (1979), pp. 33–57 ['La panique politique' in *Retreating the Political,* trans. C. Surprenant ed. S. Sparks (Routledge, 1997)] p. 40.
8. 'Was ist nun eine "Masse"' (GW, p. 76).
9. See respectively letters to Sandor Ferenzci dated 17 April 1923, and to Romain Rolland dated 4 March 1923 accompanying the sending of the book to the addressee: 'Not that I consider this work to be particularly successful, but it shows a way from the analysis of the individual to an understanding of society' in *The Letters of Sigmund Freud,* ed. E. Freud, trans. T. and J. Stern (New York, Toronto, London: McGraw-Hill Book Company, 1960), p. 342.
10. See S. Samuel Weber's discussion of the notion of the mass in 'Mass Mediauras; or, Art, Aura, and Media in the work of W. Benjamin' in *Walter Benjamin. Theoretical Questions,* ed. D. S. Ferris (Stanford University Press, 1996). On the one hand, 'nothing, Weber writes, could seem more dated than this heavy-handed notion of mass, which reeks of the collectivist discourses of the 1930s,' but on the other hand, 'the mass entails a dynamic element [in Benjamin's writing] that demands attention' (p. 34).
11. See T. W. Adorno's classical text: 'Freudian Theory and the Pattern of Fascist Propaganda' in *The Culture Industry: Selected Essays on Mass Culture,* ed. J. Bernstein (Routledge, 1991), pp. 114–35.
12. (Flammarion, 1982). The book is inspired, the author tells us, by J.-L. Nancy and Ph. Lacoue-Labarthe's arguments in 'La Panique politique'.
13. See among others, M. Henry, *Généalogie de la psychanalyse* (Presses universitaires de France, 1985).
14. *The Freudian Subject,* trans. C. Porter (Stanford University Press, 1988), p. 192. The translator follows the English translation of Freud's essay and says 'the group' where the French says 'la masse': 'la masse serait à l'origine (sans origine) de l'individu' [*Le Sujet freudien* (Flammarion, 1982), p. 239].
15. *The Interpretation of Dreams,* SE IV, p. 100.
16. Chapter VII of *The Interpretation* confirms that: 'We have thus been able to find a place in our structure for the most various and contradictory findings of earlier writers, thanks to the novelty of our theory of dreams, which combines them, as it were, into a higher unity' (p. 592).
17. Consider this statement by Freud to Lou Salomé: 'I so rarely feel the need for synthesis . . . what interests me is the separation and breaking up into its component parts of what would otherwise revert to an inchoate mass' in *Sigmund Freud and Lou Andreas Salomé – Letters,* ed. E. Pfeiffer, trans. W. and E. Robson-Scott (The Hogarth Press and the Institute of Psychoanalysis, 1963). Or else, the way in which 'The ego is an organization characterized by the urge towards synthesis. This characteristic is lacking in the id; it is, as we might say, "all to pieces", its different urges pursue their own purposes independently and regardless of another' (SE XX, p. 196).

18. 'On Dreams', SE V, p. 648.
19. See W. Granoff, J.-M. Rey, *L'Occulte, objet de la pensée freudienne* (Press universitaires de France, 1983), p. 149, n. 9.
20. See notably Gaston Bachelard in *La Philosophie du non. Essai d'une philosophie du nouvel esprit scientifique* (Press universitaires de France [1940], 1994), where the concept of mass is the point of reference for the 'demonstration of the philosophical maturation of scientific thought' ([my translation] p. 22), or Ernst Mach, *The Sciences of Mechanics, a Critical and Historical Account of its Development* [*Die Mechanik in ihrer Entwicklung historisch-kritish dargestellt*] (Open Court [1883], 1960). Walter Benjamin describes the presence of the mass in Baudelaire in a way that might extend beyond the poet's work: 'The mass is for Baudelaire so inward that in his texts one will seek its depiction in vain' [Die Masse ist Baudelaire derart innerlich, daß man ihre Schilderung bei ihm vergebens sucht.]' 'Über einige Motive bei Baudelaire' *Gesammelte Schriften* 1.2 (Frankfurt am Main: Suhrkamp Verlag, 1974), p. 621 [quoted in S. Weber, *op. cit.*, p. 219, n. 14].
21. See the Introduction to Max Jammer, *Concepts of Mass in Classical and Modern Physics* (Harvard University Press, 1961).
22. The main points of reference for this line of argument are inspired by Martin Heidegger who states in the *Zollikon Seminars*: 'For conscious, human phenomena, [Freud] also postulates an unbroken [chain] of explanation, that is, the continuity of causal connections. Since there is no such thing "within consciousness", he has to invent "the unconscious" in which there must be an unbroken [chain of] causal connections. The postulate is the complete explanation of psychical life whereby explanation [*Erklären*] and understanding [*Verstehen*] are identified. This postulate is not derived from the psychical phenomenon themselves but is a *postulate* of modern natural science. What for Kant transcends [conscious] perception, for instance, the fact that the stone becomes warm *because* the sun is shining, is for Freud, "the unconscious"' (*Zollikon Seminars. Protocols – Conversations – Letters*, ed. M. Boss, trans. Franz Mayr and Richard Askay, Northwestern University Press, 2001, pp. 207–8 [*Zollikoner Seminare, Protokolle – Gespräche – Briefe* [Klosterman GmbH, 1987]). See J. Habermas, *Knowledge and Human Interest* [*Erkenntnis und Interesse*, 1968], trans. J. J. Shapiro (Boston: Beacon Press, 1971) and P. Ricoeur, *Freud and Philosophy. An Essay on Interpretation* [*De l'Interprétation. Essai sur Freud*] (Seuil, 1965)]. A. Grünbaum in *The Foundations of Psychoanalysis, a Philosophical Critique* (University of California Press, 1984) provides an extensive bibliography on the question. See Jonathan Lear's critical commentary on Paul Ricoeur and Jürgen Habermas's endeavours, which he describes as attempts to develop 'non-causal hermeneutics accounts' of human motivation and action in *Love and its Place in Nature. A Philosophical Interpretation of Freudian Psychoanalysis* (Yale University Press [1990], 1998) p. 49, n. 36.
23. Works on that topic are numerous, see P. Mahony who, in *Freud as a Writer* (New York: International Universities Press Inc., 1982), discusses W. Schönau, *Sigmund Freuds Prosa: Literarische Elemente Seine Stils* (Stuttgart: J. B. Metzlersche Verlag, 1968); W. Muschg, 'Freud als Schriftsteller', *Die Psychoanalytische Bewegung* 2 (1977), pp. 467–509; F. Roustang, 'Du chapitre VII', *Nouvelle Revue de psychanalyse*, 16 (1977), pp. 65–95. More recently, see the influential works by S. Weber, *The Legend of Freud* (Stanford University

Press, [1982] 2000) and Malcolm Bowie, *Freud, Proust and Lacan* (Cambridge University Press, 1987).

24. See Jacques Lacan's exclusion of application: 'Psychoanalysis literally only applies as a treatment and, therefore, to a speaking subject' ['La psychanalyse ne s'applique au sens propre, que comme traitement, et donc à un sujet qui parle'], 'La Jeunesse de Gide' in *Écrits* (Seuil, 1966), p. 747.
25. See, among others, D. Ornston (ed.), *Translating Freud* (Yale University Press, 1992), and A. Bourguignon (et al.), *Oeuvres complètes de Freud/Psychanalyse (OCF.P). Traduire Freud* (Presses universitaires de France, 1989).
26. On the necessity of reflecting upon that discipline, see Étienne Balibar's preface to *La Psychologie des peuples et ses dérives*, ed. M. Kail and G. Vermès (Centre national de documentation, 1999), pp. 9–10. Balibar draws attention to what he calls the 'voisinages ou les filiations les plus étranges' between elements of late nineteenth-century 'psychologie des peuples' and other fields, such as Freud's discussion of Gustave Le Bon *La psychologie des foules*. It is these filiations which, according to him, need to be studied with respect to the evolutionism that dominates *psychologie des peuples* and its related *sciences*, such as crowd psychology.
27. See the comprehensive analyses of Jean Starobinski in his preface to the French translation of E. Jones, *Hamlet et Oedipe* (Gallimard, 1967).
28. (Act IV, Sc. 3) quoted in SE XIV, p. 320.
29. Freud notes after his comment on Macbeth that 'all genuinely creative writings are the product of more than a single motive and more than a single impulse in the poet's mind, and are open to more than a single interpretation' (SE IV, p. 266).
30. See D. Baguley, Fécondité *d'Émile Zola, Roman à thèse, évangile, mythe* (University of Toronto Press, 1973).
31. As it should become clear, the following study does not aim to detect, in the manner of a diagnostic, strategies, rivalries, dissimulations, ruses, pretensions, oblivions in Freudian thought, an approach which characterizes many current works on Freud, and which presupposes a *psychologization* of Freudian thought.

1 Psychoanalytic Concepts

1. M. Tort, 'De L'Interprétation ou la machine herméneutique', *Les Temps modernes*, 237–8 (1966), pp. 1461–92, 1487–8.
2. *Ibid.* p. 1465. Ricoeur's essay on Freud is considered to 'mark a decisive turn in the philosophical attitude towards psychoanalysis in France', J. Chemouny, *Histoire de la psychanalyse en France* (Presses universitaires de France, 1991), p. 77. The history of the philosophical interest in Freud is characterized by more than one 'decisive turn'. Consider, for example, how Jean-Luc Nancy and Philippe Lacoue-Labarthe in *Le Titre de la lettre, une lecture de Lacan* (Galilée, 1973), speak of Lacan: 'prior to Lacan, we know (but we should say that for the most part we owe him that knowledge . . .) that science and philosophy – or the authorities constituted under these names – divided their "reception" of psychoanalysis between a few traditional attitudes: silence (misrecognition or denial), open hostility, annexa-

tion, confiscation, or dedication to the immutable ends of this or that theoretical apparatus. More precisely, nothing has been thought which does not take the form of a "reception", that is to say the subordination of psychoanalysis to a ground, a justification, a truth – that is, most of the time, to a norm' (trans. F. Raffoul and D. Pettigrew [Albany State University of New York, 1992], p. 6). The authors are in turn described as the 'rare professional philosophers to have read and published on Lacan in the academy' in J. Derrida, 'Pour L'amour de Lacan', *Résistances de la psychanalyse* (Galilée, 1996), p. 79.

3. 'Freud et la philosophie', *L'Arc*, 'Freud' 34 (1968), p. 108. Tort's position with respect to what he calls 'dominant philosophies' refers us back to Louis Althusser's seminar on Lacan and psychoanalysis at the École normale supérieure during the academic year 1963–4, the year Lacan was invited to give his seminar in that institution. See L. Althusser, *Psychanalyse et sciences humaines, Deux conférences (1963–1964)* (Librairie générale française/IMEC, 1996), which provides a useful point of reference for Tort's invectives against the so-called ideological appropriation of psychoanalysis by philosophy. A passage from Althusser's lecture entitled 'Psychoanalysis within the Human Sciences' [La Place de la psychanalyse dans les sciences humaines] gives useful indications concerning the history of the encounter: 'the philosophical encounter with psychoanalysis in France passes through Sartre and Merleau-Ponty. And the origin of this encounter . . . is in Politzer [G. Politzer, *Critique des fondements de la psychologie* (Riefer, 1928)] . . . It is through Politzer that psychoanalysis has become an object of philosophical reflection' (p. 34 [my translation]). Between Freud and Politzer, however, Althusser notes the importance of Angelo Hesnard, 'the first man who has had the courage to speak about Freud in France' (p. 22), who published *L'Oeuvre de Freud et son importance pour le monde moderne* (Payot, 1960), prefaced by Merleau-Ponty. In that preface, Merleau-Ponty clearly presents phenomenology as 'the implicit philosophy of psychoanalysis' (p. 7). Even if judging on this preface alone, the rapprochement might not be as 'levelling' as Tort would make us believe. For, having stated the convergence between phenomenology and Freudian thought, Merleau-Ponty warns against the risk that psychoanalysis may be *'too well tolerated'* [Merleau-Ponty's emphasis] (p. 8). Faced with the trivialization of psychoanalytic concepts, which in 'hav[ing] lost much of their meaning and in hav[ing] become banal' provide 'the themes of a new positivity', Merleau-Ponty declares: 'one wonders if it is not essential for psychoanalysis . . . to remain, not, no doubt, an endeavour doomed to damnation and a secret science, but at least a paradox and an interrogation' (p. 8). On Merleau-Ponty and psychoanalysis, see J.-B. Pontalis, 'Note sur le problème de l'inconscient chez Merleau-Ponty', *Les Temps modernes*, 184–5 (1961), pp. 286–303; A. Green, 'Du Comportement de la chair: Itinéraire de Merleau-Ponty', *Critique*, XX, 211 (1964), pp. 1017–46.
4. A. Green, 'L'Inconscient freudien et la psychanalyse française', *Les Temps modernes*, 195 (1962), pp. 365–79, esp. p. 379. See also *L'Inconscient*, VIe Colloque de Bonneval, ed. H. Ey (Desclée de Brouwer, 1966). The passage draws attention to the contrast that commentators of Freud have perceived between 'the energetic representation (bound and unbound energy, the

diverse cathexis and counter-cathexis of this energy [*investissements et contre-investissements*]) that Freud has of the entire psychical apparatus and the method of "search of meaning" that he inaugurates', Jean Hyppolite 'Philosophie et psychanalyse' (1959), *Figures de la pensée philosophique I – 1931–1968* (Presses universitaires de France, 1971), p. 409. Schematically, Freudian thought can be assimilated to 'biological sciences' or to a 'phenomenology' according to whether one or the other aspect of the contrast is emphasized. Or else, as Ricoeur argues throughout *Freud and Philosophy: An Essay on Interpretation*, Freud's achievement lies in the way in which it reconciles the two poles. See J. Habermas, *Knowledge and Human Interest* [*Erkenntnis und Interesse*, 1968], trans. J. J. Shapiro (Boston: Beacon Press, 1971), for whom the rift in Freud constitutes what he calls a 'scientistic misunderstanding'. Habermas describes Freud's appeal to the explanatory model of distribution of energy and his confusion of that model with what is discovered by means of the therapeutic dialogue (the model for a hermeneutics) as a methodological error, that moves psychoanalysis away from self-reflexion, according to the analysis of positivism throughout the book.

5. A. Green, 'L'inconscient freudien', p. 379, Tort, 'Freud et la philosophie', p. 109.
6. 'De L'Interprétation ou la machine herméneutique', p. 1467.
7. A. Green, *ibid.*, p. 366.
8. Lecture 32, *New Introductory Lectures on Psycho-Analysis* [1932], SE XXII, pp. 92–3.
9. 'Philosophie et psychanalyse', pp. 407–8.
10. We borrow the expression 'travail du concept' from Paul-Laurent Assoun, *Introduction à L'épistémologie freudienne* (Payot, 1981), who thus refers to 'the fanstasmatic activity that conditions the metapsychological rationality' (p. 93 n. 76). See in particular the Introduction, Section 2 'Freudisme et phénoménologie', for an examination of the so-called contrast between the energetics and the hermeneutics that dominates the reception of Freud (pp. 20–30).
11. We here leave aside what marks Tort's indebtedness to Althusser's 'epistemological' reading of Marx. See L. Althusser, *Écrits sur la psychanalyse, Freud et Lacan (1964–65)* (Stock/IMEC, 1993).
12. Althusser, 'La Place de la psychanalyse dans les sciences humaines', in *Psychanalyse et sciences humaines* (p. 25).
13. 'Dérivation des entités psychanalytiques', *Vie et mort en psychanalyse* (Flammarion, 1970), p. 200.
14. See J.-B. Pontalis, 'Questions de mots', *Après Freud* (Gallimard, 1968), p. 164.
15. Laplanche's most explicit discussion of the 'borrowed character' of Freudian terminology is found in *Nouveaux fondements pour la psychanalyse* (Presses universitaires de France, 1987), it is however at issue in many other of his works, notably, as far as Freud's relation to 'biology' is concerned. See *Le Fourvoiement biologisant de la sexualité chez Freud* (Les Empêcheurs de tourner en rond, 1993). Laplanche describes the source-sciences as 'fantastic', 'false' or 'popular'.
16. Pontalis, 'La Découverte freudienne', *Après Freud*, p. 43.
17. In what follows, we will use these terms interchangeably, as Freud himself does, and designate them 'collectively' under the heading of 'figurative

language' [*Bildersprache*]. See the beginning of chapter 5 below. The 'Gesamtregister' of the *Gesammelte Werke* encourages the conflation of terms and concepts by establishing indiscriminately the 'Register der Gleichnisse, Metaphern und Vergleiche' (GW B. 18). This is underlined by W. Granoff and J.-M. Rey in *L'Occulte, objet de la pensée freudienne* (1983). The authors insist on the way in which *Gleichnis* and *Vergleich* are terms that cannot simply be reduced and translated as 'metaphor', if by metaphor, one refers to a domain of study belonging to literary theory. They point out the importance of understanding these terms (comparisons and analogies) at an epistemological level since what is at issue with them is 'le statut de l'oeuvre de Freud dans son ensemble' (p. 151).

18. See Lecture XXXII of the *New Introductory Lectures* (SE XXII, p. 95) where Freud speaks of the instincts as 'our mythology'. At the end of chapter 6 of *Beyond the Pleasure Principle,* commenting on the 'bewildering and obscure processes', Freud states, by way of justification, that one is 'obliged to operate with the scientific terms, that is to say with the figurative language, peculiar to psychology (or more, precisely, to depth psychology). We could not otherwise describe the processes in question at all, and indeed we could not have become aware of them' (SE XVIII, p. 60). This is perhaps the most often quoted passage as soon as Freud's figurative language is at issue. S. Weber discusses it in 'Observation, Description, Figurative Language' in *The Legend of Freud,* (University of Minnesota Press, 1982), p. 26 and J. Derrida in 'Spéculer sur "Freud" ', in *La carte postale, De Socrate à Freud et au-delà* (Flammarion, 1980), to mention but a few studies which underline the passage.
19. 'Questions de mots' p. 160.
20. J. Laplanche and J.-B. Pontalis, *The Language of Psychoanalysis* [*Vocabulaire de la psychanalyse* (1967)] (London: Karnac Books and the Institute of Psychoanalysis, 1973). Henceforth abbreviated as *Vocabulaire*. See 'Historique des dictionnaires de la psychanalyse', in E. Roudinesco and M. Plon, *Dictionnaire de la psychanalyse* (Fayard, 1997).
21. Samuel Weber writes: '[I]n his *Auseinandersetzung* of dreams and of the unconscious processes they entail, Freud's language is, by his own admission, contaminated by its "object".' *The Legend of Freud* (p. 85). Freud indeed admits, with respect to his work on dreams, to disliking 'the style, which [is] incapable of finding the simple, elegant expression and which lapses into overwitty, image-searching circumlocutions' which ensue from the dream itself (Freud quoted in S. Weber).
22. Among many other similar statements, consider that of the psychoanalyst François Roustang: 'I underlined on numerous occasions the extent to which Freud's style is adapted down to the slightest detail to the content of what it expresses . . . which is, after all, a banality for a style. What is less so, however, is that here the style is the creator of the object, which is to say that container and the contents are no longer separable, are even interchangeable. *The psychical apparatus that Freud builds throughout Chapter VII is Chapter VII itself.* It begins by appearing at a distance from us, through the telescope, in the simplicity of a few elements; and as we get closer to it, we see it diversifying itself . . . Each time that a new piece is introduced in the system, the entire system is transformed and must be expounded anew. But it is this expository work, which is the genuine construction of

the system, which is the system itself. The psychical apparatus is the system that gives an account of it' [Roustang's emphasis, my translation], 'Du Chapitre VII', *Nouvelle Revue de psychanalyse* 16 (Autumn 1977), pp. 65–97, 86–7. See S. Weber's formulation of the question in *The Legend of Freud, Expanded Edition* (Stanford University Press, 2000 [1982]): 'can psychoanalytic thinking itself escape the effects of what it endeavours to think? Can the disruptive distortions of unconscious processes be simply recognized, theoretically, as an object, or must they not leave their imprint on the process of theoretical objectification itself? Must not psychoanalytic thinking itself partake of – repeat – the dislocations it seeks to describe?' (p. xvi). The specificity of psychoanalysis is elsewhere understood to lie in its endeavour to 'conceive of the psychical apparatus by means of observations that are of the same nature as the observed object' [my translation], P. Lacoste 'Destins de la transmission' in S. Freud, *Vue d'ensemble des névroses de transfert, Un essai métapsychologique*, ed. I. Grubrich-Simitis (Gallimard, 1986), p. 168. See too the important work of I. Grubrich-Simitis, who displaces the question away from Freud's style towards his manuscripts, and provides an analytic reading of them in *Zurück zu Freuds Texten. Stumme Dokumente sprechen machen* (Frankfurt am Main: S. Fisher, 1993).

23. See M. Schneider, 'Philosopher après Freud', in *L'Univers philosophique, Encyclopédie philosophique universelle*, ed. A. Jacob (Presses universitaires de France, 1989), p. 726. For the psychoanalyst Sabine Prokhoris, the method of the science of the unconcious 'puts into practice a paradox still without parallel: the method is traversed, invested, even constituted by the very object it seeks to construct. Hence it cannot maintain its object at a distance from itself, since the object intimately affects both the practice and the learned discourse which seeks to enframe this object; it likewise affects the *relationship* between this practice and discourse. Accordingly, the theory – metapsychology – can by no means pose a strictly conceptual construct engendered by an act of pure reason, which has formalized a certain experience and so rendered it intelligible, while maintaining a perfect neutrality *vis-à-vis* the experience . . . Indeed, metapsychology can only function as a *metaphor* for its object, because, even though it carries its object within itself, it can come into being only at the price of putting an end to this state of affairs', *The Witch's Kitchen. Freud, Faust and Transference* [*La Cuisine de la sorcière* (Aubier, 1988, p. 14], trans. G. M. Goshgorian, Foreword M. Schneider (Cornell University Press, 1995), pp. 4–5.

24. The unification of style and object, however, depends, to a large extent, upon the idea that unconscious processes ought to be and are only 'disruptive'. Hence, the impossibility of theorizing otherwise than in an 'odd' style proves the heterogeneity of unconscious processes to rational, conscious thought. We could oppose to this valorization of 'disruptiveness' everything throughout Freud that promotes the 'ingenuousness' of unconscious processes, and their capacity to mimic rational processes [see, for example, 'The Subtleties of a Faulty Action' (1935), and obviously *Jokes and their Relation to the Unconscious* (1905)]. Classical norms of theorization are also at the disposal of the unconscious, and although Freud acknowledges the possible disruption unconscious processes may bring upon his work, he is striving towards a rational understanding – as the end of *The Future of an*

Illusion (1927) clearly states. See M. Moscovici, 'La dictature de la raison', *Nouvelle revue française de psychanalyse*, 27 (Spring, 1983), pp. 65–84, and the end of chapter 4 below.

25. 'Questions de mots', pp. 160–1. On the contestation of conceptual language, see Laplanche, 'Interpréter [avec] Freud', *L'Arc*, 34 (1968), p. 42.
26. 'Questions de mots', p. 172.
27. Laplanche, Interpréter [avec] Freud', p. 44; Pontalis, 'Préface', *Après Freud*, p. 13.
28. Laplanche: '[i]l faut arriver à entendre qu'il existe des relations complexes, des réseaux serrés entre les métaphores consciemment avancées par Freud, les métaphores inconscientes que l'interprétation de sa pensée permet de retrouver, et ces sortes de métaphores réalisées (les identifications par exemple) que la psychanalyse découvre comme constitutives de l'être humain' ('Interpréter [avec] Freud', p. 45). See 'Dérivations des entités psychanalytiques', pp. 197–214. We will not be following the path of this 'realism', which would lead us at the core of Laplanche's work.
29. J. Laplanche and J.-B. Pontalis, *Vocabulaire*. In 'Questions de mots', Pontalis asks whether the *Vocabulaire* could 'serve as a reference, indeed as a model' to similar endeavours in other disciplines and suggests that psychoanalytic language raises too unique a set of problems for this to happen (p. 160). For Nicholas Abraham and Maria Torok, in their review of the book, the *Vocabulaire* raises the following question: 'how does one include in any discourse what very precisely essentially eludes it by being its condition' [comment inclure dans un discours, quel qu'il soit, cela même qui, pour en être la condition, lui échapperait par essence?]. The discourse of psychoanalysis, constitutes, for Abraham and Torok, a 'scandalous anti-semantic' for in it, 'as soon as it enters into relation with the unconscious Kernel, any term which Freud introduces, whether he coined or borrowed it from scholarly or familiar language . . . is literally forced out of the dictionary and of language' [n'importe quel vocable introduit par Freud, qu'il l'ait forgé ou emprunté à la langue, savante ou familière . . . dès la mise en rapport avec le Noyau inconscient [that which by essence eludes discourse] . . . s'arrache littéralement au dictionnaire et au langage] 'L'Écorce et le noyau' in *L'Écorce et le noyau* (Flammarion, 1987), pp. 209–10. Such a description can however be reproduced *mutatis mutandis* with a condemning aim in mind. Witness what François Roustang says of the contradictions that the *Vocabulaire* reveals: 'Have you ever followed the meaning of a Freudian term with the help of Laplanche and Pontalis's *Vocabulaire de la psychanalyse*? The experience is always the same. Each term, through a series of transformations, is given varied meanings, which, at the end, reveal a contradiction. In other words, each term signifies something and its opposite. It could be objected that this is not a problem since the whole of the theory of the unconscious presupposes the co-habitation of opposite terms'. 'L'épistémologie de la psychanalyse', in *Le Moi et l'autre* (Aubier, 1984), p. 157.
30. 'Entretien avec J. Laplanche et J.-B. Pontalis' (1968) in R. Bellour, *Le Livre des autres, Entretiens* (Union générale d'Éditions, 1978), p. 144. The value and function of *models*, in particular, the biological *model* has remained one important preoccupation of Laplanche from *Vie et Mort en psychanalyse* onwards.

31. See 'Représenter', Laplanche, 'Terminologie raisonnée' in A. Bourguignon, P. Cotet, J. Laplanche and F. Robert, *Traduire Freud* (Presses universitaires de France, 1989), p. 137.
32. In his review of the *Vocabulaire*, the psychoanalyst Didier Anzieu provides a statistical count of concepts included in it, which Freud borrows from the 'langage allemand courant, scientifique, philosophique, voire populaire', such as, 'affect, association, compulsion, conflit, conscience, détresse, dynamique . . . identification, inconscient' as opposed to those which Freud 'fabriqué de toutes pièces' (p. 129). The classification however seems rather loose judging by the way in which, under the heading of 'fabriqu[és] de toutes pièces', Freud is said to borrow 'pulsion' but to create ('il crée') 'pulsion d'emprise', or to find '"névrose" dans la langue psychiatrique', but to invent 'névrose d'angoisse', and so on and so forth. The other categories of the list are 'néologismes' and 'mots courants' used 'en tant que métaphores' (p. 129). Notwithstanding its rather Borgesian *recensement* of Freudian terms, this review provides precious indications concerning the French reception of Freud within structuralism. It suggests that 'un des apports les plus neufs de Laplanche et Pontalis est d'avoir mis à jour le schéma structuraliste chez Freud dès le "Projet de Psychologie Scientifique de 1895"' (p. 132), which inserts the *Vocabulaire* among other contemporaneous 'return to Freud'. 'À propos du "Vocabulaire de la psychanalyse"', *Bulletin de psychologie*, XXI (1967–8), 126–32, p. 129.
33. Freud: 'we should picture the instrument which carries out our mental functions as resembling a compound microscope or a photographic apparatus, or something of the kind [*vorstellen wie ein zusammengesetztes Mikroskop*]' (SE V, p. 536). See J. Laplanche and S. Leclaire, 'L'Inconscient une étude psychanalytique' (1961) in Laplanche, *Problématiques IV, L'Inconscient et le ça* (Presses universitaires de France, 1981), for the complication to which the 'transmission' (transcription) of excitations gives rise in Freud's essay 'The Unconscious' (1915). Laplanche and Pontalis's well-known discussion of Lacan's 'comparison' between the unconscious and language develops precisely around this point.
34. Obviously notwithstanding chronology.
35. See D. E. Leary, 'Psyche's Muse', in *Metaphors in the History of Psychology*, ed. D. E. Leary (Cambridge University Press, 1990): 'a taxonomist would have to work long and hard to classify Freud's many metaphors, which were drawn from social and political life, from the fields of physical dynamics and hydraulics, physiology and natural history, anthropology and mythology, archeology and ancient history, military life and technology, the classics and popular literature, and from other realms as well. As Freud utilized these metaphors – of energy and force, flow and resistance, repression and conversion, defence and aggression, and all the rest – he was clearly following his own advice to change analogies and comparisons as often as necessary. Freud's use of multiple metaphors was occasioned by his awareness of the insufficiency of any single metaphor' (p. 18)
36. Derrida's aim in *De la grammatologie* shows a striking similarity to what he credits Freud of achieving. '*Rendre énigmatique* ce que l'on croit entendre sous les noms de proximité, d'immédiateté, de présence (le proche, le propre, et le pré- de la présence), telle serait donc la dernière intention du

présent essai. Cette déconstruction de la présence passe par celle de la conscience, donc par la notion irréductible de trace (Spur), telle qu'elle apparaît dans le discours nietzchéen comme dans le discours freudien' [my emphasis] (Minuit, 1967), p. 102.

37. 'Le retrait de la métaphore', in J. Derrida, *Psyché. Inventions de l'autre* ([1987] Galilée, 1998), p. 82.
38. *De la grammatologie*, pp. 27–30, 63. For a succint presentation of the problem of metaphor, see G. Bennington and J. Derrida, *Jacques Derrida* (Seuil, 1991), especially 'La Métaphore', pp. 114–26. See too R. Gasché, *The Tain of the Mirror: Derrida and the Philosophy of Reflection* (Harvard University Press, 1986).
39. Derrida alludes many times throughout his work to the need to confront 'the undertakings of Heidegger and of Freud'. See 'Spéculer' and 'Apories: Mourir: s'attendre aux limites de la vérité', in *Le Passage des frontières. Autour du travail de Jacques Derrida* (Galilée, 1994), among the most explicit instances. For Derrida, all Freudian *concepts* 'without exception, belong to the history of metaphysics' (p. 97), and if it is possible to draw out a conception of difference from Freud, it is by turning to 'the precautions and the "nominalism" with which Freud manipulates what he calls conventions and conceptual hypotheses'. It is thanks to these precautions that Freudian discourse cannot simply be confused with metaphysical and traditional *concepts*. But given that Freud 'never reflected upon the historical and theoretical sense of these precautions', there needs to be a 'labor of deconstruction' upon the sedimentation of metaphysical concepts within Freudian discourse (p. 198). If there is to be an exploration of the relation between the Freudian conceptuality and the 'history of metaphysics', Derrida suggests that it has to focus on the concept of time: 'we ought perhaps to read Freud the way Heidegger read Kant . . .' (p. 215); 'that the present in general is not primal but, rather, reconstituted, that it is not the absolute, wholly living form which constitutes experience, that there is no purity of the living present – such is the theme, formidable for metaphysics, which Freud, in a conceptual scheme unequal to the thing itself, would have us pursue. This pursuit is doubtless the only one which is exhausted neither within metaphysics nor within science' (p. 212).
40. Derrida proposes, right at the beginning of the essay, to let one's reading 'be guided by the metaphoric investment' of Freud's text, which will end up by 'invad[ing] the entirety of the psyche'. How is the 'entirety' of the psyche to be delimited?
41. For a discussion of the discrepancy between Freud's 'intuitions' and his 'concepts', see M. Merleau-Ponty, 'Préface', to A. Hesnard, *L'Oeuvre de Freud et son importance pour le monde moderne* (*op. cit.*). I consider this issue in relation to the concept of 'form' in 'In Spite of Appearances', *Fragmente* 'Psychoanalysis and Poetics', ed. D. Marriott and V. Lebeau, 8 (Summer 1998), pp. 39–53. Concerning the 'the gap [décalage] between the discovery and the concepts' see also, P. Ricoeur, 'A Philosophical Interpretation of Freud', in *The Conflict of Interpretations: Essays in Hermeneutics* [*Le Conflit des interprétations, Essais d'herméneutique* (1969)], ed. D. Ihde (NorthWestern University Press, 1974): 'In Freud's case the shift [décalage] is manifest. His discovery operates on the levels of effects of meaning, but he continues to

express it in the language and through the concepts of energetics of his masters in Vienna and in Berlin.' Ricoeur speaks of a 'dissonance' indeed of an 'anomaly' ('this anomaly on the part of Freudian discourse . . .') and ends up by explaining the dissonance in terms of the two levels of coherence or of the two universes of discourse with which psychoanalysis operates: that of 'force' and of 'meaning'. The 'mixed discourse' results from the fact that psychoanalysis lies at 'the flexion between desire and culture' [trans. modified]. Such a mixed character is not however a 'category mistake', Ricoeur continues, 'it comes close to the very reality which our reading of Freud revealed and which we called the semantics of desire' (pp. 166–7).

42. Chris Johnson argues that cybernetics provide a model for Derrida's analysis of Freud [*Revue internationale de philosophie* 52, 205, (1998) p. 3]. He speaks of a 'dialogue' between Freud and Derrida, while Marian Hobson in *Jacques Derrida, Opening lines* (Routledge, 2000), speaks of the 'assimilation' of one problematics to another. Freud himself uses quotations marks abundantly and conspicuously, and, as we will see, notably around his own concepts.
43. *The Interpretation of Dreams*, SE IV, p. 312.
44. One traditionally opposes the dream to the joke – respectively the egoistical product of the unconscious which is not made for communicating anything to the most social one: 'The dream is a completely asocial mental product, it has nothing to communicate to anyone else . . . A joke, on the other hand, is the most social of all mental functions that aim at a yield of pleasure' (SE VIII, p. 179).
45. 'Freud and the scene of writing', trans. A. Bass, *Writing and Difference*, p. 200. Henceforth abbreviated as 'Freud' with references inserted in brackets.
46. Derrida, p. 200. S. Freud, 'Project for a Scientific Psychology' (1950 [1895]), SE I, p. 299. Henceforth abbreviated as 'The Project' with references inserted in brackets.
47. See A. Green *Le discours vivant. La conception psychanalytique de l'affect* (Presses universitaires de France, 1973) and 'De L'Esquisse à "L'Interprétation des rêves": coupure et clôture', *Nouvelle Revue de psychanalyse* 5 (Spring, 1972).
48. For a study of the 'The Project' which considers the relationship of metapsychology to cognitive theory and neurophysiology, see K. Pribram and M. M. Gill, *Freud's 'Project' Re-Assessed, Preface to Contemporary Cognitive Theory and Neuropsychology* (New York: Basic Books, 1976). The contemporary interest in the relation between neurophysiology and psychoanalysis falls outside the scope of this book. See for example, M. Gauchet, *L'inconscient cérébral* (Seuil, 1992).
49. See *De la grammatologie* (*op. cit.*): 'Il ne s'agirait donc pas d'inverser le sens propre et le sens figuré mais de déterminer le sens "propre" de l'écriture comme la métaphoricité elle-même' (p. 27).
50. Derrida's argument opens up the question of *technè*, which he argues, Freud has not been able to raise. For an examination of this question in relation to Freud, see B. Stiegler, 'Persephone, Oedipus, Epimetheus', *Tekhnema, Journal of Philosophy and Technology*, 3 (1996), pp. 69–112.
51. SE XIX, p. 38.
52. See Marie Moscovici's description of phylogenesis in 'Un meurtre construit par les produits de son oubli', as 'a controversial and enigmatic aspect' (p.

127), which is either 'left aside' or considered to be 'inessential' (p. 129). The essay shows how the question of a genealogy of the psyche is intimately linked with the hypothesis of an archaic inheritance, that stands as a 'beginning' towards which all ulterior events converge. The idea of model runs through Moscovici's analyses, up to the point where the 'phylogenetic idea' itself is described as a 'prototype' of the relation of love and hatred of the other in me. *L'Écrit du temps* 10 (Autumn, 1985). See also I. Grubrich-Simitis, 'Métapsychologie et métabiologie', and P. Lacoste 'Destins de la transmission' in S. Freud, *Vue d'ensemble des névroses de transfert, Un essai métapsychologique* (*op. cit.*). For a recent discussion of this issue, see among others, A. Green, *Cent ans après* (Gallimard, 1998), pp. 112–25.

2 Quantity, Mass and Metaphor

1. The question of the relation between Freudian and Derridean concepts could be elaborated on by considering how Derrida speaks, on the one hand, of the concepts of *Nachträglichkeit* and of *Verspätung* as 'Freud's discovery', as the concepts that 'govern the whole of his thought', and develops the idea of 'originary repetition' on the basis of these concepts (p. 203). On the other hand, he suggests 'the concept of originary *différance* and originary "delay" were imposed upon [him] by a reading of Husserl' (p. 203 note 5). See *La Voix et le phénomène. Introduction au problème du signe dans la phénoménologie de Husserl* (Presses Universitaires de France, 1967), pp. 70–1. This may explain why Derrida speaks of a 'gap between Freud's intuitions and his concepts' (p. 215). The 'gap' would seem to be what permits the *commerce* of concepts between Husserl, Freud, and Derrida. On this problem, see my review of Derrida's *Résistances de la psychanalyse* in 'Responsibilities of Deconstruction', (eds), J. Dronsfield and N. Midgley, *Pli, Warwick Journal of Philosophy*, 6 (1997), pp. 123–31.
2. 'Freud and the Scene of Writing' in *Writing and Difference*, pp. 202, 226, 228.
3. See 'La Mythologie blanche' in *Marges – de la philosophie* (Minuit, 1972). See too R. Gasché, *The Tain of the Mirror: Derrida and the Philosophy of Reflection* (Harvard University Press, 1986), especially Part Three entitled 'Literature or Philosophy?', pp. 255–318.
4. The most recent and exhaustive work pertaining to Freud's political rhetoric is J. Brunner, 'On the Political Rhetoric of Freud's individual Psychology', *History of Political Thought*, V, II (1984), pp. 315–31; and 'A State of Mind: Metaphorical Politics in Freud's Metapsychology', in *Freud and the Politics of Psychoanalysis* (Oxford: Blackwell, 1995), pp. 47–144. This work has the merit of drawing attention to political metaphors, in particular to the military language that pervades Freudian thought. However, in spite of its very useful and rigorous *repérage*, we do not agree, for reasons which should become clearer, with the basic claim of this work: 'Freud's individual psychology contains a political thesis, formulated in metaphors and analogies borrowed from the experience of the social world and used as structuring principles in the elusive realm of the mind' (p. 316). What the author calls the 'invisible inner world of the mind' is 'shaped in terms of the outer world

of society' (p. 317). In so far as the 'outer world of society' is conceived as a source of borrowings (p. 331), the study depends upon the sharp separation of two 'realms', which it then tries to reunify by claiming that Freud's thought is essentially 'political', rather than being primarily concerned with the 'inner world'. The main thesis of the book, according to one reviewer Sebastian Gardner, is that psychoanalysis is a political discourse. Gardner begins by praising the author for 'not assigning to psychoanalysis a single, unequivocal political meaning' (p. 216) but ends up by putting into question the main procedure for arriving at such a result. Namely, the reviewer raises doubt concerning 'the transition in Brunner's argument from a theory's dependence on analogy to the metaphorical character of its content' (p. 219) and suggests that the central analogies in Freud might be not so much 'political' as more generally 'intersubjective'. Gardner's reservations towards Brunner's thesis around the claims to truth of psychoanalysis calls upon a clarification of the status of models, metaphors and analogies, in particular those belonging to the political realm (*European Journal of Philosophy*, 5, 2 (1997), pp. 216–19). M. Worbs presents a treatment of Freud's political rhetoric similar to Brunner's in *Nervenkunst, Literatur und Psychoanalyse im Wien der Jahrhundertwende* (Frankfurt am Main: Anthenäum, 1988). Referring to the metaphor of censorship, Worbs writes: 'das Politische als eine Analogie zum Psychischen ist – *nämlich identisch* mit ihm' [my emphasis] (p. 40 note 23), or that, 'Pressezensur, öffentliche Meinung im Kampf mit dem Herrscher . . . Manipulation der öffentliche Meinung durch eine von einer Minderheit beherrschten Presse – diese Metaphorik ist ein Reflex des politischen Hintergrundes, vor dem die Psychoanalyse enstanden ist. Diese politische Metaphorik ist ein Indiz für Freuds liberale politische Vorstellungswelt' (p. 43).

5. *The Ego and the Id*, SE XIX, p. 55. Another example among many others would be: 'We are very apt to think of the ego as powerless against the id; but when it is opposed to an instinctual process in the id it has only to give a "*signal of unpleasure*" in order to attain its object with the aid of that almost omnipotent institution, the pleasure principle. To take this situation by itself for a moment, we can illustrate it by an example from another field. Let us imagine a country in which a certain small faction objects to a proposed measure the passage of which would have the support of the masses. This minority obtains command of the press and by its help manipulates the supreme arbiter "public opinion", and so succeeds in preventing the measure from being passed' (SE XX, p. 92).
6. In 'Le Point de vue économique en psychanalyse' (*Évolution psychiatrique*, 30 (1965), pp. 189–213), Serge Leclaire notes that 'the whole of the economic problem [in Freud] is posited in strategical terms: movements of troops, strengths of battalions' (p. 189) rather than sending us back to the 'circulation of goods'. See J. Brunner, 'Psychiatry, Psychoanalysis, and Politics during the First Word War', *Journal of the History of Behavioural Sciences*, 27 (1991), pp. 352–65. Derrida notes the 'figure stratégico-militaire' in 'Spéculer – sur "Freud"', in *La Carte Postale, de Socrate à Freud et au-delà*, pp. 370–1, 382–3.
7. Brunner, 'On the Political Rhetoric', pp. 324, 330.
8. 'Why War' (1933 [1932]), SE XXII, p. 213.

9. One is reminded of how the mass (and the neighbouring concepts such as 'people') remain undefined even in dictionaries. See, for example, the concluding line of the entry 'peuple' in *Dictionnaire de philosophie politique*, ed. Ph. Raynaud and St. Rials (Presses universtitaires de France, 1996): 'la philosophie politique ne sait au fond pas que faire du peuple', p. 423.
10. SE III, p. 60, quoted in J. Strachey, 'The Nature of Q', SE I, pp. 395–6. See A. Green, *Le Discours vivant. La conception psychanalytique de l'affect* (Presses universitaires de France, 1973), and 'De l'Esquisse à l'*Interprétation des rêves*: coupure et clôture,' *Nouvelle revue française de psychanalyse*, 5 (1972). We could append to the remark at the end of 'The Neuro-Psychoses of Defence' (1895) what Freud says in *Totem and Taboo* (1912–13) where a problem of quantity also arises: 'No one can have failed to observe, in the first place, that I have taken as the basis of my whole position the existence of a collective mind [*wir überall die Annahme einer Massenpsyche zugrunde legen*], in which mental processes occur just as they do in the mind of an individual . . . It must be admitted that these are grave difficulties; and any explanation that could avoid presumptions of such a kind would seem to be preferable . . . Without the assumption of a collective mind [*einer Massenpsyche*], which makes it possible to neglect the interruptions of mental acts caused by the extinction of the individual, social psychology [*Völkerpsychologie*] cannot exist. Unless psychical processes were continued from one generation to another, if each generation were obliged to acquire its attitude to life anew, there would be no progress in this field and next to no development' (SE III, pp. 157–8).
11. *Ibid.* See 'First Principal Theorem: the Quantitative Conception', 'The Project', SE I, p. 295. See M. Jammer, *Concepts of Mass in Classical and Modern Physics* (Harvard University Press, 1961). The transformations of the concept of Q correspond to the way in which the 'unknown entity' takes on a more or less material character throughout Freud's work.
12. See *Moses and Monotheism: Three Essays*, SE XXIII, p. 97. See S. Weber, 'The Blindness of the Seeing Eye: Psychoanalysis, Hermeneutics, *Entstellung*', in *Institutions and Interpretation* (Minneapolis: University of Minnesota Press, 1987): 'were one to characterize what distinguishes Freud's writing so radically from that of almost all his students and followers, one could hardly do better than to examine the place it accords to the *unknown*' (p. 73).
13. *The Ego and the Id* (1923), SE XIX, p. 17.
14. In 'On Narcissism: An Introduction', *something* comes to disturb the opposition between the instincts: 'We are bound to suppose that a unity comparable to the ego cannot exist in the individual from the start; the ego has to be developed. The auto-erotic instincts, however, are there from the very first; so there must be something added to auto-erotism – a new psychical action – in order to bring about narcissism.' (SE XIV, p. 77). In *Mass Psychology and the analysis of the Ego*, what has to be elucidated is also first presented as *something*: 'If the individuals in the group are combined into a unity, there must surely be something to unite them, and this bond might be precisely the thing that is characteristic of a group.' ['so muß es wohl etwas geben . . . und dies Bindemittel könnte gerade das sein, was für die Masse charackteristisch ist']. (SE XVIII, p. 77). In the two latter cases, what is at issue is the formation of a unity – as it were by 'addition' – while

in *The Ego and the Id*, it is a problem of resemblance: 'something behaves *like* the repressed'.

15. Freud says that he calls this side of life 'higher' only 'figuratively' for want of a better expression.
16. *New Introductory Lectures*, SE XXII, p. 73. Freud refers to Geoges Groddeck, *The Book of the it: Psychoanalytic Letters to a Friend* [*Das Buch vom Es* (Psychoanalytischer Verlag, 1923)] (C. W. Daniel, 1935). He warns us against the mistake of confusing the spatial representation of the psychical apparatus with the theory of 'cerebral localization' on numerous occasions. In *The Interpretation*, for example, he writes: 'ideas, thoughts and psychical structures in general must never be regarded as localized in organic elements of the nervous system but rather, as one might say, *between* them, where resistances and facilitations [*Bahnungen*] provide the corresponding correlates' [Freud's emphasis] (SE V, p. 611).
17. 'The Unconscious' (1915) describes the way in which 'unconscious processes only become cognizable by us under the conditions of dreaming and of neurosis, that is to say, when processes of the higher, *Pcs.*, system are set back to an earlier stage by being lowered (by regression)' (SE XIV, p. 187). See P.-L. Assoun, 'La Philosophie et l'obstacle conscientialiste', in *Freud, la philosophie et les philosophes* (Presses universitaires de France, 1976), pp. 23–42.
18. See Laplanche and Pontalis, for 'substitute formation', *Vocabulaire*, p. 434. We are not however claiming that 'substitution' is the most fundamental concept of Freudian theory. Commentaries of Freud often consist in deciding upon which, of Freudian concepts, is the fundamental one. For example, for the psychoanalyst André Green, 'the fundamental concept of [Freud's] theory is not the unconscious . . . it is the drive [*la pulsion*]' which 'occupies a radically heterogeneous position with respect to the unconscious' 'Psychanalyse, langage, L'ancien et le nouveau', *Critique*, 381 (1979), p. 142. For Green, the concept of affect has been neglected on various accounts, including by Freud himself, who begins by privileging 'representation' to the detriment of the concept of affect [quantum of affect], in order to make his hypotheses acceptable, since they pertain to something which is by essence 'unknowable' (p. 180). For Green, the definition given of the id in Lecture XXXI indicates a 'slide towards affect' in so far as 'all reference to representations is left out of the description' and in so far as 'Freud even goes so far as to maintain that nothing corresponding to an idea or a content exists in the id. Nothing but instinctual impulses seeking discharge' (p. 186). Green refers Freud's difficulties around the concept of affect and representation to the 'fact that psychoanalysis is born out of hypnosis and catharsis, where pre-eminence is openly accorded to affect . . . Freud's concern to keep the originality of psychoanalysis safe from all contamination from the origins from which it has separated is doubtless responsible for this subordination of affect to representation in the beginnings of the discipline which he founded' (p. 184). See 'Conceptions of Affect' (1977) in *On Private Madness* (The Hogarth Press and the Institute of Psycho-Analysis, 1986), pp. 174–213, esp. p. 182; pp. 189–90. See Green's full-length study on the affect *Le discours vivant* (Presses universitaires de France, 1973).

19. SE V, p. 612.
20. SE XVI, p. 131/p. 137. See also in Lecture XXIII: '[symptoms] create a substitute [*Ersatz*], then, for the frustrated satisfaction by means of a regression of the libido to earlier times' (p. 365), or in *Beyond the Pleasure Principle*, where Freud speaks of the way in which '*consciousness arises instead* [*an Stelle*] *of a memory-trace*' [Freud's emphasis] (SE XVIII, p. 25). Language 'can function as a substitute for action' as Green notes referring to 'The Neuro-Psychoses of Defence', 'Conceptions of Affect' (p. 175). In *L'Enfance de l'art, une interprétation de l'esthétique freudienne* (Payot, 1970), Sarah Kofman describes how the concept of *Nachträglichkeit* involves some form of substitution: 'a memory is a substitutive construction that makes up for the lack of meaning of the thought experience' [my translation] (p. 88). See J. Derrida, 'Spéculer sur "Freud"', concerning the term *Ersatz* in Freud (p. 420).
21. L. Binswanger quoted in *Figures de la subjectivité. Approches phénoménologiques et psychiatriques* ed. J.-F. Courtine (Éditions du CNRS, 1992). (Lecture IV, SE XV, p. 61). Let us recall that in *The Introductory Lectures*, Freud begins by discussing parapraxes, then moves on to dealing with the dream and finally, with neurosis. Some commentators, such as Sarah Kofman, speak of 'the circle of Freudian method' in so far as 'works of art served as model of understanding for dream processes; the symbolism of the dream and of its processes served in turn to interpret works of art' [my translation], *L'Enfance de l'art* (p. 134). For an interesting exploration of how day-dreams relate to night-dreams in a 'circular' manner, see R. Bowlby, 'The Other day: The Interpretation of Day-dreams', in *Sigmund Freud's The Interpretation of Dreams*, ed. L. Marcus (Manchester University Press, 1999), pp. 160–82, esp. p. 166.
22. Nor is substitution the only psychical process that interests psychoanalysis. Green provides a list of what he calls the 'figures of psychoanalytic rhetoric': 'repetition-compulsion, reversal (turning into the opposite and turning against the self), anticipation, mirroring, inclusion, exclusion, formation of the complement, mediation between inside and outside, the emergence of the category of the intermediary [*Zwischen*], the situation between the same and the other, the constitution of movable limits, temporary splitting, the creation of substitutes, the setting up of screens and *finally* projective identification.' 'Conceptions of Affect', (p. 211). *Übertragung* could be said to be the general name for processes of substitution. Laplanche writes in *Vie et mort en psychanalyse* (Flammarion, 1970): '[le] terme de "représenté" [est une] articulation fondamentale de la métapsychologie freudienne . . . le modèle le plus courant employé par Freud pour rendre compte de la relation entre le somatique et le psychique utilise la métaphore d'une sorte de "délégation", pourvue d'un mandat qui ne serait pas absolument impératif' (p. 26).
23. SE IV, p. xxiii/p. vii. In the analysis of *Kultur*, Freud speaks of 'points of agreement' [*Übereinstimmungen*], as the subtitle of *Totem and Taboo* (1912–13) indicates: 'Some Points of Agreement between the Mental Lives of Savages and Neurotics' [*Einige Übereinstimmungen im Seelenleben der Wilden und der Neurotiker*].
24. *Introductory Lectures*, Lecture XXII, pp. 356, 370.

25. See 'The Economic Problem of Masochism' (1924) and 'An Outline of Psycho-Analysis' (1940 [1938]).
26. SE XVIII, pp. 8, 193–4. In 'De l'apathie théorique' (*Critique* [1975)], pp. 254–63), Lyotard discusses 'the hesitation in [Freud's] theoretical discourse' with reference to this particular passage. The principle that apparently governs Freud's exposition – the idea that the economic conception requires the 'least rigid hypothesis' – is otherwise, Lyotard argues, under the heading of *Lockerheit* [which Lyotard translates as *laxité*], a 'property of psychical energy that Freud invokes' in order 'to explain artistic activity by means of the malleability of the repressions [*des refoulements*]' (p. 261). This provides a basis for discussing Freud's theoretical discourse in terms of affect and pathos. The demonstration does not only attribute the value of *passion* to Freud's theoretical discourse, but concludes by stating that it is an 'apathetic passion' (p. 263), thus designating the co-existence in Freud's discourse of *laxité* and *désir du vrai* (p. 264). In 'Spéculer', Derrida also comments upon the *laxité* that Freud recommends in this passage (p. 298). Lyotard's analysis can be added to the commentaries that stem from the idea that Freud's discourse and object unite. See chapter 1 above.
27. SE XIX, p. 18.
28. SE XXII, p. 220.
29. See 'Mourning and Melancholia' (1917 [1915]) for an enumeration of the 'major institutions of the ego': 'conscience' [*Gewissen*], 'the censorship of consciousness' [*Bewußtseinszensur*], and 'reality-testing [*Realitätsprüfung*]' (SE XIV, p. 247).
30. According to the *Wahrig Deutsches Wörterbuch*, *Masse* as a 'Menge, große Anzahl; Vielzahl von Menschen, die ihre Individualität zugunsten der Gesamtheit zum Teil od. ganz aufgegeben haben' is a 'figurative' use of the term, as opposed to the 'literal', 'physical' meaning.
31. We cannot here enter into a discussion of Jean-Jacques Rousseau's concept of 'general will' to which Freud's comparison seems loosely to appeal. For a discussion of the relation between Freud and Rousseau, see M. Ansart-Dourlen, *Freud et les Lumières, Individu, Raison, Société* (Payot, 1985). See 'Psychanalyse et psychologie', in *Psychanalyse et sciences humaines, Deux conférences (1963–1964)* (Librairie générale française/IMEC, 1996) where Louis Althusser discusses how (Lacanian) psychoanalysis stands in relation to the 'famous eighteenth-century problem, that of the passage from the state of nature to the state of society' with reference to Rousseau's *Discours sur l'origine et les fondements de l'inégalité*, pp. 92ff.
32. See H. Kelsen, 'Le Concept d'État et la psychologie sociale, avec pour référence particulière la théorie des masses selon Freud [*Der Begriff des Staates und die Sozialpsychologie, Mit besonderer Berücksichtigung von Freuds Theorie der Masse*]' (1922), trans. F. Luce, *Confrontations*, 11 (1984), pp. 23–48. Kelsen discusses the repercussions that a substantialist conception of the 'mass' or of the 'social bond', such as the one that Freud developed, according to him, may have on a theory of the State. In a footnote added in 1923 to Chapter III of *Mass Psychology*, Freud expresses his disagreement as to whether or not the attribution of the feature characteristic of the individual to the 'group mind' constitutes a hypostasis (p. 115 note 2). For a brief discussion of Freud's 'philosophie du droit', see P.-L. Assoun,

'Psychanalyse, science du droit et criminologie', in *Freud et les sciences sociales. Psychanalyse et théorie de la Culture* (Armand-Colin, 1993), pp. 115–16. See also, among other discussions of Freud and politics, P. Roazen, *La Pensée sociale et politique de Freud [Freud's Social and Political Thought]* (1968), (Complexes, 1976), in particular, 'La Politique: le contrôle social', pp. 122–56; E. Enriquez, 'La Guerre et la mort: l'État comme figure de la guerre totale', in *De la Horde à l'état, Essai de psychanalyse du lien social* (Gallimard, 1983), pp. 163–79. Étienne Balibar discusses Freud's essay *Mass Psychology* in relation to Freudo-Marxism in his essay 'Fascism, Psychoanalysis, Freudo-Marxism', in *Masses, Classes, Ideas, Studies on Politics and Philosophy before and after Marx [La crainte des masses. Politique et philosophie avant et après Marx*] (Galilée, 1997), trans. J. Swenson (Rouledge, 1994), pp. 177–89. Balibar points out 'Freud's singular elision of the problem of the state hovering behind his analysis of the masses' (p. 186).

33. See among others, C. Schorske, *Vienna, Politics and Culture* (London: Weidenfeld, 1980); H. F. Ellenberger, *The Discovery of the Unconscious, The History and Evolution of Dynamic Psychiatry* (Basic Books, 1970), J. Le Rider, M. Plon, G. Raulet and H. Rey-Flaud, *Autour du 'Malaise dans la culture' de Freud* (Presses universitaire de France, 1998).
34. For one of the earliest discussions of Freud's essay *Mass Psychology* in France, see G. Bataille, 'La Structure psychologique du fascisme', *Oeuvres complètes, Premiers écrits 1922–1940*, vol. I (Gallimard, 1970), pp. 340–71 and for a historical discussion of it, see E. Roudinesco, 'Bataille entre Freud et Lacan. Une expérience cachée', in *Georges Bataille, Après tout* (Belin, 1995).
35. Freud attempted regularly to relate his theoretical conceptions to 'popular knowledge', 'popular wisdom'. See for example, *The Psychopathology of Everyday Life*: 'I fail to see why the wisdom which is the precipitate of men's common experience of life should be refused inclusion among the acquisitions of science' (p. 211). Can there be any other conception of the mass than a 'popular' one?
36. See Laplanche's classical study of notion of drive [*Trieb*] in relation to the notion of instinct [*Instinkt*] *Vie et mort en psychanalyse, op. cit.* Laplanche is interested in the way in which 'la pulsion sexuelle [according to the popular view on sexuality] est conçue sur le modèle de l'instinct, de la réponse à un besoin naturel, dont le paradigme est la faim' (p. 28). Central to Laplanche's demonstration is the concept of 'étayage [*Anlehnung*]', which is first attributed the value of a concept in *The Language of Psychoanalysis*. For a classical study of the idea of the 'primitive', see Laplanche and Pontalis, 'Fantasy and the Origins of the Unconscious', in *Formations of Fantasy*, ed. J. Donald *et al.* (Methuen, 1986) [*Fantasmes originaires, Fantasme des origines et origine du fantasme* (1964)].
37. Consider among numerous others, these two examples from *The Interpretation*: '[i]f this picture of the two psychical agencies and their relation to consciousness is accepted, there is a complete analogy in political life [*eine völlig kongruente Analogie*]' (p. 144).
38. The end of chapter 4 takes up again the question concerning the relation between the 'mass' and thinking.
39. It is not a coincidence if Freud compares 'comparisons' to displacement of people and to 'uprooting' on numerous occasions – the similarity between

people and 'figures' appears as soon as their 'quantity' is at stake. See chapter 4 below.

3 Sciences of the Crowd

1. See among others, J. S. McClelland, *The Crowd and the Mob, from Plato to Canetti* (London: Unwin Hyman, 1989); L. Bramson, *The Political Context of Sociology* (Princeton University Press, 1961), pp. 4–5; S. Giner, *Mass society* (London: Martin Robertson, 1976); S. Halebsky, *Mass Society and Political Conflict, Toward a Reconstruction of Theory* (Cambridge University Press, 1976), 'Intellectual Origins of and Contributions to Mass Political Theory', pp. 10–32.
2. The problem of the mass has not constituted an equally central theme for every thinker included in these studies, and the recurrent inclusion of some thinkers in them can be striking. Freud, for example, invariably features in sociological or political studies of 'mass society' thanks to *Mass Psychology and the Analysis of the Ego* (1921).
3. Since the present study partly deals with Freud's discussion of *psychologie des foules* ['crowd psychology'], and as the term crowd in German has been translated into *Masse* ['mass'], we will use both terms interchangeably. See the German translation of 'crowd' into *Masse* throughout G. Le Bon, *Psychologie der Massen*, trans. R. Eisler (Stuttgart: A. Kröner [1895], 1911). We leave aside, for the moment, the distinction between 'mass', 'crowd', 'mob', 'âme collective', 'mentalité collective' that could be made with reference to authors who battle with the difficulty of defining the idea or the phenomenon of the crowd. In this respect, see, for example, the influential study of the historian G. Lefebvre, 'Foules révolutionnaires' (1932) in *Études sur la révolution française* (Presses universitaires de France, 1963), who defines *foule* as 'an involuntary and ephemeral *aggregate* of individuals as are constituted in the surroundings of a train station . . . in a street or on the place of a town' [pp. 340–80, my translation]. This points to the essential historical work on the crowd and the French Revolution. The most influential work in this field is Georges Rudé, *The Crowd in History 1730–1848* (London: J. Wiley, 1968). Every work on the discipline: 1) designates Hyppolite Taine [*Les Origines de la France contemporaine* (Hachette, 1881), vol. II, 'La Conquête jacobine'] as the one who first granted the crowd the dignity, albeit eminently negative, of an object of study; 2) condemn Le Bon's 'pre-scientific' work, notably the 'imprecision' that surrounds his use of the notion of the 'crowd'. See Rudé, 'Faces in the Crowd', in *The Crowd in History*, pp. 195–213. On Taine, see J. van Ginneken, 'The Revolutionary Mob: Taine, Psycho-history and Regression', in *Crowd Psychology, Psychology, and Politics* (Cambridge University Press, 1993), pp. 20–51. The word 'masse' and 'levée en masse' are studied, from a lexical point of view, in M. Frey, *Les Transformations du vocabulaire français à l'époque de la révolution* (*1789–1800*) (Presses universitaires de France, 1925): 'masse: se dit pendant la révolution surtout de la foule qui commence à jouer un rôle plus considérable. ACAD., 1798 Suppl . . . Le *Néol. Fr.* et le Dict. de l'Acad. relèvent la locution célèbre qui figure dans mainte proclamation

à savoir "se lever en masse" et le subst. "la levée en masse" ("mise sur pied générale", deux expressions nouvelles qui ne sont possibles que parce que "masse" est devenu synonyme de "peuple, foule")' (p. 129). Referring to the work of Sighele, Le Bon and the others, Freud notes in *Mass psychology and the Analysis of the Ego*: 'A number of very different structures have probably been merged under the term "group" [Masse] and may require to be distinguished' (SE XVIII, p. 83). If confusion there should be, according to Freud, it can be explained by the fact that studies of the crowd have paid insufficient attention to the distinction between various types of 'crowds'. There are those which are 'of a short-lived character, those which some passing interest has hastily agglomerated out of various sort of individuals', and the 'stable groups or associations [*stabilen Massen oder Vergesellschaftungen*] in which mankind pass their lives, and which are embodied in the institutions of society. Groups of the first kind stand in the same sort of relation to those of the second as a high but choppy sea to a ground swell' (*ibid.*) Freud's doubts concerning the field of study of the crowd are not often noted among commentators, which partly explains that his inclusion in general studies on the crowd supposedly should go without saying.

4. In *Mass psychology*, Freud states concerning this discipline: 'Although group psychology is only in its infancy, it embraces an *immense number of separate issues* and offers to investigators *countless problems* which have hitherto not even been properly distinguished from one another' (my emphasis, SE XVIII, p. 70). A more recent definition of crowd psychology goes as follows: '[it is] the discipline which aims to grasp the psychological phenomena which have a collective character, whether they be coherent or destructuring.' The phenomena which it studies 'imply all the conscious and unconscious mechanisms, which constitute the life of societies, whether or not these mechanisms should pertain to stable masses or transient crowds, as well as the relation between these human wholes and their leaders'. P. Mannoni, *La Psychologie collective* (Presses universitaires de France, 1985), pp. 12–13 [my translation]. For a study of the relation of this discipline to literature, see P. Macherey, 'Autour de Victor Hugo: figures de l'homme d'en bas', *À quoi pense la littérature?* (Presses universitaires de France, 1990), or S. Moscovici, 'Les foules avant la foule', *Stanford French Review*, 'La Foule', VII, 2 (1983), pp. 151–74. The importance of Gabriel Tarde's theory in Marcel Proust's *A la Recherche du temps perdu* has been noted by Anne Henry and by Julia Kristeva, and needs to be explored further, just as Gilles Deleuze's interest in Tarde [*Différence et répétition* (Presses universitaires de France, 1969)] at a time when Gabriel Tarde does not occupy a prominent place within the French philosophical corpus.
5. For a discussion of crowd psychology as the ancestor of 'social psychology', see among others, G. W. Allport, 'The Historical Background of Modern Social Psychology', in *Handbook of Social Psychology*, ed G. Lindzey, G. Aronson and E. Aronson (New York: Random House, 1985). 'Crowd psychology', which is usually represented by Gustave Le Bon, almost invariably appears in studies of totalitarianism, and to review the field exceeds the limit of this work. See for example, Hannah Arendt, 'Le Système totalitaire', in *Les Origines du totalitarisme* (Seuil [1951], 1972), p. 39. As far as

the relation of 'psychologie des foules' to other disciplines is concerned, the most useful work to consult is J. van Ginneken, *Crowd Psychology, Psychology, and Politics* (*op. cit.*), which provides a critical review of the existing literature and ample bibliographical references on the subject. See also by the same author, 'The Killing of the Father: The Background of Freud's Group Psychology', *Political Psychology*, 5, 3 (1984), pp. 391–414. For a detailed history of crowd psychology within the 'human sciences' in France, see L. Mucchielli, 'Sociologie et psychologie en France, L'appel à un territoire commun: vers une psychologie collective (1890–1940)', *Revue de synthèse*, 4, 3–4 (1994), pp. 445–83.

6. A. Akoun, 'Relire Gustave Le Bon', *Ethnopsychologie*, 2 (1979), p. 204; P. Rieff, 'The Origin of Freud's Psychological Psychology', *Journal of the History of Ideas*, 17, 2 (1956), p. 246 quoted in Y. J. Thiec, 'Gustave Le Bon, prophète de l'irrationalisme de masse', *Revue française de sociologie*, XXII (1981), p. 409. See the influential monograph on Le Bon by R. A. Nye, *The Origins of Crowd Psychology: Gustave Le Bon and the Crisis of Mass Democracy in the Third Republic* (Beverly Hills, Sage Publications, 1975). It provides an exhaustive bibliography of Le Bon's work in medicine, photography, ethnology, physics, war, equestrian education, as well as detailed discussions of his various relations, notably with Marie Bonaparte, the first French translator of Freud. See too C. Rouvier, *Les Idées politiques de Gustave Le Bon* (Presses universitaires de France, 1986).
7. Scipio Sighele is an Italian criminologist who is the author of the first treatise on the crowd *La Folla Delinquente* (1891); the French magistrate Gabriel Tarde has written numerous books on the crowd and on public opinion such as *L'Opinion et la foule* (1901) and *Les Lois de l'imitation* (1890); and the French physician Henri Fournial wrote: *Essai sur la psychologie des foules – Considérations médico-judiciaires sur les responsabilités collectives* (1892).
8. For a discussion of the priority debate, see van Ginneken, 'The 1895 Debate on the Origins of Crowd Psychology', *Journal of the History of the Behavioral Sciences*, 21 (1985), pp. 375–81; S. Barrows, *Distorting Mirrors – Visions of the Crowd in Late Nineteenth Century France* (Yale University Press, 1981). See also E. Apfelbaum, 'Origines de la psychologie sociale en France, Développements souterrains et discipline méconnue', *Revue française de sociologie*, XXII (1981), pp. 397–407.
9. One of the most extensive study of this question is found in Laurent Mucchielli, *La Découverte du social, Naissance de la sociologie en France (1870–14)* (Éditions de la Découverte, 1998).
10. What we mean by 'methodological problems' should become clearer in what follows, notably that 'methodological' here refers to the relation between metaphors and analogies and the object of study. For other methodological aspects of the science, see D. G. Charlton, *Positivist Thought in France during the Second Empire* (Oxford: Clarendon Press, 1959), which provides necessary points of reference for a study of 'psychologie des foules' in the context of nineteenth-century positivist thought, more particularly, concerning Taine. For an overview of the philosophical context in late nineteenth-century France, see among others, Émile Boutroux, 'La philosophie en France depuis 1867' (1908) in *Philosophie, France, XIXe siècle, Écrits et*

opuscules, ed. S. Douailler, R.-P. Droit and P. Vermeren (Librairie Générale française, 1994), pp. 912–60.

11. 'It is not necessary that a crowd should be numerous' G. Le Bon, *The Crowd. A Study of the Popular Mind* [*La Psychologie des foules* (1895)], p. 43. Unless otherwise indicated, all quotations from Le Bon refer to that text and that edition, with page references in bracket.
12. Freud introduces his reflection on 'the mass' in *Mass Psychology* by commenting on Le Bon's theses during an entire chapter because the latter's description 'fits in so well with our [his] psychology in the emphasis which it lays upon unconscious mental life' (SE XVIII, p. 83), namely by granting Le Bon a considerable importance. He nevertheless believes that 'none of that author's statements bring forward anything new'. (*ibid.*) If we turn to the article on social psychology to which Freud then refers, however, the topic is presented unequivocally as a branch of sociology. Gabriel Tarde and Georg Simmel are designated as the most important writers in the field. Le Bon is mentioned as a *Nachfolger* and his work as 'zwar nicht wesentlich bereicherte, wohl aber von vornherein eine rein psychologische Untersuchung einschlug'. W. Moede, 'Die Massen- und Sozialpsychologie im kritischen Überblick', *Zeitschrift für pädagogische Psychologie und experimentelle Pädagogik*, XVI (1915), pp. 385–404, esp. p. 388.
13. We are not here merely hinting at the way in which any 'scientific' theoretical exposition (such as for example, the 'science of the crowd'), or, for that matter, any *exposition* at all, can be envisaged from a 'rhetorical' point of view, if we follow the teachings of, for example, Paul de Man's readings of the philosophical tradition (See, among others, Paul de Man, *Allegories of Reading. Figural Language in Rousseau, Nietzsche, Rilke and Proust* (Yale University Press, 1979) and R. Gasché's critical stance on de Man's approach entitled 'In-Difference to Philosophy', in *The Wild Card of Reading. On Paul de Man* (Harvard University Press, 1998)). Rhetorical analyses take on a special significance in the context of 'crowd psychology'. Let us recall that Aristotle's founding treatise on rhetoric developed its own science of the crowd in Book II. See G. Genette and R. Barthes for an analysis of the decline of the teaching of rhetoric at the end of the nineteenth-century, and the fading away of rhetoric as an 'art of persuasion' to the benefit of rhetoric as an 'art of figures'. See G. Genette 'La Rhétorique restreinte' (1970) in *Figures III* (Seuil, 1972); R. Barthes, 'L'Ancienne rhétorique. Aide-mémoire' (1970) in *L'Aventure sémiologique* (Seuil, 1985). *La Psychologie des foules* consists partly in a treatise on rhetoric, and the question arises as to what the reduction of rhetoric to a few figures might have to do with the emergence of 'the age of the masses'. The examination of this problem will be the object of further work.
14. G. Tarde, *La Philosophie pénale* (Lyon: Storck-Masson, 1890), p. 320 quoted in S. Sighele, *La Foule criminelle, Essai de psychologie collective*, 2nd edn. (F. Alcan, 1901), p. 33, respectively.
15. M. Pugliese, *Rivista di giureprudenza* (1891) quoted in Sighele, *La Foule criminelle*, p. 63.
16. Sighele, *op. cit.* p. 64. There are many other comparisons in the same book: 'la foule est un terrain dans lequel le microbe du bien meurt bien souvent, et dans lequel, au contraire, le germe du mal se développe' (p. 65). The com-

parative nature of the argumentation is no less striking: '[d]e même que la moyenne de plusieurs nombres ne peut évidemment être égale au plus élevé de ces nombres, de même un agrégat d'hommes ne peut refléter dans ses manifestations les facultés les plus élevées,' (p. 60), '[d]e même qu'il est des animaux qui pour s'effacer . . . prennent la couleur du milieu dans lequel ils vivent, de même les hommes qui se trouvent dans une foule prennent la *teinte morale,* de ceux qui les entourent' (p. 69); see also pp. 56 and 73.

17. It remains to be seen to what extent 'circulation' and 'propagation' can be considered as synonyms for Le Bon's guiding thread: 'suggestions are contagious in every human agglomeration' (p. 39). The question arises as to whether one should attribute an 'analogical' value to the 'scientific' discourses to which 'contagion' and 'suggestion' send us back.
18. See among others, van Ginneken, *op. cit.* Chapter 2 on 'The Emergence of Positivist Criminology in Italy', pp. 49–57.
19. Sighele, *La Foule criminelle,* (p. 153).
20. It is interesting to confront Le Bon's insistence on 'la mobilité des foules' to the way in which, in his 'theory of words', an emphasis is put on the fact that 'words, then, have only mobile and transitory significations which change from age to age and people to people; and when we desire to exert an influence by their means on the crowd what it is requisite to know is the meaning given them by the crowd at a given moment, and not the meaning which they formerly had or may yet have for individuals of a different mental constitution' (p. 106). Le Bon gives, as examples, the words 'democracy, socialism, equality, liberty' (p. 103), or 'republic', 'fatherland', 'the "king" and the "royal family"', and argues that there can be no resemblance between the use of these words, not only at different epochs, but most importantly, in different peoples (pp. 104–5). Detaching 'words' from 'signification', and linking the character of words to that of the crowd, keeps the domain of 'signification' guarded against the 'multitude', whose relation to 'words' consists in a relation to 'images', and, notwithstanding the vagueness with which Le Bon appeals to it, to 'figures de rhétorique'. Since no *peuple* can have access to the signification that words have for another one, language provides a means of differentiating peoples and a guarantee against the latter ever coming together as one unified 'crowd'. This is another respect in which, as note 13 above suggested, Le Bon's treatise would motivate a detailed study of it from the point of view of rhetoric and language. (This might help us to understand Hannah Arendt's references to the topic of 'verisimilitude' throughout *The Origins of Totalitarianism.*)
21. See Mucchielli for a description of the naturalism that dominates late eighteenth-century and nineteenth-century anthropology, which host evolutionist theories of race. Chapter I – 1. 'De la race aux sociétés', pp. 27–75.
22. Tarde writes: 'si diverses qu'elles soient par leur origine, comme par tous leurs autres caractères, les foules se ressemblent toutes par certains traits', 'Le Public et la foule' (1901) in *L'Opinion et la foule,* Introduction by D. Reynié (Presses universitaires de France, 1989), p. 54.
23. For a discussion of the political contents of Le Bon's treatise, see among others Nye, *The Origins of Crowd Psychology,* 'The Dilemna of the Third Republic: The Conjunction of Collective Psychology and Political Theory', pp. 83–121.

24. Later in the book, Le Bon speaks of the way in which 'nations [*les peuples*] were submitted to secret forces analogous to those which compel the acorn to transform itself into an oak or a comet to follow its orbit.' (p. 115).
25. 'Le Bon's unconscious more especially contains the most deeply buried features of the racial mind [*Rassenseele*], which as a matter of fact lies outside the scope of psychoanalysis. We do not fail to recognize, indeed, that the ego's nucleus, which comprises the "archaic heritage" of the human mind [*Menschenseele*], is unconscious; but in addition to this we distinguish the 'unconscious repressed', which arose from a portion of that heritage. This concept of the repressed is not to be found in Le Bon' (SE XVIII, p. 75 note 1). We will see in chapter 5 how a concern for analogies and comparisons, if apparently moving us away from Le Bon's *âme de la race*, is indispensable when dealing both with the concept of 'archaic heritage' and of 'the return of the repressed'. It might be useful to refer to the sociologist René Worms, who writes in 'Psychologie collective et individuelle' shortly after Le Bon wrote his treatise: 'The majority of psychological and sociological theories deem that expressions such as "national mind" [*esprit national*] or "family mind" [*esprit de famille*] [we could add Le Bon's *âme de la race*], only have a metaphorical meaning. They do not, according to these theories, designate a concrete reality, a substance endowed with unity and permanence, they simply serve to mark a set of properties, of characters which are found to be identical in the mind of a great enough number of individuals', *Revue internationale de sociologie* (1899), pp. 249–73, esp. p. 253 [my translation].
26. Le Bon speaks of 'multitude of peoples [*une foule de peuples*]' with reference to Napoléon to whom he alludes on numerous occasions (p. 67). The examination of the 'racial' theory of Le Bon exceeds the scope of the present inquiry and is already well discussed in the existing literature. Borch-Jacobsen writes in *The Freudian Subject*: 'For Le Bon, the "racial soul" already marks a first degree of crowd *organization* . . . since it is the same for all individuals, it is what gives them the unity and identity of a "people"' (p. 138). What for Le Bon comes *prior to* 'the racial soul' is the 'simple multitude' or the 'multitudes sans cohésion' [translated as 'the multitudes composed of different races'] (p. 156), an example of which is, for Le Bon 'the barbarians of very diverse origin who during several centuries invaded the Roman Empire' (p. 155). Note, however, that, without referring to any specific epoch, Le Bon describes individuals in a 'psychological crowd' as 'barbarians'. It is difficult to distinguish between what Le Bon calls the crowd in the ordinary sense and the psychological crowd since, in Le Bon's account, they both send us back to 'the simple multitude' or to 'barbarity'.
27. See the discussion of Le Bon's notion of the unconscious in Borch-Jacobsen, *op. cit.*, pp. 170–3, see especially Nye, *The Origins of Crowd Psychology*.
28. See Sighele pp. 4ff. on the analogy between man and human society with reference to Spencer, Comte and Schopenhauer.
29 Le Bon argues against Spencer that 'in the aggregate which constitutes a crowd there is in no sort a summing-up of or an average struck between its elements. What really takes place is a combination followed by the creation of new characteristics, just as in chemistry certain elements, when brought into contact – bases and acids, for example – combine to form a new body possessing properties quite different from those of the bodies that have served to form it' (p. 27).

30. Chapter 5 discusses the context in which Freud speaks of analogies that 'kommt der Identität naher'. A page later Freud contests Le Bon's assimilation of the transformation of the individual into a crowd on the ground that he overlooks a serious point: 'We cannot avoid being struck by a sense of deficiency when we notice that one of the chief elements of the comparison, namely the person who is to replace the hypnotist in the case of the group, is not mentioned in Le Bon's exposition' (SE XVIII, pp. 76–7). Borch-Jacobsen argues that the proximity between Le Bon and Freud becomes apparent, among other places, in Freud's insistence on Le Bon's so-called poor treatment of the question of the leader, despite the fact that the latter devotes a great deal of his treatise to them (p. 138). See also in *The Freudian Subject*, 'An-archy' (in particular, pp. 142ff.). What the author calls 'the leadership thesis' ['a leader, a *Führer* is peremptorily assigned' (p. 144)] refers to the fact that the leader in Le Bon's exposé is introduced in the manner of a *Diktat*, because it is believed that 'les foules ... veulent un chef' (p. 144). This is what Freud mistakenly reproduces in his book *Mass Psychology*, in order to ward off the fear of what Borch-Jacobsen calls 'an-archy', in too strict obedience to 'the schema of the Subject'.
31. If we referred to late nineteenth-century scientific theories on hypnosis, contagion and suggestibility, however, we could find various 'psychological' treatises that aim not only to establish distinctions between these three phenomena, but that also provide competing accounts of each of them separately. A detailed discussion of late nineteenth-century theories of hypnosis, suggestion and contagion as well as of the relation between hypnosis and psychoanalysis would demand an entire chapter. Arguments around the failed rejection of hypnosis by psychoanalysis are abundantly discussed and well documented. See L. Chertok and I. Stengers, *Le Coeur et la raison, L'hypnose en question de Lavoisier à Lacan* (Payot, 1989) and *La Suggestion, hypnose, influence, transe*, ed. D. Bougnoux, Colloque de Cerisy (Les Empêcheurs de penser en rond, 1991). 'Hypnosis', in *The Freudian Subject* is said to provide 'the highly paradoxical model of a pre-individual, presubjective psychology' in so far as, according to Borch-Jacobsen, 'the hypnotized person is a non-individual, a quasi-individual, since he is literally penetrated by (the discourse of) the other; and if there is an unconscious, in this instance, it must be said, strictly speaking, to belong to no subject (it comes from the other, through the other)' (p. 141). Here, the author appears to elaborate on such an understanding of hypnosis mostly with reference Le Bon's appeal to hypnosis. For an exploration of hypnosis that moves beyond the technical aspect of this phenomenon, see M. Borch-Jacobsen, E. Michaud and J.-L. Nancy, *Hypnoses* (Galilée, 1984). Hypnosis is an opportunity, for these authors, to reflect upon the 'question de la passivité' (p. 11). These texts as well as Freud's discussion of Le Bon, raise the question as to whether or not 'hypnosis' refers to an empirical manifestation (even if it is an elusive one) or if 'hypnosis' is a term of analogy. This question does not only arise around hypnosis, but as we indicated in the first chapter, with all the sciences and the domains to which Freud appeals. It should become clear that we are wondering whether the idea of the 'mass' or the 'crowd', indeed the 'individual' cannot also function as terms of

analogy, even though what is at issue is not a science (like archaeology, thermodynamics, etc.), a technical object, or a domain of activity (like politics or war). See note 17 above.

32. Freud writes: 'At bottom, all that is left over as being peculiar to Le Bon are the two notions of the unconscious and of the comparison with the mental life of primitive people, and even these had naturally often been alluded to before him' (SE XVIII, p. 82).

4 On a Large Scale

1. SE I, pp. 304, 361.
2. SE I, p. 225; SE XXII, p. 160; 'On Narcissism', pp. 145, 147.
3. SE IV, p. 176. Other examples include: 'Es wimmelt natürlich in der Träumen von solchen Mischgebilden' translated into 'Dreams are of course a mass of these composite structures' (p. 324). 'If it were really the business of dreams to relieve our memory of the "dregs" of daytime recollections by a special psychical activity, our sleep would be more tormented and harder worked than our mental life while we are awake. For the number of indifferent impressions from which memory would need to be protected is clearly immensely large: the night would not be long enough to cope with such a mass [*die Summe zu bewältigen*]' (*ibid.*, p. 178).
4. SE XXI, Editor's note, p. 7. See also Lecture XXXV of the *New Introductory Lectures on Psycho-Analysis* (1933 [1932]).
5. SE XXI, p. 64; SE XXII, p. 161. What is also called the 'lower-strata of our own society' is likened to primitive men or even sometimes to peoples of antiquity, notably with respect to their belief in the prophetic nature of dreams (SE XI, p. 34).
6. 'Why War' (1933 [1931]), pp. 212, 206. Marthe Robert compares Freud's incomprehension for the people [*le peuple*] to his attitude towards the Jewish people in the following manner: 'We must consider an important point that can easily give rise to misunderstandings. That is Freud's lack of sympathy and understanding for "the people" as such, an idiosyncrasy, which some writers, on the strength of spotty observations and traditional prejudices, have termed typically Jewish. True, Freud's aversion for "the people" is well attested, but here we must ask what he meant by "people". For him the word had two distinct meanings, relating to two distinct spheres of experience. The one was an immediate self-evident reality; the other was remote and problematic since, inextricably bound up with the movements of history, it could be apprehended only through a complex interplay of contradictions and conflicts. The first – the Jewish people – was to Freud a living organism to which he belonged by birth, which he knew without effort and would have known even if he had forgotten it or lost all interest in its existence. Concerning the second – the German people or "the people" in general – he had only indirect information, insufficiently controlled images which, too blurred or too clear, at once abstract and charged with the obsessive memory of frenzied racial hatreds, little more than blind forces suddenly set in motion, anonymous crowds suddenly seized with delirious convulsions. Thus while the Jewish people was for

Freud a familiar reality which, independently of all value judgments, reassured him by its warmth and its familiarity, on the other side the notion of "the people" had an occult, sinister ring; it was the Sphinx, the absent one, a visitation from the world of irrational darkness, terrifying when it makes its appearance on the scene of history (*From Oedipus to Moses, Freud's Jewish Identity*, trans. R. Manheim, Routledge and Kegan Paul, 1976 [*D'Oedipe a Moïse: Freud et la conscience juive* (Calmann-Lévy, 1974)], pp. 43–4). According to Robert, the referent for Freud's declarations concerning 'the people' or 'the rabble' (indeed 'la masse') is the people of Jewish ghettos from which Freud attempts to distinguish himself by aspiring to another aspect of this culture (the spiritual aspect) to which his family does not gives him access.

7. See 'Postscript' (1927) to 'The Question of Lay-Analysis' (1926), where 'crowd behaviour' is explicitly linked with America and where Freud refers the reader to a work on the crowd by E. Dean Martin, *The Behaviour of Crowds* (1920). See also *Civilization and its Discontents* where, paraphrasing Janet, Freud speaks of 'the psychological poverty of groups' [*das psychologische Elend der Masse*] and refers to America as a particular opportunity to study 'the damage to civilization' that can be done for lack of 'control of the instincts' (SE XXI, pp. 115–16). See J.-M. Rey in 'Freud et l'écriture de l'histoire' (in *L'Écrit du temps* [1984], pp. 23–42), concerning Freud's relation to Jung, whom he accuses of adapting his ideas to the desires of the multitude.
8. That the 'masses' should be allied with what is oldest and comes the earliest is suggested by the odd concluding sentence of Part VI of *The Future*: 'it would be more remarkable still if our wretched, ignorant and downtrodden ancestors [*unseren armen, unwissenden, unfreien Vorvätern*] had succeeded in solving all these difficult riddles of the universe' (SE XXI, p. 33).
9. Lecture XXXIV, SE XXII, p. 138. Note that in *Psychopathology of Everyday Life*, Freud describes the 'collective forgetting of name' as 'ein Phänomen der Massenpsychologie' (pp. 48–50). 'Collective' here refers to the way in which forgetting names can be contagious, but also to the way in which 'whole chains of names' can be withdrawn from memory (SE VI, pp. 40–2).
10. 'Human civilization rests upon two pillars, of which one is the control of natural forces and the other the restriction of our instincts', but we are here leaving aside the 'control of natural force'. See 'Why War', SE XXII, p. 212.
11. SE IX, p. 186.
12. SE XXI, p. 97.
13. SE XXII, p. 73.
14. SE XXI, pp. 8–9.
15. *Ibid.*, p. 117.
16. It remains to be explored just how the mass may be a figure of the uncanny, and refer us back to the uncanny. See Freud's Letter 12 May 1919 to S. Ferenczi in which we learn that, incidentally, Freud worked on the mass at the same time as working on 'The Uncanny': 'J'ai non seulement terminé le projet de l'Au-delà du principe de plaisir . . . mais aussi repris pour vous ce petit rien sur l'inquiétante étrangeté et tenté, au moyen d'une idée simple, de donner une base à la psychologie des foules' [I have not only

finished the project of 'Beyond the pleasure principle' . . . but also taken up again for you this little nothing on the 'Uncanny' and attempted, by mean of a simple idea, to give a psychoanalytic basis to crowd psychology] S. Freud, S. Ferenczi, *Correspondance t. II 1914–19* (Calmann-Lévy, 1966), pp. 391–2.

17. SE XXI, pp. 97, 10.
18. *Ibid.*, p. 136.
19. SE XXII, p. 95. The justification for the interchange of terms can sometimes be perplexing. In Lecture XXIV of the *Introductory Lectures of Psycho-Analysis* (1916–17) Freud indeed calls upon 'euphony' in order to account for the fact that 'he made it hard for [his audience] to understand how many of the technical terms [he] used *meant the same thing*' (p. 378). Concerning the lack of precision of the concept of instinct, See 'An Autobiographical Study' where 'instinct in general is regarded as a kind of elasticity of living things, an impulsion towards the restoration of a situation which once existed but was brought to an end by some external disturbances' (SE XX, p. 57).
20. SE XVIII, p. 70.
21. The concept of identification with that of the ego-ideal soon become the main concerns of the essay. Freud's earlier discussion of the concept of identification however already involves a 'crowd'. See *The Interpretation of Dreams*, where the concept of hysterical identification is defined as the ability 'to suffer on behalf of a whole crowd' (SE IV, p. 149). Does this not come close to the way in which Freud describes the redemption of mankind from the sense of guilt that religion claims to have achieved. 'In Christianity', writes Freud, redemption is achieved 'by the sacrificial death of a single person, who in this manner takes upon himself a guilt that is common to everyone' (*Civilization and its Discontent*, SE XXI, p. 136). The idea of redemption seems to underlie Freud's description of the occasional need to favour illness over health in *Introductory Lectures on Psycho-Analysis* (1916–17): 'It is not his [the physician] business to restrict himself in every situation in life to being a fanatic in favour of health. He knows that there is not only neurotic misery in the world but real, irremovable suffering as well, that necessity may even require a person to sacrifice his health; and he learns that a sacrifice of this kind made by a single person can prevent immeasurable unhappiness for many others' (SE XVI, p. 382).
22. See SE XXI, pp. 136–7.
23. Freud uses the idea of scale in various contexts, including in the analysis of *Kultur*, notably in his conceptualization of thinking 'as a small-scale kind of acting' in the *New Introductory Lectures* (SE XXII, p. 89).
24. Letter to Romain Rolland dated 4 March 1923 in *The Letters of Sigmund Freud*, ed. E. Freud, trans. T. and J. Stern (New York, Toronto, London: McGraw-Hill Book Company, 1960), p. 342.
25. SE XVI, p. 389.
26. SE XX, p. 72.
27. Civilization is in turn compared to 'a people' or a 'stratum of its population' in the same essay: 'Civilization behaves towards sexuality as a people [*ein Volkstamm*] or a stratum of its population [*Schichte der Bevölkerung*] does which has subjected another one to its exploitation' (SE XXI, p. 104).

28. *Ibid.*, p. 144.
29. See Jean-Luc Nancy's discussion of this passage in *Le Sens du monde* (Galilée, 1993), 'Psychanalyse': 'inasmuch as psychoanalysis is in principle placed under the heading of a therapy . . . but inasmuch as, precisely, it does not find anything in the world as a normal and healthy state on which to regulate its procedure, psychoanalysis cannot simply be conceived as a therapy of the world itself, of "everyone" [*de tout le monde*]. This is to what *Mass Psychology* and *Civilization and its Discontents* may appear to respond by an admission of failure' (pp. 77–82) and in 'La panique politique', *Confrontations*, 2 (1979), pp. 33–57.
30. For anthropomorphic descriptions of comparisons, see *New Introductory Lectures*, Lecture XXXI: 'analogies [*Vergleiche*], it is true, decide nothing, but they can make one feel more at home [*daß man sich heimischer fühlt*]' (p. 105). *The Interpretation*, concerning the relation of 'just as' favoured by the dream and the processes of unification, identification and composition [*Mischbildung*]. In particular, the way in which in dreams, 'localities are often treated like persons' (SE IV, p. 320). According to the idea that the object of study mingles with the science devoted to it, we could say that the reasoning by analogy that is the main theoretical tool in the analysis of *Kultur* acquires the characteristics of what it is supposed to explain. The 'larger scale' which might turn out to have more than one name: 'human masses', 'primitive masses', 'crowd', appears to designate a place, including that of theoretical elaboration – where analogical reasoning takes on the features of classical descriptions of the masses as a particular kind of unruly gathering.
31. SE XVII, pp. 167–8.
32. The rejection of hypnosis by psychoanalysis has inspired numerous studies. See for example, Chertok, L. and I. Stengers. *Le Coeur et la raison, L'hypnose en question de Lavoisier à Lacan* (Payot, 1989). See chapter 3 above.
33. SE XXI, p. 118.
34. *Ibid.*, p. 139.
35. *Ibid.*, p. 140.
36. *Ibid.*, p. 122.
37. See Freud's comments on the League of Nations in his exchange with Einstein in 'Why War' (1933 [1932]), p. 207.
38. SE XIII, pp. 157–8.
39. SE XXI, p. 115.
40. 'Psycho-Analysis' (1926), SE XX, pp. 266–7. In 'The Goethe Prize Address' (1930), Freud speaks of 'the construction of a mental science which makes it possible to understand both normal and pathological processes as parts of the same natural course of events' (SE XXI, p. 208). Dreams occupy a special position in that they have the 'greatest external similarity and internal kinship with the creations of insanity' and are also 'compatible with complete health in waking life'. They are '"normal" illusions, delusions and character-changes' (SE XI, pp. 33–4). In 'Five Lectures on Psycho-Analysis' (1910 [1909]): 'The deeper you penetrate into the pathogenesis of nervous illness, the more you will find revealed the connection between the neuroses and other productions of the human mind, including the most valuable' (p. 49). 'The neuroses have no psychical content that is peculiar to

them and that might not equally be found in healthy people' (p. 50). Or else, as Jung has expressed it, 'neurotics fall ill of the same complexes against which we healthy people struggle as well. Whether that struggle ends in health or in neurosis, or in a countervailing superiority of achievement, depends on *quantitative* considerations, on the relative strength of the conflicting forces' (p. 50). See Freud's discussion of the critics of the concept of the unconscious who prefer to conceive of it in terms of 'a great variety of gradations of intensity or clarity'. The processes that we experience which are only 'faintly, hardly even noticeably conscious' are according to the investigators that Freud has in mind, 'the ones to which psychoanalysis wishes to apply the unsuitable name "unconscious"'. The idea of 'gradations of clarity' that Freud rejects in his critics is otherwise at issue in dream-interpretation. The intensity (which is equivalent in the following passage with clarity) of certain elements of the dream shows that they are those on which 'the greatest amount of condensation has been expended' (SE IV, p. 330), since 'in the process of condensation . . . every psychical interconnection is transformed into an *intensification* of its ideational content' (SE V, p. 595). The clarity or indistinctness of dreams may also be 'part of the material which instigated the dream', according to the principle that the '*form of a dream or the form in which it is dreamt is used with quite surprising frequency for representing its concealed subject-matter*' (Freud's emphasis, SE IV, p. 332).

41. SE XII, p. 210; 'Types of Onset of Neurosis' (1912), p. 237; Lecture XXXIV, *New Introductory Lectures*, SE XXII, p. 145. See 'An Outline of Psycho-Analysis' where Freud speaks of the 'hubbub of illness' SE XXXIII, p. 202.
42. SE XVI, p. 456. In 'Delusions and Dreams in Jensen's *Gradiva*' (1907 [1906]), however, Freud writes that 'the frontier between states of mind described as normal and pathological is in part a conventional one and in part so fluctuating that each of us probably crosses it many times during the course of a day' (SE IX, p. 44).
43. *Ibid.*, p. 457. This takes up again what *The Interpretation* had already explicitly stated: 'psycho-analytic research finds no fundamental, but only quantitative, distinction between normal and neurotic life; and indeed the analysis of dreams, in which repressed complexes are operative alike in the healthy and the sick, shows a complete identity both in their mechanisms and in their symbolism' (SE V, pp. 373–4).
44. SE XXII, pp. 121, 59. See *The Interpretation*: 'It is not my belief, however, that psycho-neurotics differ sharply in this respect from other human beings who remain normal – that they are able, that is, to create something absolutely new and peculiar to themselves. It is far more probable . . . that they are only distinguished by exhibiting on a magnified scale feelings of love and hatred to their parents which occur less obviously and less intensely in the minds of most children' (SE IV, p. 261). It would be wrong however for psychiatry to limit itself 'to the study of the severe and gloomy illnesses that arise from *gross injuries* to the *delicate* apparatus of the mind. Deviations from health which are slighter and capable of correction, and which to-day we can trace back no further than to disturbances in the interplay of mental forces, arouse its interest no less' (SE IX, p. 44, my emphasis). The latter seems to correspond to a *juste milieu* on the basis of which

to understand 'normal' states as well as 'severe' illness, that act as counterpart to each other. Could what Freud calls *disturbances* not in fact describe 'the interplay of mental forces' itself? Hence, it is 'only through the medium of these' that any understanding of the delicate apparatus can be obtained (*ibid.*). In what this strata, level or *locality* consist is the question that we raise at the end of this chapter. The essay in fact abounds in statements about normal and pathological states which each present slightly modified versions of the psychoanalytic procedure. After having found a 'complete agreement' between the findings of Gradiva and those of psychoanalysis, Freud concedes of differences (p. 90), notably as far as the method for arriving at them is concerned: 'Our procedure consists in the conscious observation of abnormal mental processes in other people so as to be able to elicit and announce their laws.' Departing from its initial moments, psychoanalysis is here based on the observation of 'other people' as opposed to Gradiva who directs his attention 'to the unconscious of his own' (p. 92). Just how 'normal' or 'healthy' behaviour is described on the basis of the observation of disorders is indicated in 'The Loss of Reality in Neurosis and Psychosis' (1924) where a 'normal' behaviour is one that 'combines certain features of both reactions towards reality that characterize these two forms of mental disorder. Namely, it is "normal" if it disavows the reality as little as does a neurosis, but if it then exerts itself, as does a psychosis, to effect an alteration of that reality' with the only difference that the alteration is made to the external and not solely to the internal world. The description of action in the external world is thus based on the second step of psychosis, that has the nature of reparation and that consists in 'creating a new reality' (SE XIX, p. 185). 'In psychosis, the transforming of reality is carried out upon the psychical precipitates of former relations to it – that is, upon the memory-traces, ideas and judgements which have been previously derived from reality and by which reality was represented in the mind' (*ibid.*).

45. SE XIV, p. 82. In 'The Aetiology of Hysteria' (1896), however, the potential rejection of the therapeutic procedure Freud has been describing in the essay is brought into the field of histology. It is not pathological processes that 'enlarge' but the procedure: 'This procedure is new and difficult to handle, but it is nevertheless irreplaceable for scientific and therapeutic purposes . . . one cannot properly deny the findings which follow from this modification of Breuer's procedure so long as one puts aside and uses only the customary method of questioning patients. To do so would be like trying to refute the findings of histological technique by relying upon macroscopic examination' (SE III, p. 220). See the comparison of the apparatus with 'the microscope and the telescope' in *The Interpretation of Dreams*, SE IV, p. 536 and 'An Outline', p. 197.
46. SE VII, p. 290. See 'The Future Prospects of Psycho-Analytic Therapy' (1910) for an allusion to how, so long as the hallucinations of the Virgin Mary 'brought a flock of believers', 'the visionary state of the girls [who were subject to these hallucinations] was inaccessible to influence' (SE XI, p. 149).
47. On the association of the crowd with disease, see S. Barrows, *Distorting mirrors Visions of the Crowd in Late Nineteenth Century France* (Yale University Press, 1981). In 'The Neuro-Psychoses of Defence' (1894), Freud speaks

of a 'psychosis through simple intensification' of an *Überwältigungspsychose*, 'a psychosis of overwhelming' (SE III, p. 55).

48. SE XVIII, p. 69.
49. SE XIV, p. 94.
50. *Ibid.*, p. 95.
51. *Ibid.*, p. 96.
52. SE XVIII, p. 129.
53. 'Size' is related to the 'higher' sides of the human. See note 93 below.
54. SE XVIII, p. 131.
55. SE XIV, p. 169.
56. This condensation allows one to mitigate the idea of progress. In a letter to Richard Dyer-Bennett dated 9 December 1928, Freud reproaches to his addressee his idea of progress. He suggests that apart from an 'a very limited elite', 'all the old cultural levels – those of the Middle Ages, of the Stone Age, even of animistic prehistory – are still alive in the great human masses', *The Letters of Sigmund Freud*, ed. Ernst L. Freud, trans. T. and J. Stern, (New-York: Basic Books, 1960), p. 384.
57. See 'Education' in Part III of 'The Project'.
58. *The Interpretation*, SE IV, p. 268 n. 1. In the last paragraph of *Jokes and their Relation to the Unconscious* (1905), the mechanics of humorous, comic pleasure and of jokes are referred to the economy of expenditure, or to the recovery of mental expenditure in the following manner: 'The euphoria that we endeavour to reach by these modes [humour, comic and jokes] is nothing other that the mood of a period of life in which we were accustomed to deal with our psychical work in general with a small expenditure of energy – the mood of our childhood, when we were ignorant of the comic, when we were incapable of jokes and when we had no need of humour to make us feel happy in our life' (SE XVIII, p. 236). In the association of childhood with 'smallness' we seem to be dealing with what Freud calls in the same work 'ideational mimetics [*Vorstellungsmimik*]' whereby the size (of movement – Freud takes the example of the perception of movement) is correlated to the large or small amount of expenditure necessary for producing the idea corresponding to the perception of the movement (SE VIII, pp. 192–3). Pleasure coincides with the economy of a *large* amount of mental expenditure.
59. *The Ego and the Id* (SE XIX, p. 35). Psychoanalysis proposes the 'transvaluation of all psychical values' by disturbing the equation whereby the 'higher mental function . . . will find access to consciousness assured to it' and by demonstrating that 'difficult intellectual operations . . . can be carried out preconsciously and without coming into consciousness' and more strangely by suggesting that, 'conscience [*Gewissen*] can be "unconscious"'. Freud speaks of the 'transvaluation of all psychical value' in the context of a discussion of psychical intensity in dreams (SE IV, p. 330). Elsewhere the 'scale of value' has a moral sense: 'If we come back to our scale of values, we shall have to say that not only what is lowest but also what is highest in the ego can be unconscious' (SE XIX, p. 27).
60. *Ibid.*, pp. 36–7.
61. The question of observation is at issue in C. Borck's article on 'The Rhetoric of Freud's Illustration' in *Freud and the Neuro-Sciences, From Brain Research*

to the Unconscious, ed. G. Guttmann and I. Scholz-Strasser (Verlag der Österreichischen Akademie der Wissenschaften, 1998). Borck demonstrates among other things, 1) that there is a continuity between the illustrations that Freud did as a medical student and researcher and those that he did in the metapsychological essays; 2) that what preoccupies Freud is above all the insufficiency of any visual representation. Yet we may wonder why the representation of the 'libidinal constitution of a crowd' in *Mass psychology* is not included among the illustrations that Borck discusses. Borck's study raises the question as to what distinguishes the *Bildersprache*, the verbal auxiliary constructions from the visual ones. Is the one means more apt to provide 'representations' than the other?

62. The first pages of 'The Work of Condensation' are eloquent in this respect, but we could say, more generally, that the impossibility of measurement is one of the most persistent problems of *The Interpretation* (SE IV, p. 279).
63. *Ibid.*, p. 38. 'It is here that the gulf between an actual individual and the concept of a species becomes evident' (p. 38).
64. *Ibid.*
65. *Ibid.*, p. 58.
66. SE XXI, p. 208. See *The Interpretation*, the idea that 'the interpretation of dreams is like a window through which we can get a glimpse of the interior of that apparatus' (SE IV, p. 219) and the 'All of them [dreams] are completely egoistic: the beloved ego appears in all of them, even though it may be disguised' (SE IV, p. 267). What sort of grouping does the *Witz*, as the 'social manifestation' of the unconscious depends upon? In *Mass Psychology*, it is the ego rather than the 'psychical apparatus' that is at issue. What is at stake is the passage from the first topography to the second, that is, from a mechanistic to an anthropomorphic model of the psyche. Is the functioning of the mental apparatus to be relegated to the mechanistic side of Freud's work or is the knowledge that psychoanalysis seeks to gain not based on the unique 'instrument' that is yet not easily reconcilable with the idea of an ego, a subject, or even of a 'mass'?
67. SE XX, p. 254.
68. Let us imagine what kind of work *The Interpretation* would constitute if it comprised only the review of the existing literature of dreams. As far as observation is concerned, the topic of the mass fits in, within Freud's work, among the other topics of inquiry that are not studied by means of direct observation or regular therapeutic contact. *Mass Psychology* therefore goes together with, for example, Freud's work on Woodrow Wilson, on President Schreber, on Leonardo. See P. Lacoste, 'L'observation. Freud et la scénographie clinique', *Revue Internationale de philosophie*, 'Freud 1939–1989', (4/1989 no. 171), pp. 480–505.
69. This raises the classical question prevalent in the discourses on the crowd as to whether the crowd is capable or not of 'elevated' acts. The existing literature on dreams partly believes that dream-life provides a release from 'the dictates of morality'. See chapter 3 above, and chapter II 'The Morality of Crowds' in Gustave Le Bon, *The Crowd. A Study of the Popular Mind* (London: Ernst Benn Limited [19th edn], 1947), pp. 56–9. The main points of this section pertain to the way in which the 'moral standard of crowd is very low' because the crowd gives impunity to the individual, who would not otherwise 'gratify his instincts' (pp. 56–7).

70. SE XVIII p. 72. Freud's definition of an individual as a 'psychical id' is not made to simplify matters.
71. *Ibid.*, p. 73.
72. This interrogative can be drawn together with Part II of *The Ego and the Id*, where Freud speaks of 'a quantitative and qualitative something' (SE XIX p. 22).
73. *New Introductory Lectures*, SE XXII, p. 67; SE XVIII, p. 116. 'Many equals, who can identify themselves with one another, and a single person superior to them all – that is the situation that we find realized in groups which are capable of subsisting [*in der lebensfähigen Masse*].'
74. SE XVIII, pp. 91, 101. The formula is found again in *The Ego in the Id*: 'Social feelings rest on identifications with other people, on the basis of having the same ego ideal' (SE XIX, p. 37).
75. See 'Psycho-analysis and the Establishment of the Facts in Legal Proceedings' (1906), SE IX, p. 110, where Freud speaks of the 'indirect representation' in which word associations consist. In another register, we could paraphrase what Michel Schneider says about thought in Freud. Instead of speaking of psychoanalysis as 'pensée du non-pensé, et peut-être de l'impensable' we could say 'thought of the non-perceived, perhaps of the non-perceivable'. 'A quoi penses-tu?', *Nouvelle revue française de psychanalyse* 'Le trouble de penser', no 25 (1982), p. 11.
76. In the appendix to 'The Neuro-Psychoses of Defence' on Freud's fundamental hypothesis, the editor writes: 'The fact was, no doubt, that the formulations and hypotheses which Freud put forward in neurological terms had actually been constructed with more than half an eye to psychological events; and when the time came for dropping the neurology it turned out that the greater part of the theoretical material could be understood as applying, indeed applying more cogently, to purely mental phenomena' (SE III, p. 64).
77. Lecture XXXI, SE XXII, p. 70.
78. 'Five Lectures on Psycho-Analysis', (1910 [1909]), SE XI, p. 39.
79. 'The Question of Lay-Analysis', SE XX, p. 188.
80. *The Future of an Illusion*, SE XXI, p. 31.
81. *Ibid.*, p. 53.
82. See J.-B. Pontalis, 'L'Illusion maintenue', in 'Effets et formes de l'illusion', *Nouvelle revue française de psychanalyse*, no 4 (1971), pp. 3–11.
83. *The Future*, p. 21. See too 'Obsessive Actions and Religious Practices' (1907) SE IX, pp. 126–7.
84. SE XXII, p. 175.
85. 'Leonardo da Vinci and a Memory of his Childhood', SE XI, p. 123.
86. SE XXII, p. 161.
87. *The Future*, p. 17.
88. 'Leonardo', p. 123. The modelling of God on fathers is a matter of what we called 'scale' too: 'The common man cannot imagine this Providence otherwise than in the figure of *an enormously exalted Father* [*eines großartig erhörten Vater*]' [my emphasis], *The Future*, p. 74.
89. SE XXII, p. 206. See *The Future*, p. 37. See 'On Repression' for the idea of 'techniques'.
90. See 'Types of Onset of Neurosis' (1912), SE XII. Freud speaks of the subject breaking down 'from his inflexibility' in front of the demands of reality in

the second type of precipitating cause of falling ill, given that the problem lies in a developmental process (p. 233). Illness depends upon the libido 'resisting displacement' (p. 234), on the latter's 'pathogenic fixations'. See 'Conclusion' below.

91. See *The Language of Psychoanalysis*, which draws out the apparent tension between 'an approach which appeals otherwise to an absolute determinism' and the term 'choice' [*Wahl*] which suggests that 'an act on the subject's part is required if the various historical and constitutional determinants which psychoanalysis brings out are to become meaningful and attain the force of motivating factors' (p. 69).
92. 'Dostoevsky and the Parricide', SE XXI, p. 179. Concerning science and art: 'at present we can only say figuratively that such satisfactions are [*bildweise*] "finer and higher" [*feiner und höher*]' (*ibid.*).
93. SE XXI, pp. 85–7.
94. *Ibid.*, p. 81. In 'Five Lectures on Psycho-Analysis', 'to-day neurosis' is said to take 'the place of the monasteries which used to be the refuge of all whom life had disappointed or who felt too weak to face it' (SE XI, p. 50). One finds an early version of 'mass-psychology' in Draft H of the Fliess Paper about paranoia as regards the Franco–Prussian War of 1870: 'The "*grande nation*" cannot face the idea that it can be defeated in war. *Ergo* it was not defeated; the victory does not count. It provides an example of mass paranoia and invents the delusion of betrayal' (SE I, p. 210). See 'Some Points for a Comparative Study of Organic and Hysterical Motor Paralyses', SE I for what the editor deems to be one of the earliest 'applications'. It should have become clear that there is more than one 'first' application of psychoanalysis.
95. SE XXI, p. 84.
96. 'Leonardo', p. 123.
97. *The Future*, p. 44.
98. (Lettre de Freud à Laforgue, 5–02–1928) in *Nouvelle Revue française de psychanalyse*, no 15 (1977), p. 292.
99. *The Future*, p. 53.
100. *Ibid.*, p. 39. As the *New Introductory Lectures* reiterates: 'Our best hope for the future is that intellect – the scientific spirit, reason – may in process of time establish a dictatorship in the mental life of man [*die Diktatur im menschlichen Seelenleben einzuräumen*]' (SE XXII, p. 171).
101. *Ibid.*, pp. 52, 54.
102. *Ibid.*, p. 55.
103. See the 'A Difficulty in the Path of Psychoanalysis' (1917) and 'The Resistances to Psycho-analysis,' SE XIX, p. 221.
104. 'Instincts and their Vicissitudes' (1915), SE XIV, p. 117.
105. See P.-L. Assoun, *Introduction à l'épistémologie freudienne* (Payot, 1981), p. 147. See the whole of Chapter III 'De la dynamique à l'économique. Le modèle Fechnero-Helmholtzien', pp. 145–87.
106. Yet, consider Freud's scornful attitude towards the provisional nature of religious truths. Lecture XXXV, pp. 172–3.
107. 'The Resistances to Psycho-Analysis' (1925 [1924]), SE XIX, p. 216.
108. Concerning the artistic gift, everyone knows that 'it is a psychological mystery' to psychoanalysis (SE XI, p. 50). In his preface to Theodor Reik's

'Das Ritual', Freud says that psychoanalysis was brought into contact with the lives 'not only of the sick, but of the healthy, the normal and the super-normal [*Übernormal*],' referring no doubt to artists (SE XVIII, p. 259).

5 Figurative Language According to Freud

1. 'On Narcissism' formulates a very similar epistemological pronouncement: A science based on 'empirical observation', Freud contends, 'will not envy speculation its privilege of having a smooth, logically unassailable foundation, but will gladly content itself with nebulous, scarcely imaginable basic concepts which it hopes to apprehend more clearly in the course of its development, or which it is even prepared to replace by others. For these ideas are not the foundation of science, upon which everything rests: that foundation is observation alone. They are not the bottom but the top of the whole structure, and they can be replaced and discarded without damaging it' (SE XIV p. 77). See *New Introductory Lectures on Psycho-Analysis* (1933 [1932]), Lecture XXXII on 'Anxiety and Instinctual Life', where it is the experimental activity of the ego that is at issue. The latter 'makes use of an experimental cathexis and starts up the pleasure–unpleasure automatism by means of a signal of anxiety. After that several reactions are possible or a combination of them in varying proportion . . .' (SE XXII, p. 90). It is worth mentioning some of the numerous models that are scattered throughout Freud. For example, in Lecture XXXII, birth is said to be the model [*Vorbild*] of an anxiety state (p. 93) and later in the same essay, defaecation 'the model of the act of birth' (p. 100). Also, 'in sadism and in masochism', Freud writes, 'we have before us two excellent examples of a mixture of the two classes of instinct, of Eros and aggressiveness, and we proceed to the hypothesis that this relation is a model one . . .' (pp. 104–5), or in *The Ego and the Id* (1923): 'Pain, too, seems to play a part in the process, and the way in which we gain new knowledge of our organs during painful illnesses is perhaps a model of the way by which in general we arrive at the idea of our body' (SE XIX, p. 26).
2. SE XIV, p. 117. Paul-Laurent Assoun claims that 'all the essential propositions which constitute Freudian methodological capital are found in this text', in *Introduction à l'épistémologie freudienne* (Payot, 1981), p. 74.
3. SE XXIII, p. 159.
4. There are numerous well-known pronouncements throughout Freud concerning the way in which philosophers like Schopenhauer conceived of the unconscious before psychoanalysis, not to mention those referring, by paralipsis, to Nietzsche. See P.-L. Assoun's classical study *Freud, la philosophie et les philosophes* (Presses universitaires de France, 1976). Assoun argues that Freud develops two parallel discourses on philosophy (in a nutshell, one of rejection and one of sanction), the conflictual relations of which alone can tell us something about Freud's attitude towards philosophy. See also, P. Herzog, 'The Myth of Freud as an Anti-philosopher', in *Freud: Appraisals and Reappraisals*, ed. P. E. Stepansky (The Analytic Press, 1988); S. Kofman, 'Freud et Empédocle', in *Quatre romans analytiques* (Galilée, 1973), pp. 46–66. That any philosophical consideration of psychoanalysis should

engage the question of Freud's use of models and concepts borrowed from other sciences clearly emerges in E. Escoubas, '"La Fatale différence" Ontologie fondamentale et archéologie de la psyche: Heidegger et Freud', in *Figures de la subjectivité* (Éditions du CNRS, 1992), pp. 147–64, notably as far as the understanding of Freud's naturalism by Heidegger is concerned.

5. For a discussion of the concept of analysis in Freud with respect to the analogy of chemistry, see A. Rey de Castro, 'La Notion d'analyse dans la psychanalyse: chimie d'un oubli', in *La Notion d'analyse*, ed. G. Granel and E. Rigal (Toulouse: Presses universitaires du Mirail, 1992), pp. 229–48.
6. See *Civilization*: 'auxiliary organs [*Hilfsorgane*]' (SE XXI, p. 92) and 'auxiliary constructions' [*Hilfskonstruktionen*] (*ibid.*, p. 75).
7. See 'Why War' (1933 [1932]): 'It may perhaps seem to you as though our theories are a kind of mythology and, in the present case, not even an agreeable one. But does not every science come in the end to a kind of mythology like this? Cannot the same be said to-day of your own Physics?' (SE XXII, p. 211).
8. 'A Difficulty in the Path of Psycho-Analysis' (1917), SE XVII, p. 137. For a recent rejection of such therapeutic claims, see M. Borch-Jacobsen's *Remembering Anna O., A Century of Mystification [Souvenirs d'Anna O.]* (1995) trans. K. Olson, X. Callahan and the author (New-York and London: Routledge, 1996). Borch-Jacobsen seems to have maintained only the terms, if one dare say so, of his sophisticated analysis of the ·'mythical status' of psychoanalysis developed in the last part of *Le Sujet freudien* (Flammarion, 1982). Myth in *Remembering* has indeed become a term of abuse, in so far as it points to the fact that psychoanalysis has, from the start, and thanks to various 'dissimulations', developed as a 'delusive therapeutic technique'. One of the most important dissimulations would be the influence of hypnosis on Freud and Breuer's hysterical patients. This 'influence' is demonstrated with reference to a general, public interest in spectacles involving hypnosis, with which the hysterics *cannot not* have become acquainted. Space and incentive are lacking here for entering into a debate upon the arguments developed in this book. Let us simply note that the latter appears to be largely determined by contemporary debates in America designated under the heading of the 'False Memory Syndrome'. One senses in it an intense fascination with the guarded and secretive nature of Freud's (and the psychoanalytic movement) archives, a fascination that is apparent in the way in which, when finally obtained, the means for gaining access to 'incriminating' documents, are described with the greatest amount of details.
9. In the same chapter, Freud prefaces the exposition of the spatial representation of the psychical apparatus with the following statement: '[w]e are justified, in my view, in giving free rein to our speculations [*Vermutungen*] so long as we retain the coolness of our judgement and do not mistake the scaffolding for the building [*das Gerüste nicht für den Bau halten*]. And since at our first approach to something unknown [*Unbekanntes*] all that we need is the assistance of *provisional ideas* [*Hilfsvorstellungen*], I shall give preferences in the first instance to hypotheses of the crudest and most concrete description [*die rohesten und greifbarsten Annahmen*]' (p. 685). Freud begins by comparing the 'instrument which carries out our mental functions as

resembling a compound microscope or a photographic apparatus or something of the kind' (p. 684). He inserts a justificatory comment about the use of analogies: 'Analogies [*Gleichnisse*] of this kind are only intended to assist us in our attempt to make the complications of mental functioning intelligible by dissecting the function and assigning its different component constituents to different parts of the apparatus' (p. 685).

10. SE V, p. 538. J. Laplanche and J. B. Pontalis, *The Language of Psychoanalysis* (1967) trans. D. Nicholson-Smith (The Hogarth Press and the Institute of Psychoanalysis, 1973) p. 358. In Chapter VII of *The Interpretation of Dreams*, more particularly in the section devoted to 'Wish-Fulfilment', the reflex apparatus represents an 'earlier stage' of the psychical apparatus: 'at first the apparatus efforts were directed towards keeping itself so far as possible free from stimuli' (p. 719). This description of the psychical apparatus is, later in the same chapter, referred to as 'the fiction of a primitive psychical apparatus [*die Fiktion eines primitiven psychischen Apparats*] (p. 757).
11. M. Hesse, *Models and Analogies in Science* (Notre-Dame University Press, 1966), p. 130.
12. 'An Outline of Psychoanalysis' (SE XXIII, p. 395)
13. These 'analogies' are found in *The Interpretation*, as far as 'language' is concerned, see in particular 'The Means of Representation', p. 430 note 1 on K. Abel's *The Antithetical Meaning of Primal Words* (1884) and Freud's review of this book entitled 'The Antithetical Meaning of Primal Words' (1910). The work of language could be considered as a source of borrowing. The way in which dreams 'treat the category of contraries [*Gegensatz*] and contradictories [*Widerspruch*] is highly remarkable', writes Freud, '[t]hey show a particular preference for combining contraries into a unity and for representing them as one and the same thing. Dreams feel themselves at liberty, moreover, to represent any element by its wishful contrary; so that there is no way of deciding at a first glance whether any element that admits of a contrary is present in the dream-thoughts as a positive or a negative' (p. 430). It is with respect to the treatment of 'contraries and contradictories' that Freud refers to Abel: according to this philologist and others too, '*the most ancient languages behave exactly like dreams [die ältesten Sprachen sich in diesem Punkte ganz ähnlich benehmen wie der Traum]*' [my emphasis] (p. 430). See J. Forrester, *Language and the Origins of Psychoanalysis* (Macmillan, 1980).
14. See J. Laplanche, *Nouveaux fondements pour la psychanalyse* (Presses universitaires de France, 1987).
15. Freud, *Collected Papers*, ed. E. Jones, Vol. IV (Basic Books, 1959), p. 7.
16. SE IV, p. 100. In 'My Contact with Josef Popper-Lynkeus' (1932), Freud writes: 'by applying to [my patient's] dreams, and more particularly to my own dreams, the procedure which I had already used for the study of other abnormal psychological structures, I succeeded in answering most of the questions which could be raised by an interpretation of dreams' (SE XXII, p. 220). In chapter VII of *The Interpretation*: '[i]n view of the complete identity [*der vollen Identität*] between the characteristic features of the dream-work and those of the psychical activity which issues in psychoneurotic symptoms, we feel justified in carrying over [*übertragen*] to dreams the

conclusions we have been led to by hysteria. Consequently we borrow [*entnehmen*] the following thesis from hysteria' (p. 756).

17. For a useful discussion of the concept of *Kultur* in Freud (in particular as far as the genealogy of the terms *Kultur* and *Civilization* is concerned), see Assoun, chapter 10 'La Kultur et son malaise', in *Freud et les sciences sociales. Pychanalyse et théorie de la Culture* (Armand-Colin, 1993), pp. 119–33. See too H. and M. Vermorel, 'De *l'Avenir d'une illusion au Malaise dans la culture*', *Revue française de psychanalyse*, IV (1993), pp. 1095–111, and J. Le Rider, M. Plon, G. Raulet and H. Rey-Flaud, *Autour du Malaise dans la culture de Freud* (Presses universitaires de France, 1998). For a broader discussion of the distinction, see J. Starobinski, 'Le Mot civilisation', in *Le Remède dans le mal, Critique et légitimation de l'artifice à l'âge des Lumières* (Gallimard, 1989), pp. 11–59.
18. SE XX, p. 72.
19. SE IX, p. 117.
20. SE IX, p. 38.
21. In *De l'Interprétation. Essai sur Freud,* Paul Ricoeur writes: 'the whole of the Freudian theory of culture can be considered as a merely analogical transposition of the economic explanation of the dream and of neurosis' [my translation] (Seuil, 1965), p. 76. This implies that the Freudian theory of *Kultur* begins beyond the analogical moment, whereas on our reading, it lingers on the complications that it generates.
22. Let us recall once again what Freud says concerning the hypothesis of phylogenesis in *The Ego and the Id* (1923): 'the attempt must be made – in spite of a fear that it will lay bare the inadequacy of our whole effort' (SE XIX, p. 38).
23. In *Freud and the Legacy of Moses* (Cambridge University Press, 1998), Jay Bernstein carries out a 'close reading' of *Moses,* in order to show that one must take particularly seriously the subtleties of Freud's arguments, including the 'analogical transposition'. According to this author, in spite of the 'strange' character of the book (p. 2), *Moses* is a sustained attempt on Freud's part to reflect upon the concept of religious tradition and to deal with the questions concerning the 'essential nature of being a Jew', which he himself raises. Bernstein is responding to recent discussions of Freud's last book by Jewish historians such as J. Yerushalmi (*Freud's Moses: Judaism Terminable and Interminable* [Yale University Press, 1991]), following Jacques Derrida who first took issue with this historian in *Mal d'archives* (Galilée, 1995). For Yerushalmi and other commentators, *Moses* provides an opportunity to pick out Freud's reliance on discredited Lamarckian beliefs. It is against what Bernstein considers ill-founded criticisms, that the call for a 'close' reading of Freud's text is made. We agree on many points with Bernstein's analysis, notably with the way in which he gives the analogical transposition, even if perhaps a little too rigidly, a temporal dimension (p. 71). One of the claims of the present study, however, is that the fundamental uncertainties which the analogical reasoning carried out in the essays on *Kultur* brings about, extend well beyond the later essays and themes, throughout the whole of Freud's writings, including those which are manifestly not concerned with the 'application' of psychoanalysis or with the understanding of 'mass psychology'. As far as the issue of Freud's Lamarckism is

concerned, see L. B. Ritvo's reference work: *Darwin's Influence on Freud* (Yale University Press, 1990).

24. See among others M. Moscovici, 'Préface' to *L'Homme Moïse et le monothéisme, trois essais* trans. C. Heim (Gallimard, 1986), pp. 15–59; M. de Certeau, 'L'Écriture de *Moïse et le monothéisme*', in *L'Écriture de l'histoire* (Gallimard, 1975); J.-J. Goux, 'Moïse, Freud, la prescription iconoclaste' and 'Freud et la structure religieuse du nazisme' in *Les Iconoclastes* (Seuil, 1978); L. Poliakov, 'Freud et Moïse' (1968) in *Les Juifs et notre histoire* (Flammarion, 1973), pp. 227–47. J. Assman, *Moses the Egyptian: The Memory of Egypt in Western Monotheism* (Cambridge, MA. Harvard University Press, 1997).
25. Letter dated 30 September 1934. S. Freud and A. Zweig, *Correspondance 1927–39* (1968), trans. L. Weibel and J.-C. Gehrig (Gallimard, 1973), p. 129. See too Freud's detailed letter about his 'historical novel of sort' to Lou Andreas-Salomé, dated 6 January 1935, *Sigmund Freud and Lou Andreas Salomé – Letters [Sigmund Freud-Lou Andreas-Salomé Briefwechsel*], ed. E. Pfeiffer, trans. W. and E. Robson-Scott (The Hogarth Press and the Institute of Psychoanalysis, 1963), where he recalls: 'The strength of religion lies not in its *material*, but in its *historical* truth' (p. 205).
26. In the first essay of *Moses*, Freud compares the distortion [*Entstellung*] of a text to 'a murder', but the essay indeed crucially pertains to 'a murder' (p. 115). On *Entstellung* and *Moses*, see J.-F. Lyotard, 'Le Travail du rêve ne pense pas', in *Discours, figure* (Klincksieck, 1978), pp. 241–3.
27. The Standard Edition says: 'people in the mass'.
28. It would be possible to underline the fact that Freud uses 'human masses' descriptively in an essay written on the eve of exile in 1938–39, whereas the presupposition of a *Massenpsyche* occurs in an essay written more or less in safety in 1912–13, long before Freud was forced to leave Vienna. See Henri Ellenberger's historicist description of *Mass Psychology* in *The Discovery of the Unconscious. The History and Evolution of Dynamic Psychiatry* (Basic Books, 1970): '*Group Psychology and the Analysis of the Ego* obviously was inspired by the collapse of the Hapsburg Empire at the end of 1918, with the panic and distress that followed' (p. 528) and a similar approach in J. van Ginneken, 'The Killing of the Father: The Background of Freud's Group Psychology', *Political Psychology*, 5, 3 (1984), pp. 391–414.
29. SE XVIII, p. 70.
30. See 'Why War' (1933 [1932]) where 'conflict of opinion' represents a higher level of abstraction and therefore a step higher in the process of *Kultur* than conflict settled with muscular strength (SE XXII, p. 204)
31. See P. Lacoste, 'Destins de la transmission', in S. Freud, *Vue d'ensemble sur les névroses de transfert, Un essai métapsychologique* (1915), trans. P. Lacoste (Gallimard, 1986), pp. 165–210. We cannot here embark upon a close examination of Freud's twelfth metapsychological essay, that is, consider Freud's ambitious project of establishing a 'parallèle entre la succession des névroses selon leur ordre d'apparition et l'historique des générations' (p. 169) and compare it with the other 'analogical' transpositions with which we have been concerned so far (Lacoste speaks of homology). This would involve examining the way in which, as Lacoste indicates, the phylogenetic point of view always threatens to be assimilated to the theory of hereditary etiology (p. 170).

32. If *Kontaktstellen* had its 'opposite' and formed a 'pair of opposites' [*Gegensatzpaar*], it would be with what we are calling here 'points of heterogeneity'. See Laplanche and Pontalis, *The Language of Psychoanalysis* (*op. cit.*): 'the idea of the pair of opposites is part of a permanent and essential element in Freud's thinking – namely, the basic dualism which provides the ultimate explanation of psychical conflict' (p. 295).
33. That 'völlig kongruente Analogie' should quickly lose their character of 'completeness' might be referred to Freud's explanation of 'Cognition and Reproductive Thought' in the 'Project for a Scientific Psychology', as we saw as the end of chapter 2.
34. See the end of 'The Primal Band', in *The Freudian Subject* (*op. cit.*) where the opposition between individual and mass psychology is presented in terms of 'the familiar quarrel: psychoanalysis contesting its own prehistory' (p. 147). Such an interpretation on Freud's unease with everything that has to do with hypnosis and suggestion partly implies that the 'truth' of psychoanalysis has to be sought for in its *prehistory*, a claim that seems inspired by Freudian hypotheses around the *Urgeschichte* of either the individual or the mass. This said, it is possible to find in *Moses* explicit references to the rival approaches to problems of *Massenpsychologie* (notably to Jung and to the notion of 'collective unconscious'), but we are not here attempting to draw out, from the point of view of the history of the psychoanalytic movement, Freud's various rivalries. To diagnose Freud's notorious rivalrous 'tendencies' towards his disciples, other sciences or other thoughts, does not add, it seems to us, anything to our understanding of these problems.
35. For the complaint that the essays on *Kultur* have been misread, See A. Green, 'Culture(s) et civilisation(s), malaise ou maladie?' *Revue française de psychanalyse*, 4 (1993), pp. 1029–56. Green argues with others, for a 'historical' reading of them that makes them dialogue with contemporary events and intellectual movements of ideas.
36. Let us recall that when Freud speaks, at the beginning of '*Beyond the Pleasure Principle*', of the 'least rigid hypothesis' concerning the sensation of unpleasure and of pleasure, whereby unpleasure corresponds to an *increase* and pleasure to a *diminution*, he specifies that, 'the factor that determines the feeling is probably the amount of increase or diminution in the quantity of excitation *in a given time*' (SE XVIII, p. 8). The examination of the demarcation between mass and individual psychology, when brought back to a question of quantity, calls for an examination of 'time' and 'temporality' throughout the metapsychological essays. The apparently extrinsic topic of the 'mass', thus turns out to lead us straight into some of the most difficult but crucial aspects of Freudian thought, that of temporality, that cannot be studied only on the basis of the concept of 'deferred action' [*Nachträglichkeit*].
37. The distinction between the two deserves more attention: 'the traumas are either experiences on the subject's own body or sense perceptions, mostly of something seen and heard – that is experiences and impressions' (SE XXIII, pp. 162–3).
38. What complicates the exposition is not only that Freud calls upon, in the manner of 'An Outline of Psycho-Analysis' (1940 [1938]), most of the fundamental concepts of psychoanalysis, but that their explanation depends

upon a set of evolutionist ideas (p. 81) which constitutes the most controversial aspect, for Freud himself, of the earlier expositions of these concepts. This is the case here with the theory of sexuality, which, Freud claims, is 'confirmed by the anatomical investigation of the growth of the internal genitalia; it leads us to suppose that the human race is descended from a species of animal which reached maturity in five years and rouses a suspicion that the postponement of sexual life and its diphasic onset are intimately connected with the history of hominization' (p. 75). See Lacoste, 'Destins de la transmission' (*op. cit.*). Elsewhere, and apparently in another register, Freud writes in 'The Unconscious' (1915): 'the content of the *Ucs* may be compared [*vergleichen*] with an aboriginal population in the mind [*Urbevölkerung*]. If inherited mental formations exist in the human being – something analogous to instinct in animals *[etwas dem Instinkt der Tiere Analoges gibt*], these constitute the nucleus of the *Ucs*.' (SE XIV, p. 195).

39. See more particularly, the last sections of the Fourth Essay of *Totem et Taboo*, where Freud is forced to postulate 'ambivalence' as fundamental data in order to circumvent the problem as to which family, the primitive one or the late nineteenth-century one of his patients, is the model of the other.
40. Freud appeals to 'the idea of evolution' to say that it 'no longer leaves room for doubt' that the human species has a prehistory (p. 80).
41. On *Totem and Taboo*, see among others, J. Derrida, 'Préjugés', in *La Faculté de juger* (Minuit, 1985), pp. 87–139, around the invention of the concept of the 'repressed'.
42. The 'first difficulty' pertains to the fact that the Jewish religion is only one example among many others with which Freud admits of not being able to deal satisfactorily, for lack of knowledge of them.
43. Freud is not preoccupied with the conservation of written records; in any case, such permanent traces are, as it happens, tied up with those who 'possess' them in the form of knowledge ('such knowledge'). See the introduction to *The Future of an Illusion* (1927) where the demarcation between those who possess knowledge and those who do not is limpid (SE XXI, pp. 5–9), and chapter 4 above.
44. See Derrida's *Mal d'archive*, pp. 47–8. What we are drawing out does not pertain so much to collective or individual memory, but rather to the way in which the demarcation between individual and mass psychology, notably as far as *impressions* are concerned, sends us back particularly sharply to the 'figurative' aspect of the psychoanalytic conceptuality.
45. SE XIX, p. 15.
46. *Ibid.*, p. 17.
47. We leave aside the fact that Freud also claims to reduce 'the gulf which earlier periods of human arrogance had torn too wide apart between mankind and the animals' (p. 100). *Instinkt* is associated with the biological and the naturalism from which, at least manifestly since Lacan, psychoanalysis ought to be sharply distinguished. Language might stand the furthest remove from naturalism or biologism. In view of the last section of this essay, however, it is doubtful whether language can be subtracted from such a framework. Freud indeed repeats the argument in favour of an archaic heritage, but this time, with respect to language: 'the "innate" symbolism which derives from the period of development of speech, which is

familiar to all children without their being instructed, and which is the same among all peoples despite their different languages' and the reaction of children which does not correspond to their 'own experience, but instinctively, like the animals, in a manner that is only explicable as phylogenetic acquisition [*sondern instinktmäßig, den Tieren vergleichbar*]' (p. 132). See J. Forrester, *Language and the Origins of Psychoanalysis* (*op. cit.*).

48. Let us recall the following statement from 'Repression' (1915): '[repression] is a concept which could not have been formulated before the time of psychoanalytic studies' (p. 146). In the context of a study of the 'mass' in Freud and concerning the 'invention' of the concept of repression, one cannot but be struck by Ludwig Binswanger's marginal remark in 'La conception freudienne de l'homme' which interestingly finds an anticipation of the concept of repression in what is recognized as one of the founding texts of 'crowd psychology': 'J'ai trouvé chez Taine une anticipation particulièrement instructive du concept freudien de refoulement, et cela dans sa description de la "souveraineté des passions libres en 1790" [*Les Origines de la France contemporaine*, IV, 96): "Une grande expérience va se faire sur la société humaine: grâce au relâchement des freins réguliers qui la maintiennent, on pourra mesurer la force des instincts permanents qui l'attaquent. Ils sont toujours là, même en temps ordinaire; nous ne les remarquons point, parce qu'ils sont refoulés, mais ils n'en sont pas moins actifs, efficaces, bien mieux, indestructibles. Sitôt qu'ils cessent d'être réprimés, leur malfaisance se déclare comme celle de l'eau qui porte une barque et qui, à la première fissure, entre pour tout submerger."' The note ends by alluding to more concordances between Taine's psychological naturalism and Freud's. 'La Conception freudienne de l'homme' in *Analyse existentielle, psychiatrie clinique et psychanalyse. Discours, parcours et Freud*, trans. R. Lewinter, Preface P. Fédida (Gallimard, 1970), p. 217.

6 Conclusion: 'On Transience'

1. SE XIV, p. 304.
2. On the concept of 'clinging', see J. Derrida, 'Entre crochets', in *Points de suspension* (Galilée, 1992), who discusses briefly the concept of the 'instinct de cramponnement' developed by Imre Hermann in *L'Instinct filial*, introduced by N. Abraham, 'Introduction à Hermann' (Denöel, 1972), pp. 14–17.
3. 'Mourning and Melancholia' (1917 [1915]) SE XIV, p. 243.
4. 'Beyond the Pleasure Principle' (p. 60). See F. Robert, 'Glossaire', in *Traduire Freud* (Paris, Presses universitaires de France, 1989), for the cognates of *Vergänglichkeit*. Malcolm Bowie discusses briefly 'On Transience' in his book on *Lacan* (Blackwell, 1991). He sees in that short essay written in hommage to Goethe during World War I, an opportunity to draw Freud and Leornardo's 'scientific' mind together: 'For Freud, as for Leonardo, the individual bloom could be described both in the multitude of its separable parts and in its power of cohesion; described in either way, it bore no prophetic sign of its imminent passing. There it was – complete, self-contained, in equilibrium, a stronghold against disaster. And for Freud those *mental* objects that comprise the subject-matter of psychoanalysis were the more

useful as explanatory tools the more they resembled simple whole things from the physical world. Theories themselves, in so far as they sought to explain the causal structure of mental processes, were expected to possess separable parts and cohesive power in the manner of material objects: theories were of course acknowledged as transient conventions, powerless to resist the catastrophic upheavals of nature, but for the brief spell in which they held together and worked, they were splendid timeless fixities. Indeed they were useful in psychoanalytic practice only in so far as they represented a stable supra-individual causality in the light of which individual passions, drives and appetites could be understood' (pp. 9–10).

5. 'An Outline of Psycho-Analysis' (1940 [1938]), p. 391.

Index

Abraham, Nicholas, Maria Torok, 149 n. 29
Adorno, Theodor W., 142 n. 11
'Aetiology of Hysteria, The' (1896), 172 n. 44
Althusser, Louis, 145 n. 3, 158 n. 31
âme collective, 62–3
âme de la race, 58, 165 n. 25
analogy, *see* model
'Antithetical Meaning of Primal Words, The' (1910), 179 n. 13
Anzieu, Didier, 150 n. 32
Apfelbaum, Erika, 162 n. 7
archaic heritage, 129, 130, 165 n. 25, 183 n. 47
  see also memory-trace; phylogenesis; tradition; transmission
Arendt, Hannah, 161 n. 5, 164 n. 20
artistic gift, 88
Assman, Jan, 181 n. 24
Assoun, Paul-Laurent, 146 n. 10, 156 n. 17, 176 n. 105, 177 n. 2, n. 4, 180 n. 17
'Autobiographical Study, An' (1925 [1924]), 13, 71
auxiliary constructions (*Hilfsvorstellung*), 41, 73, 87, 95, 96, 103, 139
  see also Bildersprache; intellectual scaffolding (*Hilfskonstruktion*); model

Bachelard, Gaston. 143 n. 20
Balibar, Étienne, 51, 144 n. 26, 159 n. 32
Barrows, Susanna, 162 n. 8
Barthes, Roland, 163 n. 13
Bataille, Georges, 159 n. 34
Baudelaire, Charles. 143 n. 20
Beispiel, 98
  see also Bildersprache
Benjamin, Walter, 143 n. 20
Bennington, Geoffrey, 151 n. 38
Bernstein, Jay M., 180 n. 23, 142 n. 11
Beyond the Pleasure Principle (1920), 18, 21, 30, 45, 100, 147 n. 18
Bildverbot, 109
Bildersprache, 98, 103–4, 106, 108, 111, 113, 118, 131, 139–40, 146 n. 17, 147 n. 18, 174 n. 61
  see also model
Binswanger, Ludwig, 44, 48
biology, 12, 16, 100, 129, 146 n. 4, n. 5, 183 n. 47
Bonaparte, Marie, 162 n. 7
Borch-Jacobsen, Mikkel, 5, 165 n. 30, 166 n. 26, 178 n. 8
Borck, C. 173 n. 60
borrowings, 16, 102–3, 108, 110, 146 n. 15
Bourguignon, André, 144, n. 25
Boutroux, Émile, 162 n. 10
Bowie, Malcolm, 144 n. 23, 184 n. 4
Bowlby, Rachel, 157 n. 21
Bramson, L., 160 n. 1
Breuer, Joseph, 105, 172, n. 45, 178 n. 8
Brunner, José, 153 n. 4

Cannetti, Elias, 4
Certeau, Michel de, 181 n. 24
'Character-Types met with in Psycho-Analytic Work, Some' (1916), 11
Charlton, Donald Geoffrey, 162 n. 10
Chemouny, Jacques, 144 n. 2
Chertok, Léon, Isabelle Stengers, 166 n. 31
childhood, 78, 79, 87, 89, 120, 173 n. 58
  of humanity, 86
childlessness, 11
children, 78, 124, 130
Christianity, 122, 124, 169 n. 21
Civilization and its Discontents (1930 [1929]), 1, 65, 66, 70, 72, 73, 87, 106, 168 n. 7, 169 n. 21

'"Civilized" Sexual Morality and Modern Nervous Illness' (1908), 66, 107
collective responsibility, 55
  forgetting, 168 n. 5
  mind (in Le Bon), 57, 59, 61 (*see also* group mind; *âme de la race*; *Massenpsyche*)
condensation, 7, 46, 78, 79, 122, 171 n. 41
'conditions of representability', 7, 8, 79
conscience (*Gewissen*), 43
  moral conscience, 67, 68, 77, 78, 79
consciousness, 60, 61, 79, 83, 84, 93, 98–9, 101–2, 127, 132, 140, 173 n. 59
'Constructions in Analysis' (1937), 85, 142 n. 6
'Contact with Joseph Popper-Lynkeus, My' (1932), 1, 46, 47, 179 n. 16
contagion, 40, 164 n. 17, 168 n. 9
creative writing, 85, 117, 158 n. 26
crowd, 53–60, 64, 75, 76, 111
  as a term of analogy for the unconscious, 60
  see also psychological group
crowd psychology (*psychologie des foules*), 10, 40, 161 n. 4
  see also group; mass; social psychology; *Massenpsychologie*

Darwin, Charles, 11, 122
delayed effect (*Verspätung*), 25, 109–10, 119, 128, 182 n. 37
Deleuze, Gilles, 161 n. 4
'Delusions and Dreams in Jensen's *Gradiva*' (1907 [1906]), 171 n. 42
Derrida, Jacques, 9, 23–36, 54, 147 n. 18, 151 n. 39, 180 n. 23, 183 n. 41, n. 44, 184 n. 2
'Difficulty in the Path of Psycho-Analysis, A' (1917), 178 n. 8
disavowal [*Verleugnung*], 114
displacement, 46
distortion (*Entstellung*), 46, 75, 109–10, 111, 115–16, 117, 127
dream, 7, 26, 43, 44, 74, 105, 157 n. 21, 167 n. 3, 170 n. 40, 171 n. 43, n. 44, 174 n. 66, 179 n. 13
dream-work, 7, 43, 46, 104
drive (*Trieb*), 101, 102
  death, 2, 68, 72, 74, 77, 99
Dyer Bennett, R., 173 n. 56

'Economic Problem of Masochism, The' (1924)
economics of thought, 97
  of the libido, 87
economy, 16, 38, 44, 79, 80
  of life and death, 34
ego, 5, 9, 38, 39, 42, 65, 79, 84, 96, 106, 127, 128, 137, 142 n. 17, 173 n. 59, 174 n. 66
Ego and the Id, The (1923), 35, 76, 77, 79, 173 n. 58, 175 n. 72, 74, 177 n. 1, 180 n. 22
ego-ideal, 76, 77, 78, 79, 82, 94
Ellenberger, Henri, 159 n. 33, 181 n. 28
energetics of force, 24, 36
  see also hermeneutics
epistemology, 8, 9, 15, 35, 54, 85, 93
Eros, 72, 73, 74, 77, 177 n. 1
Escoubas, Eliane, 178 n. 4
evolution, Darwin theory of, 113
evolutionism, 3, 26, 78, 144 n. 26, 164 n. 21, 182–3 n. 38
external world, 93–7, 120–21, 128, 136, 172 n. 44
Ey, Henri, 145 n. 4

falsification (*Verfälschung*), 115
  see also distortion
family, 121, 122, 124
Ferenzci, Sandor, 142 n. 9, 168 n. 16
Fiktion, *see Bildersprache*
'Five Lectures on Psycho-Analysis' (1910 [1909]), 170 n. 40, 176 n. 94
Forrester, John, 179 n. 13, 184 n. 47
foule, 53, 160–1 n. 4
  see also mass; crowd; group
Fournial, Henri, 53, 162 n. 7

Frey, M., 160 n. 2
Future of an Illusion, The (1927), 10, 64, 69, 85, 86, 90, 91, 94, 96, 106, 149 n. 24, 168 n. 8, 183 n. 43
'Future Prospects of Psycho-Analytic Therapy, The' (1910), 172 n. 46

Garner, Sebastian, 154 n. 4
Gasché, Rodolphe, 151 n. 38, 153 n. 3, 163 n. 13
Gasset, Ortega y, 4
Genette, Gérard, 163 n. 13
Giner, Sandor, 160 n. 1
Ginneken, Jan van, 160 n. 2, 181 n. 28
Gleichnis, see Bildersprache
Goethe, 11
'Goethe Prize Address, The' (1930), 81, 170 n. 40
Goux, Jean-Joseph, 181 n. 24
Granoff, W. 143 n. 19, 147 n. 17
Green, André, 14, 145 n. 3, n. 4
Groddeck, Georg, 43, 156 n. 16
group mind (*Massenseele*), 59
  see also âme de la race; collective mind
group psychology, 107–8, 117, 125, 129
  and the analysis of the ego, *see* group psychology
  see also mass psychology; social psychology; *Massenpsychologie*
Grubrich-Simitis, Ilse, 148 n. 22, 153 n. 52
Grünbaum, Adolf, 143 n. 22

Habermas, Jürgen, 143 n. 22
Halebsky, Sandor, 160 n. 1
happiness, 87
health, 75, 86, 170 n. 40
Heidegger, Martin, 24, 143 n. 22, 151 n. 39
Heller, Hugo, 10
helplessness (*Hilflosigkeit*), 86
Henry, Michel, 142 n. 13
hereditary influences in Le Bon's notion of the unconscious, 58
  see also âme de la race
heredity, 12, 25, 26, 34, 35, 129
  see also archaic heritage; memory-traces; phylogenesis
Hermann, Imre, 184 n. 2
hermeneutics, 14, 146 n. 10, n. 4, 151 n. 41
Hesnard, Angelo, 145 n. 3
Hesse, Mary, 179 n. 11
historical truth, 89
'History of an Infantile Neurosis, From an' (1918 [1914]), 121
Hobbes, Thomas, 4
Hobson, Marian, 152, n. 44
hoi polloi, 51
'human masses' (*Menschenmassen*), 35, 67, 111, 112, 124, 116, 134
  and time, 111
hypnosis, 62
  hypnotic suggestion, 105
Hyppolite, Jean, 15, 146 n. 4

id, 42, 43, 45, 48, 50, 79, 96, 106, 128, 175 n. 70
idealization, 77
identification, 5, 68, 82, 121, 123, 169 n. 21
illness, 75, 88
individual, 2, 25, 34, 58, 59, 60–2, 70–2, 73, 80, 81, 96, 98, 106, 109, 117–20, 125, 129, 133
intellectual scaffolding (*Hilfskonstruktion*), 98, 102, 134, 139
  see also Bildersprache
intellectuality, progress in, 88
interpretation
  decoding method *en détail*, 6–7
  of Freud's work, 6
  of *Mass Psychology and the Analysis of the Ego* (1921), 6
  symbolic method *en masse*, 6–7
Interpretation of Dreams, The (1900), 6–7, 18, 31, 35, 65, 78, 103, 111, 142 n. 16, 169 n. 21, 171 n. 41, 172 n. 45, 173 n. 58, 174 n. 66, 179 n. 10, n. 13, n. 16
'Instincts and their Vicissitudes' (1915), 91, 100–1, 176 n. 105

instinctual renunciation, 67, 68
Introductory Lectures on Psycho-Analysis (1916–17 [1915–17]), 6, 43, 169 n. 21
introspection, 92–4

Jammer, Max, 143 n. 21
Johnson, Chris, 152, n. 44
joke (*Witz*), 152 n. 44, 173 n. 58, 174 n. 66
Jokes and their Relations to the Unconscious (1905), 173 n. 58, 183 n. 38
Jones, Ernest, 104
Judaism, 122, 124
Jung, Carl, 25, 168 n. 7, 171 n. 4, 182 n. 34

Kant, Immanuel, 143 n. 22, 151 n. 39
Kelsen, Hans, 158 n. 32
knowledge, 8, 44, 126, 138, 177 n. 1
  and science, 90–97
  domain of, 10, 50, 85, 88
  institutionalization of, 53
  lack of, 83 (*see also* unknown)
  popular, 16, 71, 159 n. 35
  of the psychical apparatus, 82
  of the unconscious, 18
Kofman, Sarah, 157 n. 21, 177 n. 4
Kompression, 78
Kristeva, Julia, 161 n. 4
Kultur, 67–9, 77, 78, 79, 86, 106–7, 108, 131
Kulturprozeß, 66, 69, 86, 106–7, 111, 133

Lacan, Jacques 144, n. 24, 183 n. 47
Lacoste, Pierre, 148 n. 23, 181 n. 31
Lacoue-Labarthe, Philippe, 142 n. 7, n. 12, 144 n. 2
Laforgue, René, 89, 176 n. 98
language, 179 n. 13
  conceptual, 3, 19
  figurative, *see Bildersprache*; model
  Le Bon's theory of, 55, 130
  ordinary, 17
  scientific, 98–100, 134
Laplanche, Jean, 9, 16–17, 23, 141 n. 1, 149 n. 3, 175 n. 82, 159 n. 36, 182 n. 32
latency, 109, 114, 116, 120, 121
  Incubationszeit, 114
Le Bon, Gustave, 4, 53–63, 160 n. 3, 161 n. 5, 174 n. 68
Le Rider, Jacques, 159 n. 33, 180 n. 17
leader, 4, 54–5, 66, 112, 114, 166 n. 30
Leary, M., 150 n. 35
Leclaire, Serge, 150 n. 33, 154 n. 6
Lefebvre, Georges, 160 n. 2
Lévinas, Emmanuel, 24
libido, 87, 135–6, 137
'Lines of Advance in Psychoanalytic Therapy' (1919 [1918]), 65
Lipps, Theodor, 83
literature, 10, 16, 116–17
'Loss of Reality in Neurosis and Psychosis, The' (1924), 172 n. 44
Lyotard, Jean-François, 181 n. 26

Mach, Ernst, 143 n. 20
Macherey, Pierre, 161 n. 4
Man, Paul de, 163 n. 13
Mannoni, Pierre, 161 n. 4
many, the, 38, 40, 64, 66, 70, 124, 139
Marx, Karl, 4
mass, 1, 8, 5, 42, 126, 131
  delusion (*Massenwahn*), 71, 85, 88, 90
  and Freud's mode of argumentation, 38–40, 42, 117–18
  illusion, 10 (*see also* religion)
  libidinal structure of the, 4, 76, 82
  neurosis (*Massenneurosis*), 71, 80
  physical concept, 8, 64–5, 80, 102
  popular conception, of, 48
  psychology, 118, 122, 124, 131–2, 134
  therapy, 65
  traditional concept, 7, 9, 66, 67, 170 n. 30
  see also multitude; crowd; group

Mass Psychology and the Analysis of the Ego (1921), 2–4, 6, 62, 65, 66, 68, 75, 76, 78, 80, 81, 82, 112, 122, 140, 141 n. 1, 155 n. 14, 158 n. 32, 160 n. 2, 161 n. 3, n. 4, 170 n. 29, 173–4 n. 61
Masse, 47, 52, 64, 65, 73, 77, 112, 141 n. 1
Massenbildung, 73, 77
Massenheit, 73
Massen-Ideal, 65
Massenphantasie, 65
Massenpsyche, 73, 111, 112, 155 n. 10
Massenpsychologie, 110, 111, 112, 113, 115, 116, 119, 125, 141 n. 1
Massenseele, 64, 73, 82, 85
material truth, 115
  see also historical truth
McClelland, John S., 160 n. 1
McDougall, William, 141 n. 1
memory, 28–31, 34–5
memory-trace, 25, 26, 34, 35, 41, 116, 118, 125, 126, 130, 131, 132, 134, 172 n. 44
mental processes, 120, 129
  normal and pathological, 74, 75, 76, 80, 81, 85, 105, 170 n. 40, 171–2 n. 44
Merleau-Ponty, Maurice, 145 n. 3, 151 n. 41
metaphor
  political, 38–40, 153–4 n. 4
  see also model
metapsychology, 3, 21–2, 41, 68, 96, 98, 99, 103, 104, 148 n. 23
Michaud, Eric, 166 n. 31
minority/majority, 66, 67, 154 n. 5
misère psychologique, 74
mob, 5, 46, 64, 65
model, 5, 8–9, 15–18, 20, 22, 23, 26, 35, 42–9, 48, 53–4, 69, 70–1, 80, 98–9, 103, 107–8, 109, 100, 110, 113, 117–19, 121, 123, 124, 127, 131, 133, 139, 147 n. 17, 177 n. 1
monotheism
  Egyptian, 110, 125, 132
  Jewish, 109, 113, 115, 116, 118, 125, 132 (*see also peuple*)
morality, 3, 59, 106
Mosaic religion, 110–11, 113, 116
  mob-characteristics (*Pöbelhaftigkeit*), 66
  tradition, 114
Moscovici, Marie, 148 n. 24, 152 n. 52, 181 n. 24
Moses and Monotheism: Three Essays (1939 [1937–9]), 1, 3, 10, 35, 66, 71, 88, 89, 98, 107–34
mourning, 135–40
'Mourning and Melancholia' (1917 [1915]), 139, 158 n. 29
Mucchielli, Laurent, 162 n. 5, n. 9
multitude, 51, 56, 58, 60, 64, 65, 78, 85
  see also mass; crowd; mob
murder of Moses, 114, 125, 126
Muschg, Walter, 143, n. 23
Muster, see model

Nachträglichkeit, Verspätung, 25
Nancy, Jean-Luc, 142 n. 7, n. 12, 144 n. 2, 166 n. 31, 170 n. 29
'Narcissism: An Introduction, On' (1914), 75, 76, 77, 80
natural sciences, 16, 92, 101, 102, 104, 106
naturalism, 8, 183 n. 47, 184 n. 48
neurological fable, 34
neurology (mythological), 35
neurosis, 44, 69, 75, 86, 104–5, 120–22, 133, 170–1 n. 40
  communal, 70
  genesis of human, 117–18
  obsessional, 107
  traumatic, 109, 114, 120
  universal, 88
neurotic symptom, 43, 44, 74, 105, 118, 120, 121
neurotics, 78, 81, 85, 88, 131, 171 n. 43
'Neuro-Psychoses of Defence, The' (1894), 41, 175 n. 76
New Introductory Lectures on Psycho-Analysis (1933 [1932]), 42, 66, 75, 169 n. 23, 170 n. 30, 175 n. 73, 176 n. 100, 177 n. 1

Nietzsche, Friedrich, 24, 43, 177 n. 4
'Note upon the "Mystic Writing-Pad", A' (1925 [1924]), 26–34
number
  factor of, 112
  the great, 65, 66, 69, 71, 80, 82 (*see also* many)
Nye, Robert A., 162 n. 7, 164 n. 23

observation, 79, 81, 82, 91, 99, 101, 148 n. 23, 177 n. 1
  self-observation, 94
'Obsessive Actions and Religious Practices' (1907), 107, 175 n. 83
omnipotence, 123
  of thought, 76
Ornston, D., 144 n. 25
'Outline of Psycho-Analysis, An' (1940 [1938]), 35, 94, 101, 128, 171 n. 41, 172 n. 45, 182 n. 38, 185 n. 5
overestimation, 76

parapraxes, 43
people (*Volk*), 111, 112
persuasion, 55, 105
peuple, 58, 155 n. 9, 161 n. 3, 167 n. 6
  psychologie des peuples, 144 n. 26
philosophy, 3, 13–15, 16, 17, 93, 94, 101, 144 n. 2, 145–6 n. 3, n. 4
phylogenesis, 9, 26, 35, 38, 79, 80, 87, 129, 130, 131, 132, 181 n. 31
  see also memory-traces; transmission; heredity
pleasure principle, 28, 45, 96
Plon, Michel, 147, n. 18
poetry, 18, 16, 116–17
Poliakov, Léon, 181 n. 24
Politzer, Georges, 145 n. 3,
Pontalis, Jean-Bertrand, 9, 18–19, 23, 145 n. 3, 175 n. 82
'Postscript' to 'An Autobiographical Study' (1935), 69, 108
primal
  family, 123
  father, 87, 109, 122, 123, 126, 130, 132
  horde, 121, 122, 123, 126, 132
  phantasy, 129
'Project for a Scientific Psychology, The' (1950 [1887–1902]), 1, 28–31, 35, 48, 49, 83, 142 n. 3, 150 n. 32, 182 n. 33
Prokhoris, Sabine, 148 n. 23
Proust, Marcel, 161 n. 4
psychical
  apparatus, 3, 20–2, 27, 32, 33, 34, 37, 44, 45, 64, 82, 85, 89, 90, 93–4, 96, 97, 101, 103, 113–14, 128, 148 n. 22, 171–2 n. 44, 174 n. 66, 179 n. 10 (means of picturing, 95, 173–4 n. 61)
  localities, 20, 82, 128
  processes, 26, 44, 82–3, 84, 102, 104, 122, 127
  reality, 83
'Psychical (or Mental) Treatment' (1890), 75
psychoanalysis
  application (*Anwendung*) of, 2, 3, 10, 67, 69, 74, 80, 104–5, 117–19, 122, 123, 124, 129, 131, 133, 144 n. 24
  in Derrida's 'Freud and the Scene of Writing', 9, 25, 34
  means of representation at the disposal of psychoanalysis, 6
  and religion, *see* religion
  and therapy, 2, 82, 84, 131, 146 n. 4, 172 n. 45
'Psycho-Analysis' (1926), 170 n. 40
'Psycho-Analysis, On' (1913 [1911]), 74
'Psycho-Analysis and the Establishment of the Facts in Legal Proceedings' (1906), 175 n. 75
psychoanalytic concepts, 9, 14, 16–17, 69–70, 98–102, 120, 127, 131, 133
  analogical/figurative use of, 14, 108, 111, 113,
psychological
  crowd, 60, 57, 61
  group (*Menschenmenge*), 60
psychology, 23, 41, 50, 74, 76, 83, 93, 101, 107–8, 117–18, 131

see also individual; group; mass; social psychology
psychosis, 121
overwhelming, 173 n. 47
public opinion, 77, 154 n. 5

quality, 46, 101, 127, 128
quantity, 3, 7, 38, 28–9, 38, 40–2, 45, 50, 68, 70, 75, 77, 80, 123, 131
mysterious Q, 41, 42
quantum of energy, 75
'Question of Lay-Analysis, The' (1926), 81, 105, 168 n. 7
'Postscript' (1927), 107
quota of affect, 41, 156 n. 18

rabble, 5
see also mob; mass; crowd; multitude
rational thought, 8, 90
realism, 19, 149 n. 28
reason, 10, 94
dictatorship of, 39
Reich, Wilhelm, 141 n. 1
Reik, Theodor, 176–7 n. 108
religion, 3, 35, 59, 64, 67, 69, 79, 85, 88, 106, 107, 108–9, 111, 113–14, 116, 119, 122, 133
religious illusions, 69, 86, 89–90, 93
repetition (originary), 30
repression, 42, 46, 66, 68, 74, 84, 107, 111, 115, 121, 123, 123–9, 132, 133, 165 n. 25
'Repression, On' (1915), 175 n. 89, 184 n. 48
resistances, 113, 117
'Resistances to Psycho-Analysis, The' (1925 [1924]), 66, 92, 93
Rey, Jean-Michel, 143 n. 19, 147 n. 17, 168 n. 7
Rey de Castro, A., 178 n. 5
rhetoric, 54, 163 n. 13
Ricoeur, Paul, 13, 143 n. 2, 146 n. 4, 151 n. 141, 180 n. 18
Rieff, R., 162 n. 7
Ritvo, P. B., 181 n. 23
Roazen, Paul, 159 n. 32
Rolland, Romain, 142 n. 9, 169 n. 24
Roudinesco, Elisabeth, 147 n. 18, 159 n. 34
Rousseau, Jean-Jacques, 158 n. 31
Roustang, François, 143, n. 23, 147 n. 22, 149 n. 29
Rudé, Georges, 160 n. 2

Salomé, Lou Andreas, 142 n. 17, 181 n. 25
Sartre, Jean-Paul, 145 n. 3
Schneider, Monique, 175 n. 75, 148 n. 23
Schönau, Walter, 143 n. 23
Schopenhauer, Arthur, 177 n. 4
Schorske, Carl, 159 n. 33
science, 10, 64, 82–5, 88, 90–7, 98, 113–14
self, 84–5
see also observation
sexuality, 2, 67, 120, 129, 183 n. 38
Sighele, Scipio, 53, 55, 63, 140, 161 n. 3, 163 n. 14, 162 n. 7
Simmel, Georg, 163 n. 11
social psychology, 51–2, 80, 161 n. 5, 163 n. 12
see also crowd; group; mass psychology; *Massenpsychologie*
sociality, 20, 25, 37, 40
society, 2, 4, 77
origin of, 112
Spinoza, Baruch, 4
Strachey, James, 65
style, 8, 18, 147 n. 21, n. 22
see also theorization
substitution, 43, 74, 136–40, 156 n. 18, 157 n. 20
suggestibility, 62
auto-suggestion, 105
super-ego, 42, 43, 68, 76, 77, 79, 80, 106, 128
suppression of instincts, 67, 68, 106–7
symbolism, 129, 130

Taine, Hyppolite, 160 n. 2
Tarde, Gabriel, 53, 161 n. 4, 162 n. 7, 163 n. 11, 163 n. 14, 164 n. 22
theorization
classical norms of, 18, 148 n. 24

theorization *cont.*
  and construction, 124
  and the mass, 40, 117–18
  mode of, 2, 8, 9, 23–5, 118–19
Thiec, Y. J., 162 n. 7
thinking, 49, 50, 90, 97, 120, 127
time, 109, 113–14, 115, 122, 125, 126, 132, 140, 180 n. 23, 182 n. 36
Tort, Michel, 13–17, 145 n. 3
totalitarianism, 5, 65
Totem and Taboo (1912–13), 35, 66, 73, 87, 106, 109, 111, 112, 122, 157 n. 23, 183 n. 39
tradition, 114–16, 118, 120, 125, 126, 129, 133, 134
transference, 125
transience (*Vergänglichkeit*), 135–6, 137
'Transience, On' (1916 [1915]), 135
transmission, 35, 113, 115–16, 125, 126
  of psychical content, 26, 150 n. 33
  of an archaic heritage, 36, 38, 79
  see also falsification; heredity; memory-trace; phylogenesis
trauma 120, 121, 129
'Types of Onset of Neurosis' (1912), 175 n. 90

uncanny, 168 n. 16
unconscious, 6, 8, 15, 19, 83, 84, 91, 105, 126, 127, 128, 133, 140, 171 n. 40
  and barrenness, 11
  collective (*Kollektive*), 108
  Le Bon's notion, 58–9, 165 n. 25
  processes, 7, 8, 9 (*see also* psychical processes)
  sense of guilt, 42, 68, 73, 169 n. 21
  and style, 148 n. 24
  text, 32
'Unconscious, The' (1915), 150 n. 33
unknowability of, 8, 100–2
unknown, 23, 83, 104, 111, 116, 131, 134
  content, 43
  means of picturing, 42, 54
  nature of Q, 40
  in psychoanalysis, 3, 38, 49
Urgeschichte, 124, 125, 182 n. 34

Vergleich, 98
  see also Bildersprache
Vermorel, H. and M., 180 n. 17
Voragine, Jacques de, 1
Vorbild, *see* model

war, 135–6, 138, 139
Weber, Samuel, 142 n. 10, 147 n. 18, n. 21, 155 n. 12
'Why War', 168 n. 9, 170 n. 37, 178 n. 7, 181 n. 30
Worbs, Michael, 154 n. 4
Worms, René, 165 n. 25

X, 70, 99, 103

Yerushalmi, Josef Hayim, 180 n. 23